GRAPHICAL
COMMUNICATION
PRINCIPLES:
A
PRELUDE
TO CAD

Also Available from McGraw-Hill

Schaum's Outline Series in Engineering

Most outlines include basic theory, definitions, and hundreds of solved problems and supplementary problems with answers.

Titles on the Current List Include:

Acoustics
Advanced Structural Analysis
Basic Equations of Engineering Science
Computer Graphics
Continuum Mechanics
Descriptive Geometry
Dynamic Structural Analysis
Engineering Economics
Engineering Mechanics, 4th edition
Fluid Dynamics, 2d edition
Fluid Mechanics & Hydraulics, 2d edition
Heat Transfer
Introduction to Engineering Calculations
Introductory Surveying
Lagrangian Dynamics
Machine Design
Mathematical Handbook of Formulas & Tables

Mechanical Vibrations
Operations Research
Programming with C
Programming with Fortran
Programming with Pascal
Reinforced Concrete Design, 2d edition
Space Structural Analysis
State Space & Linear Systems
Statics & Mechanics of Materials
Statics & Strength of Materials
Strength of Materials, 2d edition
Structural Analysis
Structural Steel Design, LRFD Method
Theoretical Mechanics
Thermodynamics, 2d edition
Vector Analysis

Schaum's Solved Problems Books

Each title in this series is a complete and expert source of solved problems containing thousands of problems with worked out solutions.

Related Titles on the Current List Include:

3000 Solved Problems in Calculus
2500 Solved Problems in Differential Equations
3000 Solved Problems in Electric Circuits
2500 Solved Problems in Fluid Mechanics & Hydraulics
1000 Solved Problems in Heat Transfer
3000 Solved Problems in Linear Algebra
2000 Solved Problems in Mechanical Engineering Thermodynamics
2000 Solved Problems in Numerical Analysis
700 Solved Problems in Vector Mechanics for Engineers: Dynamics
800 Solved Problems in Vector Mechanics for Engineers: Statics

Available at your College Bookstore. A complete list of Schaum titles may be obtained by writing to: Schaum Division
McGraw-Hill, Inc.
Princeton Road, S-1
Hightstown, NJ 08520

GRAPHICAL COMMUNICATION PRINCIPLES: A PRELUDE TO CAD

Robert J. Foster
Hugh F. Rogers
Richard F. Devon

Pennsylvania State University

McGraw-Hill, Inc.
New York St. Louis San Francisco Auckland Bogotá
Caracas Lisbon London Madrid Mexico Milan
Montreal New Delhi Paris San Juan Singapore
Sydney Tokyo Toronto

**GRAPHICAL
COMMUNICATION
PRINCIPLES:
A
PRELUDE
TO CAD**

4 5 6 7 8 9 0 VNH VNH 9 5 4 3

P/N 021643-6
PART OF
ISBN 0-07-909898-3

This book was set in Times Roman by Waldman Graphics, Inc.
The editors were B.J. Clark, Anne Duffy, and Jack Maisel;
the designer was Merrill Haber;
the production supervisor was Richard A. Ausburn.
Von Hoffmann Press, Inc., was printer and binder.

Library of Congress Cataloging-in-Publication Data

Foster, Robert J. (Robert Jay), (date).
    Graphical communication principles: a prelude to CAD / Robert J.
Foster, Hugh F. Rogers, Richard F. Devon.
        p.   cm.
    Includes index.
    ISBN 0-07-909898-3 (set)
    1. Computer graphics.   2. Computer-aided design.   I. Rogers,
Hugh F.   II. Devon, Richard F.   III. Title.
T385.F664   1991
620′.00425′0285—dc20   90-38968

ABOUT THE AUTHORS

Robert J. Foster is program chairman of Engineering Graphics at the University Park Campus of The Pennsylvania State University. He has a masters degree in mechanical engineering and a doctorate in higher education, both earned at Penn State. He has been active in the Engineering Design Graphics Division of the American Society for Engineering Education (ASEE), where he has held several offices, including chairman.

Professor Foster's interests are teaching engineering graphics and studies of student retention. He has published several articles in these areas. He is the author of two McGraw-Hill texts—*Graphic Science and Design,* 4th ed. (French, Vierck, Foster) and *Engineering Drawing & Graphics Technology,* 13th ed. (French, Vierck, Foster).

Hugh F. Rogers is currently an associate professor of engineering graphics at The Pennsylvania State University. He has taught machine and technical drafting design, technical illustration, architectural graphics, nomography, and related subjects for thirty-three years at the college level.

Professor Rogers is the author of several engineering and architectural graphics workbooks. Workbooks published with McGraw-Hill are *Graphic Science Problems Book, Engineering Drawing and Graphic Technology Problems Book,* and *Engineering Drawing and Graphic Technology Problems Book II.* He has worked in industry and private practice as a draftsman, designer, and surveyor.

Richard F. Devon is an associate professor of engineering graphics at the University Park Campus of The Pennsylvania State University. He has taught first-year engineering courses there for the past eight years. His particular responsibility has been in generating computer curricula in programming, CAD, and computer graphics.

Professor Devon has three year's experience in industry as a civil engineer, including a brief period on the site of the Sydney Opera House. He is author and coauthor of two small books on programming and of a number of articles on engineering education and the social context of technology.

CONTENTS

PREFACE

This text represents a bridge between the traditional large graphics books and direct application of software for computer-aided drafting (CAD). It is generally accepted that a person about to use a CAD system needs to have basic knowledge about graphical concepts and relationships. One needs to know about orthographic projection systems, dimensioning procedures, and three-dimensional relationships among other basics. One does not need to know about extensive hand lettering, inking, and intricate intersections of solids, for example, to successfully operate a CAD system.

The intent of the text is to present in a concise, streamlined manner with clear illustrations those topics of graphics most needed by beginning CAD operators. The text leaves to other sources, such as CAD reference manuals, exploration of techniques of operating a particular CAD software package. The many software systems are best learned with instruction from specific literature devoted exclusively to that software.

Note that all CAD software formats assume that the reader is familiar with basic concepts of graphics. Hence one must know where a left-side view appears, where a half-section is to be placed, or where dimensioning should be properly located. This text provides a full but CAD-tailored background in graphical concepts to support CAD users.

The text is organized into five parts, Parts A to E, respectively: Tools and Techniques of Manual Graphics, Representation of the Three-Dimensional World, Clarification of Shapes and Sizes, Spatial Analysis, and Visual Techniques to Communicate and Analyze Data. Each part is fully illustrated. Representative problems are found at the end of each chapter.

Part A, Tools and Techniques of Manual Graphics, includes Chaps. 2 through 4. Use of basic instruments, such as the compass and dividers, is covered so that a CAD user will be comfortable doing simple initial trial layouts prior to starting a CAD project. Lettering techniques available in CAD software are discussed. Also tangencies and other basic geometric relationships are described.

Part B, Representation of the Three-Dimensional World, stresses x, y, z axis systems and visualization of objects in 3-D space. Chapters 5 through 7 take the reader carefully through the conversion from 3-D formats to the 2-D orthographic system. There is emphasis on sketching ability.

Part C, Clarification of Shapes and Sizes, utilizes Chaps. 8 through 10 to convey information on sectioning, dimensioning, and tolerancing. These topics are vital to the intelligent use of a CAD system.

Part D,   Spatial Analysis, uses Chaps. 11 and 12 to guide the reader through an understanding of auxiliary views so that later effective use can be made of such facilities on a CAD system. The basic concepts are covered, such as the true length of a line, edge view, true surface of a plane, and relationships among lines and planes. Artwork is largely new and intended for ease of understanding.

Part E,   Visual Techniques to Communicate and Analyze Data, is a one-chapter section to aid the reader in presentation graphics and analysis of data. The design of effective charts and graphs of lower-order curves is also discussed.

A new workbook by Professor Hugh F. Rogers has been developed to supplement the text material. The plates are carefully designed to allow one to sketch the solutions or to use traditional hand instruments. A facility in sketching is a valuable asset to a CAD user. One often needs to think while using a pencil and perhaps a straightedge. A basic sketch for the problem approach desired on a CAD system can save time and minimize idle time while one is sitting at the CAD console.

A supplement entitled *Technical Drawing with AUTOCAD* by Leendert Kersten (University of Nebraska, Lincoln) is available from McGraw-Hill. This paperback will teach a student the skill of using AutoCAD, while explaining the concepts.

The authors seek comments from users of this text. This is a new endeavor that grows out of the rich legacy of traditional graphics but aiming toward CAD use. Therefore the text strives to include that graphical background which is needed prior to beginning with a CAD system. A coupling of this text with a specific CAD-software manual should be of maximum benefit to the CAD user. Please provide feedback from your experiences.

McGraw-Hill and the authors would like to thank the following reviewers for their many helpful comments and suggestions: Russell M. Echols, Texas A&M University; Frederick T. Fink, Michigan State University; Leendert Kersten, University of Nebraska, Lincoln; Michael B. McGrath, Colorado School of Mines; and Manjula B. Waldron, Ohio State University.

Robert J. Foster
Hugh F. Rogers
Richard F. Devon

INTRODUCTION

1. NEED FOR GRAPHICAL COMMUNICATION

We live in a world of graphical symbols and pictures. If we traveled about the world in a car, we would often see the symbol in Fig. 1. We would be expected to know what it means. Our travel comfort could be affected by understanding that symbol.

Figure 1
A symbol important to travelers.

Very often people communicate with one another in a graphical mode. Each day we see pictures on TV and in magazines. We absorb them almost automatically. If we did not, in a sense we would be illiterate. Some pictures simply entertain, of course. Others instruct us in some way. If we are going to drive an unfamiliar car, we look for symbols for the lights, windshield washer, and seat adjustment, for example.

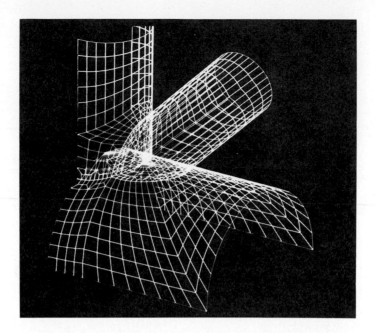

Figure 2
Abstract design from a computer.

People who design and build products use lots of graphical symbols and pictures. The builders receive their instructions from the designers through graphical means. Information may be abstract, as in the three-dimensional representation of intersecting surfaces in Fig. 2. This particular figure was computer-generated. Figure 3 shows more specific information for a hand-drawn part of a diesel engine. You are not expected to understand yet all that is implied in this two-view figure, but it transmits information to the informed builder. The rocker arm of Fig. 3 is shown half size; that is, 1 inch (in) on the drawing represents 2 actual inches. The scale

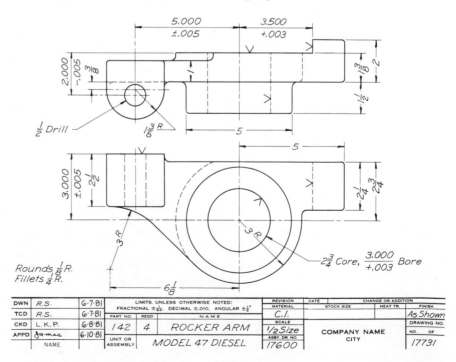

Figure 3
Hand-drawn engine part.

Figure 4
A portion of the United States geological survey map.

is thus 1 = 2. The map in Fig. 4 is a one-view drawing at a much smaller scale, where 1 in equals 1000 feet (ft). Figure 4 conveys very real but different information from the other figures.

In all the pictures seen so far, we would be expected to see or *visualize* what is being shown. A key factor in understanding any drawing is the ability to visualize. This book emphasizes visualization, often through freehand sketching.

2. PURPOSE OF OUR STUDY

Much drafting today is done by *computer-aided drafting* (CAD). A system such as that in Fig. 5 allows the user to generate drawings via the computer. The user gives input through means such as a keyboard, "mouse," or graphics tablet. Output can be put on paper by means of pen plotters, laser printers, or dot-matrix printers, to name three. Computer-generated drawings offer speed and high-quality linework. However, CAD systems are really just sophisticated tools to create drawings. Any CAD system waits for commands to be inputted. The user must give proper commands, knowing what is desired in the way of a drawing.

Figure 5
A system for generating drawings using a computer. (Courtesy Hewlett-Packard.)

All CAD systems operate on specific software which provides a particular format for entering drafting commands. There are also commands for loading, editing, and saving drawings, plus numerous other manipulations. Each software package has its own unique commands, although all software allows the same basic operations to be done. For example, each software program will easily permit lines and circles to be drawn, combined, rescaled, moved, or copied.

Every CAD system has one feature in common: the human being needed to give information to the computer. This human being *must* understand basic graphical concepts in order to input intelligent information to the CAD system. For example, where does a top view properly go, how should the sectioned view look, and what is proper dimensioning technique? A person illiterate in graphical concepts cannot operate a CAD system with any degree of efficiency or competence.

The purpose of our study is to provide clear, concise knowledge of graphical concepts so that you may then use a CAD system with confidence. This book gives background which allows you to use *any* CAD system when supplemented by specific information for a specific CAD system. Each software company, whether it offers AUTOCAD, CADKEY, VERSACAD, or other graphics software, provides complete, thorough manuals on the operation of its software. An operator of a CAD system should always make good use of company information. Also a number of excellent references are available which assume that users know the principles underlying graphics. These books go immediately into useful details of a particular software.

Our study therefore explains the principles of graphic communication which have universal application. Applications can be for CAD as well as hand-drawn manual uses, including both freehand sketching and instrument drawing. In this book, however, we do not dwell on graphical aspects unrelated to CAD, such as instruction in the creation of hand-inked drawings.

In addition, we emphasize the understanding of principles needed for computer-aided *drafting* as opposed to computer-aided *design*. The term *CAD* may mean different things to different people, because the letter D can stand for either *drafting* or *design*. Sometimes we see the term *CADD,* which means computer-aided drafting and design.

This book teaches drafting, not design. Design is indeed a very important aspect of technology in which knowledge is analyzed and integrated to create a product. Design is often learned in upper-level engineering courses or during on-the-job training. Drafting is a tool used to assist in design and is a necessary element of design. Drafting may be done via CAD or manual methods, depending on the situation. By knowing well the principles of good drafting, one can become a better designer. Proper use of drafting principles can lead to the development of complex designs, as seen in Fig. 6.

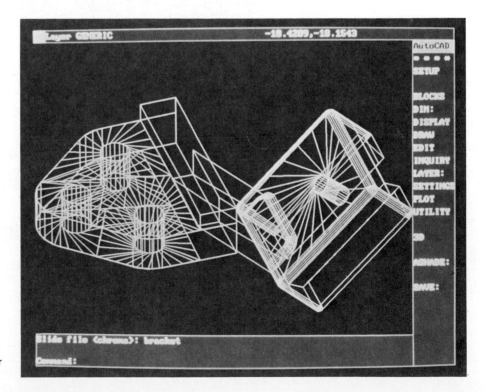

Figure 6
A complex shape seen on a computer screen. (Courtesy Autodesk, Inc.)

■ 3. HOW CAD CAME TO BE

For centuries people have expressed their designs on paper by hand. Whether it is a freehand sketch, as in Fig. 7, or a drawing done by using manual instruments, as in Fig. 3, the human hand controlled its accuracy and quality. Computers had little commercial application until the late 1950s, when major corporations such as aircraft manufacturers began to use huge computers for complex calculations needed in design. These computers also were employed in *computer numerical control* (CNC) of machining operations. A computer could control the path of a cutting tool for a propeller, for example.

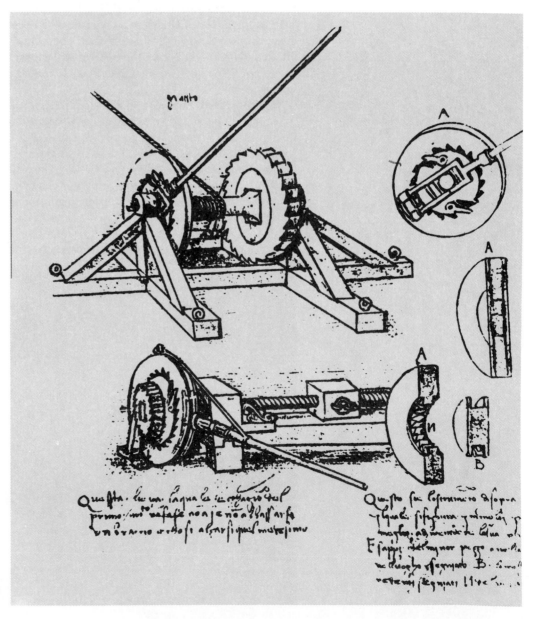

Figure 7
A historical sketch by Leonardo da Vinci (about 1500).

The use of CAD arrived by the 1960s. Large computers were still needed, but the CAD operator could interact with the drafting and design procedure, making revisions easily. This ease of design modification shown on a computer monitor screen was a great advantage over the tedious manual method of making changes.

Early CAD use was essentially limited to two-dimensional (2-D) layouts. Much good work could be done, but the computer memory needed for three-dimensional (3-D) work was still too costly for most applications. Large mainframe computers were still required for CAD work.

By the late 1970s, advances in computer technology had progressed so that memory capacities formerly reserved for mainframe computers could be incorporated into microcomputers. The resulting reduction in cost vastly widened the market. Many more drafters and designers could afford to use CAD. Software was still largely restricted to 2-D formats, but by the middle 1980s 3-D software was available and more cost-effective.

At present CAD systems can be afforded by even small companies. The range of hardware and software is extensive. The question for drafters becomes not whether a drawing can be done, but whether it *should* be done on a CAD system. Virtually all drafters now have the option of doing a drawing via CAD rather than manually.

4. PRESENTING GRAPHICAL INFORMATION

Graphical information can be defined as that information presented in the form of a picture, as opposed to mathematical equations or a written narrative. Our discussion relates to graphical material used primarily in a technological sense. The material includes freehand sketches, as in Fig. 8, and design drawings, as in Fig. 6. Also included are graphs, as in Figs. 9 and 10. The material typically does *not* include photographs, artwork, musical scores, or posters.

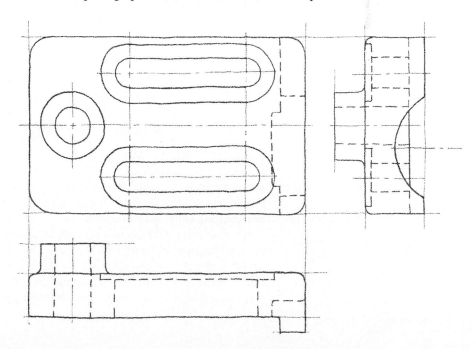

Figure 8
A freehand drawing.

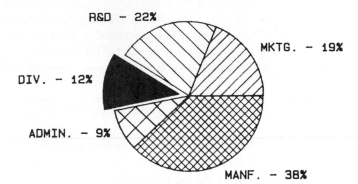

Figure 9
A pie chart as drawn on a computer-driven plotter. (Courtesy Hewett-Packard.)

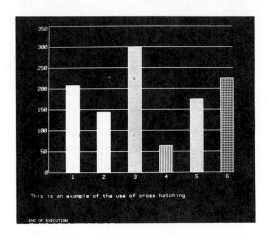

Figure 10
A bar chart with textured bars drawn by a computer program.

Graphical information can be presented manually, either by freehand sketching or by use of instruments. It can also be presented by using CAD. When would we use freehand sketching versus instrument drawings versus CAD? Each has its place, as we shall see.

a. The Case for Freehand Sketching

Sketching ability is valuable when you wish to jot down the general shape of an object or plot data quickly to note the trend of data in a graph. Sketching is quick and completely versatile. You can sketch on a mountaintop with a simple, lightweight pad and pencil, far removed from the need for electric power for a computer or a drafting table and instruments.

Also the brain interacts quickly with the human hand. Ideas flow from the mind through the hand to paper with a natural ease. Great concepts are often born with a modest sketch. We can also readily share ideas with others via sketches. Sketches can be great communicators of information. While sketches are not often the endpoint of a design, they are often the beginning stage of a designed product.

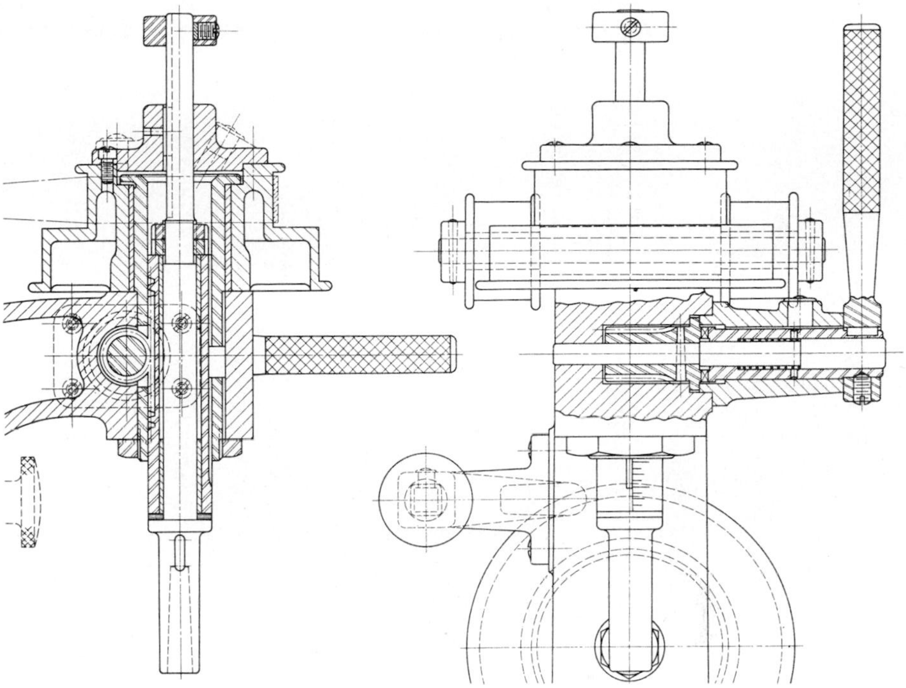

Figure 11
A portion of a design layout. Notes and specifications accompany the drawing.

b. The Case for Instrument Drawings

Sketches may be the beginning point of a design, but sketches in themselves go only so far. They express ideas well, but their accuracy is limited. Also for complex designs, such as that in Fig. 11, sketching becomes very tedious and difficult because of the intricate shapes and many assembled parts.

In that case, using hand-held instruments gives an advantage over sketching. Alignment between views is maintained, and good accuracy ensures a better understanding of the interrelationship of parts. In Chap. 2 we discuss many instruments, including the compass, dividers, and triangles. These instruments have existed for hundreds of years, evolving slowly as technical improvements have been made. Instruments were used in the design of the ships in which Columbus discovered the New World in 1492 and in shipbuilding today, for example.

Instruments are of real value when a drawing is to be done *once* for a product and is not expected to be revised frequently. On a personal level, if you were to design a dining room table for your home, using hand-held drafting instruments would be a natural choice.

c. The Case for Drawings by CAD

The last paragraph above gives a clue to at least one advantage of CAD drawings. Instrument drawings are well suited to drawings that are done *once* and are not expected to be revised often. But if drawings are to be *repeated* and *revised* often, CAD offers powerful advantages.

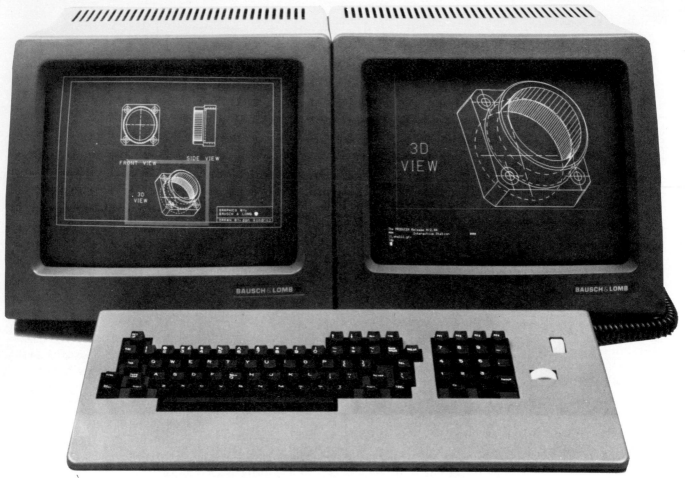

Figure 12
Both 2-D and 3-D drawings can be shown on this dual raster display. (Courtesy Interactive
Graphics Division, Bausch & Lomb.)

Once data are entered into a computer, a CAD system can deliver fast, highly accurate variations of a basic drawing. Different views of an object can be created quickly in both 2-D and 3-D views, as in Fig. 12. Standard features can be repeated, modified, or deleted quickly, such as the size and number of windows on a given floor of an office building. Versatility, accuracy, and speed are virtues of CAD systems, once the basic data have been entered.

The data entered into CAD systems can also be used to help control manufacturing processes through computer-aided manufacturing (CAM). The database can be a powerful link between the design of a part and its production. Other texts discuss in depth the role of computer databases in production.

The intent of this book is to prepare you to use a CAD system intelligently from the standpoint of understanding the needed graphical principles of drawing layouts. Section 5 lists the various sections of the book and what they plan to accomplish.

5. LAYOUT OF OUR STUDY

The book is divided into five parts, with each having a special emphasis. Each part comprises two or three chapters (except Part E). The purposes of the sections are listed below.

a. Tools and Techniques of Manual Graphics

We have discussed the particular advantages of manual drafting by using instruments. This part helps you understand the use of basic drafting instruments, lettering, and geometric relationships among lines, circles, and curves. When you understand these factors, two things are possible. First, you can do modest drawings with instruments and achieve reasonably accurate, neat results. Second, you can better appreciate and use the various options in CAD software. You can, for example, be knowledgeable about lettering styles and relationships between lines, such as parallelism and perpendicularity.

b. Representation of the Three-Dimensional World

This important part teaches you to show objects in three dimensions by various methods. This information is valuable when you are using CAD. You can then understand the options offered by a particular CAD system. The concepts of the conversion between 3-D and 2-D formats are thoroughly discussed. Again, this is very helpful when you are using CAD software. Freehand sketching techniques are also stressed. So you can do some useful preliminary thinking on paper before laying out the problem using CAD.

c. Clarification of Shapes and Sizes

Three chapters are devoted to the areas of sectioning, dimensioning, and tolerancing. You must understand Part C before attempting to use CAD. A CAD system will only do (but do well) what you instruct it to do. It waits for instructions. Knowledge of good practices in sectioning, dimensioning, and tolerancing is essential if your final drawing, done by using CAD, is to be correct and understandable.

d. Spatial Analysis

This part deals with a study of the interaction of lines and planes within 3-D space. For example, how do you find the angle between two lines or between two planes? These questions, and many others, can be answered after studying this section. When designing parts or structures, often you need to know how to analyze lines, planes, and even solids to get a readout of vital information. A drafter or designer must understand spatial concepts to intelligently instruct a CAD system for assistance. Although the information in Part D is useful for manual solutions, it is equally useful in CAD applications.

e. Presentation Graphics

A final chapter deals with the presentation and analysis of data. Data can exist in a variety of forms: dollars of business sales, rainfall per month, horsepower versus engine speed. How can data be presented both effectively and honestly? What formats and techniques are available for graphical presentation? How can data be placed on a chart or graph to best indicate the trend?

Presenting data well is not a mysterious science but rather a process that follows sensible guidelines. Use of proper procedures can ensure that the results will be as effective as possible, whether you use manual methods or computer software. Chapter 13 will be very helpful to CAD users because the operator of a CAD system will be aware of appropriate techniques for data presentation. Graphical output should therefore be highly readable and usable.

PART A

TOOLS AND TECHNIQUES OF MANUAL GRAPHICS

C H A P T E R 2

BASIC DRAFTING TOOLS

■ 1. OVERVIEW

You may wonder what basic drafting tools have to do with computer-aided drafting. Cannot the CAD user simply let the computer do all drafting? It is certainly true that good software will permit the user to generate all necessary drafting procedures on the screen and then permit high-quality pen plots on the paper of choice. Also CAD software and hardware are being improved continuously with more options and higher quality at lower cost.

There is, however, one constant in the CAD process. This element is the human operator who must convey ideas from her or his brain to the CAD system. The concept of a design or part must pass from the operator's brain, through the fingers, and into a CAD keyboard, mouse, or other input device. A person does not create design and drafting concepts instantly. The CAD system is a tool to facilitate the creation of a design.

Many CAD users find that making an initial hand sketch or simple layout of the part to be designed is extremely helpful. These CAD users are not manual drafters in the full sense of the word, but they do find utility in some basic drafting tools. Knowing how to use a proper pencil, paper, and scale, for example, allows you to make a quick "thinking" sketch or drawing. Details and the final form are then done on the CAD system. Figure 1 shows a simple sketch which can be finalized by using CAD. Figure 2 illustrates the final drawing on a CAD system.

15

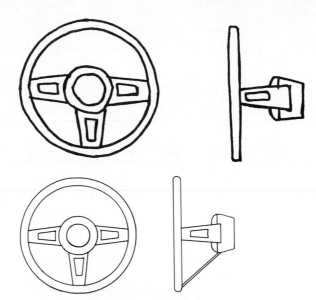

Figure 1
A pre-CAD sketch.

Figure 2
CAD drawing of Figure 1.

This chapter concentrates on those basic drafting tools that support the CAD user. The tools are light and therefore easy to carry around, whether you are out at an installation site or in the computer room or office. The tools are also basic, meaning that they have a wide range of use and are simple to manipulate. Highly specialized manual tools, such as inking equipment, are not covered. Comments on inking relate to CAD plotters.

2. PENCIL AND LEAD: A USEFUL COMBINATION

In this section we look at pencil and lead types and how they are used. The proper selection and use of these items can make the sketching or layout of parts easier and more effective. First we describe the pencils and leads themselves; then we briefly discuss their uses.

a. Types of Pencils

Everyone is familiar with the commonest of pencils, the wood pencil with graphic lead. Every desk drawer contains several. They usually have an eraser on the end and merely require occasional sharpening. Companies often give away pencils stamped with their names. Unfortunately the lead in these pencils is of uncertain hardness and quality. Many have lead which is too soft for engineering work.

A step up from the common lead pencil is the drafting wooden pencil with carefully controlled lead hardness options. Such a pencil usually does not have an eraser. The one disadvantage of these pencils is that they grow shorter as they are sharpened. Figure 3 shows a representative pencil of this type.

Figure 3
A wooden drafting pencil.

U.S.A. KOH-I-NOOR RAPIDOGRAPH, INC.   1500-I Drawing   2H

Figure 4
Mechanical pencil with ¹⁄₁₆-in lead.

Figure 5
Thin-lead mechanical pencil. (Courtesy J. S. Staedler, Inc.)

Many persons prefer a mechanical pencil with replaceable leads. In this way, the lead holder is permanent. Only the lead is variable. The higher initial cost is soon offset by the lower cost of replacing leads, not the entire pencil, as with wooden pencils. Also there is a choice of lead hardness to be used.

Mechanical pencils come in two styles. One has a lead of about ¹⁄₁₆-in [1.5-millimeter (mm)] diameter which must be sharpened. Figure 4 shows one such pencil. Thin-lead mechanical pencils are becoming increasingly popular because they do not need sharpening. A typical one is seen in Fig. 5. Two common lead sizes are 0.3 and 0.5 mm. Various lead hardnesses are available. (See the discussion of leads below.) Thin leads wear down quickly, but they are easily replaced and their lack of need for sharpening is appreciated.

b. Types of Leads

Leads may vary in diameter, as mentioned, and in hardness, which is of vital interest to the user. Lead hardness is denoted by number and letter, as in Fig. 6. One rarely needs a lead as hard as 9H or as soft as 7B. A 4H or 5H lead would be suitable for making very light lines for initial layouts. On finalized drawings one could use H, 2H, or 3H leads, which give suitable blackness without smudging. Leads of H or F grade are good for lettering. The F, HB, and softer leads are good for sketching. In every case, the user must match his or her hand pressure to the

Figure 6
Chart of led hardness.

Hard grades		Medium grades		Soft grades	
9H	Hardest	3H	Hardest	2B	Hardest
8H		2H		3B	
7H		H		4B	
6H		F		5B	
5H		HB		6B	
4H	Softest	B	Softest	7B	Softest

lead selected. A person who has a light touch can use a softer lead than someone who bears down hard on the lead. Recall that thin-lead pencils (Fig. 5) do not require sharpening. However, leads of ¹⁄₁₆-in (1.5-mm) diameter do need to be sharpened. Sharpening may be done with a sandpaper pad (Fig. 7) or a lead pointer (Fig. 8). In either case, a conical point is desired for all general work. If only straight lines are to be made, a wedge point is sometimes used since it wears better than a conical point.

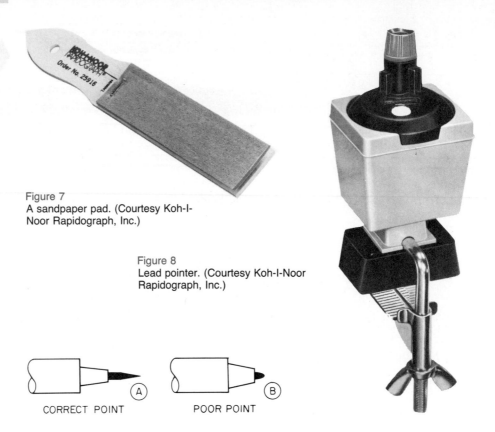

Figure 7
A sandpaper pad. (Courtesy Koh-I-Noor Rapidograph, Inc.)

Figure 8
Lead pointer. (Courtesy Koh-I-Noor Rapidograph, Inc.)

Figure 9
Comparison of lead points.

The quality of the drawn line is extremely dependent on the sharpness of the lead. Nothing hurts quality more than a dull lead. Keeping a lead sharp is so simple to do, yet it is easy to neglect this main ingredient of line quality. The badly worn point in Fig. 9B can never give the line quality of the correct point in Fig. 9A. It is also good to wipe a freshly sharpened lead on a cloth or tissue to prevent graphite dust from dropping onto the drawing. Graphic dust soon creates ugly smudges and blotches.

3. LINE TYPE

As you create parts or designs, you will need various types of lines. Line types are equally valid for manual and CAD work. You must select the correct line type for the particular need. Figure 10 shows a part which incorporates all needed lines. Note them carefully. Line conventions are covered in Y14.2M of the American National Standards Institute (ANSI) (Line Conventions and Lettering). Line widths between 0.016 and 0.032 in (0.35 and 0.7 mm) will cover the great majority of needs. If a drawing is to be reduced, greater widths on the original are helpful.

In CAD work, the ink pens for the plotter are available in various thicknesses, although often a plot is done in only one size. Various colors are also possible. Large drawings are sometimes plotted with slightly greater line widths than small drawings. You must keep fresh pen tips in the plotter to ensure dark, crisp lines.

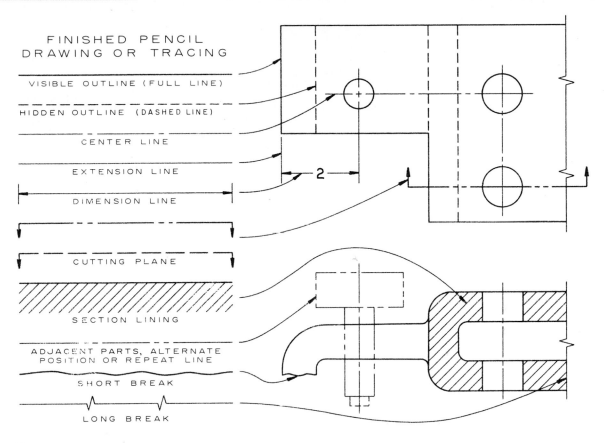

FINISHED PENCIL
DRAWING OR TRACING

VISIBLE OUTLINE (FULL LINE)

HIDDEN OUTLINE (DASHED LINE)

CENTER LINE

EXTENSION LINE

DIMENSION LINE

CUTTING PLANE

SECTION LINING

ADJACENT PARTS, ALTERNATE
POSITION OR REPEAT LINE

SHORT BREAK

LONG BREAK

Figure 10
Line types.

▪ 4. ERASER

A tool given too little credit in the working world is the eraser. You never outgrow your need for an eraser. A useful type is the white plastic form seen in Fig. 11. Such types are available for both pencil and ink. An erasing shield (Fig. 12) is helpful in limiting the area to be erased. If erasing is common in your work, an erasing machine (Fig. 13) may be a worthwhile investment. All drawings, including CAD draftings, sometimes need a touchup correction, and erasing is therefore a necessary process. Why replot a large drawing if a quick fix is available by erasing or by another process such as using White-Out or doing a paste-over?

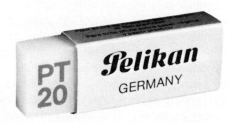

Figure 11
Plastic eraser. (Courtesy Koh-I-Noor
Rapidograph, Inc.)

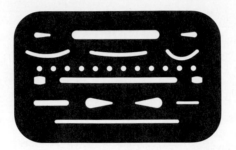

Figure 12
An erasing shield. (Courtesy Pickett Industries.)

Figure 13
An erasing machine. (Courtesy Keuffel & Esser Co.)

■ 5. DRAWING-SHEET MATERIAL

Several types of materials are available on which to sketch or draw. You simply pick the type appropriate to your need. For our discussion, we need to know whether the material is for manual sketching or drawing prior to the final CAD drawing or for the CAD plotter itself. Material for the preliminary work done by hand need not be as elegant as that for the CAD plotter output.

a. Sketch Pads

Such pads are commonly $8\frac{1}{2} \times 11$ in or larger. They are used almost exclusively for sketching, as the name implies. The material is usually common paper in a choice of colors. Pads may be plain or gridded. A gridded background, such as that seen in Fig. 14, is very helpful in the alignment of views (discussed in Chap. 6). In addition to common ''typewriter'' paper, pads can be obtained in vellum, described below.

b. Separate Paper Sheets

Some people may need more flexibility in size than is readily available in pads. For them, single sheets of one of the standard sizes may be ideal. Figure 15 lists the common sizes. The smaller sizes may be preferred for initial sketches. The larger sizes may be selected for the output plotter, assuming the plotter has the capacity to handle them. Some plotters also can work with rolls, as in Fig. 16.

Paper comes in two common types: *detail paper* and *tracing paper*. Detail paper is opaque; tracing paper is translucent. Detail paper is available in white or colors that are easy on the eye, such as buff or cream. Its opaqueness means that reproduction must be done by some photographic process, whereas tracing paper can

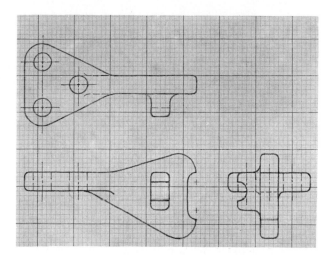

Figure 14
Gridded sketch paper.

USA size, in	Closest international size, mm
A (8.5 × 11.0)	A4 (210 × 297)
B (11.0 × 17.0)	A3 (297 × 420)
C (17.0 × 22.0)	A2 (420 × 594)
D (22.0 × 34.0)	A1 (594 × 841)
E (34.0 × 44.0)	A0 (841 × 1189)

Figure 15
Comparison of paper sizes.

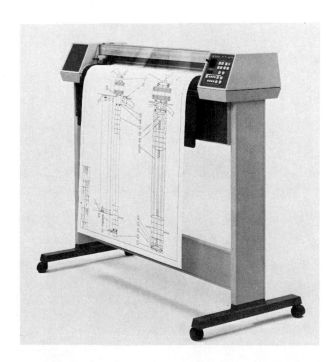

Figure 16
CAD plotter using roll paper.

be reproduced by ozalid or other relatively inexpensive methods. Tracing paper tends to be too thin for use in CAD plotters and does not erase as well as detail paper.

c. Vellum

This material is extremely popular for both manual and CAD use. It is made of 100 percent rag and is sufficiently translucent for all reproduction methods. It is coated on one side with a resin which gives a good surface for accepting pencil or ink and which also gives it good erasing characteristics. Vellum is reasonably strong and feeds well in CAD plotters. Its cost is usually higher than that for paper, but its superior drafting properties make it a favorite with drafters.

d. Film

This once exotic material is seeing greater use in recent years. Made of polyester plastic, film has a mat finish which accepts well both pencil and ink. Film has excellent properties in terms of strength, dimensional stability in humid or dry conditions, and long shelf life. Its expense is offset by its desirable qualities. It is unlikely that a preliminary sketch would be done on film, but a designer might select it as an output medium for a drawing.

6. DRAWING SURFACE

For a simple sketch, a clipboard may do well, or perhaps a tabletop or horizontal surface on the terminal may be handy. For more serious sketching or drawing, a basic drawing board is convenient. The type shown in Fig. 17 is inexpensive, or for additional cost the type in Fig. 18 features a built-in parallel straightedge. The

A basic drawing board. (Courtesy Gramercy Corp.)

Parallel straight-edge drawing board. (Courtesy Gramercy Corp.)

Figure 19
A drafting machine. (Courtesy
Gramercy Corp.)

ultimate in surfaces would be the large drafting table complete with drafting machine, seen in Fig. 19. Few CAD users, however, would be apt to spend many
hours on this professional setup to create manual drawings. In the touch-up of large
CAD drawings, though, you might well utilize the fine surface offered.

■ 7. T SQUARE AND TRIANGLES

These tools in combination have provided drafters with valuable assistance for
many decades. They are classical tools in the sense that they never really go out
of style. Their use is as basic as that of a pencil. The head of the T square runs
along the edge of a drafting board or table, as in Fig. 20. Horizontal lines are
drawn by pulling the pencil along the edge of the T square.

Figure 20
Use of a T square.

A plastic triangle, seen in Fig. 21, is used to create vertical lines. By sliding the horizontal edge of the triangle along the edge of the T square, you can draw as many verticals as you wish. Triangles are usually of the 45°-45°-90° and 30°-60°-90° varieties, seen in Fig. 22. Any 15° increment can be drawn by using these two styles of triangles in combination, as shown in Fig. 23. You can also buy an adjustable triangle which can be set and locked to the desired angle.

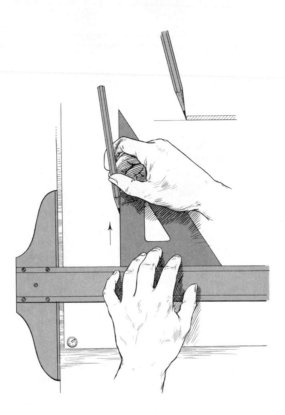

Figure 21
A triangle used for vertical lines.

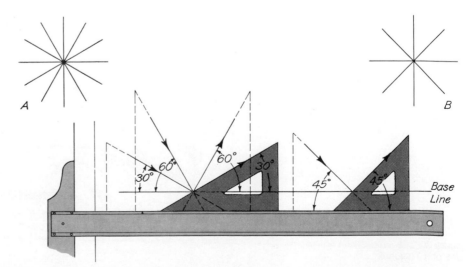

Figure 22
Basic positions of 30°–60° and 45°–45° triangles.

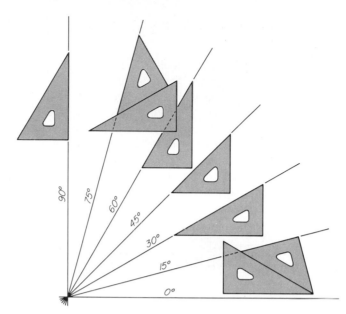

Figure 23
Using 45° and 30°–60° triangles to give 15° increments.

A very worthwhile manipulation is seen in Fig. 24. You can generate perpendiculars to any line, as in Fig. 24A. You simply rotate the triangle to provide the perpendicular. Parallel lines also can be made, as in Fig. 24B. You can create a parallel to an existing line by sliding the triangle along the edge of the T square. A T square is not mandatory for the creation of perpendicular and parallel lines. You may use the edge of a large triangle instead of the edge of the T square, as in Fig. 25.

Note one aspect of the illustrations in this section. All those involving the T square are for right-handed people. The position of the head of the T square is reversed for left-handed people. The head is on the opposite (right-hand) side of the table. Also the triangle, as shown in Fig. 21, is flipped to the mirror-image position for left-handed people.

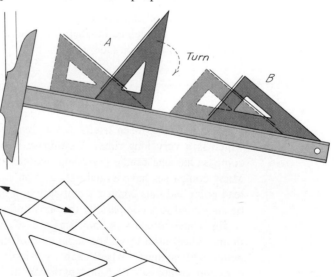

Figure 24
Using triangles to generate perpendiculars.

Figure 25
Using a triangle edge as an alternate to a T square.

8. DIVIDERS

This helpful tool has a long history. As Fig. 26 shows, the tips of both legs are needle points. The legs are separated the desired distance, and the position is held by friction within the upper pivot joint. The primary purpose of dividers is to transfer any selected distance from one place to another. Ocean navigators have long used dividers to track distances across a map. You could use dividers on a road map to estimate a distance, by walking the dividers along a selected route. With the dividers set to some known distance, you could simply count the number of steps taken and multiply by the set distance of the dividers. For example, 15 steps at 10 miles (mi) per step gives 150 mi.

Figure 26
Dividers.

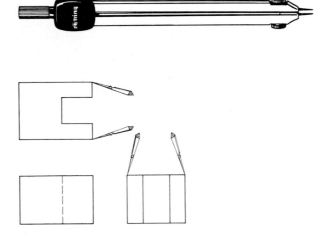

Figure 27
Matching distances with dividers.

On drawings, a divider is very useful in setting off a distance in one view to match that in another view. In Fig. 27 there are three views of an object: top, front, and right side (explained in Chap. 6). The depth in the top view is matched by the same depth in the right-side view.

9. COMPASS

A compass has been useful for as long as people have been drawing circles, which is a very long time. A compass is built much as a divider except that a compass has one needle point and one point containing a lead (or ink dispenser). Many compasses have a dual nature. You can insert a needle point in place of the lead point and thus convert a compass to a divider. The instrument in Fig. 28 can be converted to a compass by the substitution of one point.

This same compass is known as a *bow compass* because it features a threaded thumb wheel used to set the separation of the legs. The separation distance holds better with a thumb wheel than by friction alone within the pivot joint. Most common compasses of 6-in length can give about a 5-in maximum radius. An extender beam (Fig. 29) allows for much greater radii.

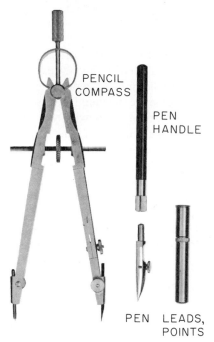

Figure 28
Dual-purpose compass.

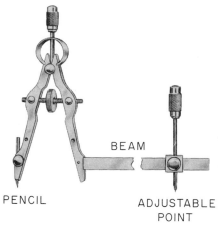

Figure 29
An extension-beam compass.

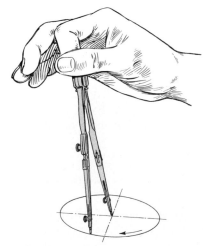

Figure 30
Use of a compass.

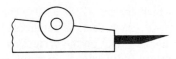

Figure 31
Wedge point for compass.

You can use a compass to generate a circle easily by following the method in Fig. 30. Apply most of the pressure from your hand to the needle point at the center of the circle to be drawn. Lean the compass into the direction of travel, and slowly twirl the compass between your thumb and forefinger. As a variation of style, note that the compass of Fig. 30 does not have the thumb wheel seen in Fig. 28.

The condition of the lead in the compass point is important to ensure good arc quality. The hardness of the lead should never exceed that being used for straight lines with the pencil. If lines are being drawn with an H lead, the arcs should also be done with an H lead or even one grade softer (F lead). Most people do not press as hard on the compass lead point as they do on a pencil. Therefore a lighter touch with a softer lead can give the same darkness as greater pressure with a harder lead.

The shape of the lead point is important, too. The wedge shape shown in Fig. 31 keeps its sharpness longer than a conical point. A conical point is helpful in a pencil because you rotate the pencil as you use it. This is not so in a compass, which moves in a fixed circular direction.

10. SCALES

The scale of a drawing tells the user the size of the part on the drawing relative to the part's actual size. If the drawing scale were 1 = 2, the user would know that 1 unit of length on the drawing represented 2 units of length on the actual part. A feature 3 in long on the drawing is really 6 in long on the actual part. (But the *dimension* of the feature on the drawing will say 6 in. See Chap. 9.) Note that when using a CAD system you would enter any dimension using its real value. You can then adjust the size of any part on the screen to suit your needs.

The scale of a drawing follows the equation $U = A$, where U is the *unit length* on the drawing and A is the *actual length*. For example, if you use the scale 1 in = 4 ft, then 1 in on the drawing represents 4 ft (48 in) on the actual part. The ratio 1 : 48 means that all features on the drawing are to be multiplied by 48.

A scale such as 1 : 48 is suitable for large objects, such as buildings. Many scales are available. Their use is equally valid for manual and CAD drawings.

a. General Classification

There are basically just two types of scale: those in English units and those in metric units. Scales in English units use an inch-foot fractional system or a decimal system. Scales in metric units are in base 10 and normally use the millimeter (mm), centimeter (cm), or meter (m) as units.

b. Scales in English Units

Examples are offered for the inch-foot fractional and decimal systems.

1. Inch-foot system.   This system uses the architect's scale and is expressed as $x = 1'-0''$, where x in inches may be one of these values: $\frac{3}{32}$, $\frac{1}{8}$, $\frac{3}{16}$, $\frac{1}{4}$, $\frac{3}{8}$, $\frac{1}{2}$, $\frac{3}{4}$, 1, $1\frac{1}{2}$, 3, 6, 12.

Therefore if $1'' = 1'-0''$, then 1 in on the drawing represents 1 ft (12 in) on the actual part. The ratio of the scale is 1 : 12, since 1 in = 12 in. Every feature on the drawing is multiplied by 12, meaning that the part on the drawing is one-twelfth actual size.

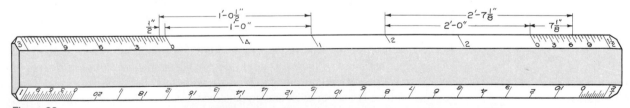

Figure 32
Reading an architect's scale.

Figure 32 shows how to read an architect's scale. Two scales are found along the same edge. The left-hand edge is marked 3, which means $3'' = 1'-0''$. The right-hand edge is marked 1½, meaning $1\frac{1}{2}'' = 1'-0''$. Each scale is subdivided only within an *extra* foot provided at each end. To read $1'-0\frac{1}{2}''$ on the scale $3'' = 1'-0''$, the 1-ft value is set within the undivided portion, while the ½-in value is picked up within the subdivided foot. Similarly, to read $2'-7\frac{1}{8}''$ on the scale $1\frac{1}{2}''$

= 1'–0", read 2 ft within the undivided portion and 7⅛ in within the subdivided foot. Incidentally, the ratio for the scale 1½" = 1'–0" is found by

$$1\tfrac{1}{2}'' = 1'\text{–}0'' = 12''$$
$$\tfrac{3}{2}'' = 12''$$
$$1 : 8 \text{ (ratio)}$$

2. Decimal format. This format uses the civil engineer's scale, also known as the *engineer's scale*. This scale is expressed as $1'' = Y \times 10^n$, where Y is any integer, commonly 1, 2, 3, 4, 5, or 6. The exponent n is an integer of the user's choice. The units of Y are also the user's choice. Here are some examples:

$$1'' = 2 \text{ ft} \times 10^2 = 200 \text{ ft}$$
$$1'' = 4 \text{ lb} \times 10^1 = 40 \text{ lb}$$
$$1'' = 5 \text{ ft/s} \times 10^0 = 5 \text{ ft/s}$$
$$1'' = 3 \text{ ft} \times 10^{-1} = 0.3 \text{ ft}$$

We can see that the engineer's scale has great versatility. In effect, the user sets the decimal point and the units.

Refer to Fig. 33 for two examples. Case A shows a full-size scale which is actually 1 = 1. This scale is marked 10 at the end, which means only that 1 in is subdivided into 10 parts. If one drops the zero within 10, the resulting true multiplier, 1, is revealed. The value of 2.15 read may be 2.15 in, ft, ft/s, or any unit desired by the user. The unit of feet per second, for example, might be chosen if one were plotting a graph of velocity in feet per second vs. time in seconds.

In case B of Fig. 33, a scale 1 = 300 is desired, that is, $1 = 3 \times 10^2$. The exponent of 2 is needed, which means that any value on the scale is multiplied by 10^2, or 100. Therefore a value read as 5.8 becomes 580. The number 580 could be 580 in, 580 ft, or whatever is desired.

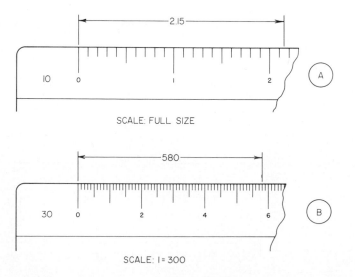

Figure 33
Reading a civil engineer's scale.

Note also that if the zero were dropped in the 30 at the scale's end, the true multiplier, 3, would be given. The number 30 is merely the number of subdivisions in one actual inch. Comparing 3 to the desired multiplier of 300, we see that all values read must be multiplied by 100.

c. Scales in Metric Units

Metric scales use base 10, a decimal base. As such, they are read much as the engineer's scales discussed above. The only difference between a metric scale and an engineer's scale is the units. The engineer's scale is based on inches while metric scales are in millimeters, centimeters, or meters. A scale of $1 = 6$ on the engineer's scale means that 1 in equals 6 of something (say, inches, feet, pounds). All features on the drawing are to be multiplied by 6. A multiplier of 6 on a metric scale is expressed as $1 : 6$, where a colon is used instead of an equals sign. The value 1 could be 1 mm, 1 cm, or 1 m, as long as the unit value is expressed in a note on the drawing, such as "All dimensions in mm."

Reading a metric scale is just like reading an engineer's scale. See Fig. 34. A scale of $1 : 1$ means that the multiplier is 1, that is, the scale is read directly. If the scale has units of millimeters, then the value 43 becomes 43 mm, as shown. The 10 at the left-hand side merely means that 1 cm is divided into 10 parts, making each subdivision equal to 1 mm. Dropping the zero from the 10 marking on the scale gives the true multiplier, 1. This situation was seen also on the engineer's scale.

Again in Fig. 34, if you need a scale of $1 : 30$, you choose the 30 scale. Realize that the true multiplier of the scale is 3, not 30, because you must drop the zero to get the actual multiplier. If the true multiplier is 3, you must multiply all values read on the scale by 10, to get a scale $1 : 30$. Therefore the value read as 155 becomes 1550. The units are millimeters because values on this particular scale are in millimeters.

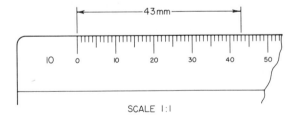

SCALE 1:1

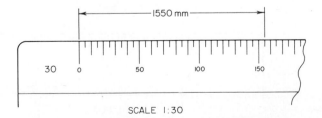

Figure 34
Reading the metric scale.

SCALE 1:30

11. IRREGULAR CURVES

Irregular curves are very helpful when you wish to fit a smooth curve along points which are not part of a circle. A *French curve* is another term for an irregular curve. These plastic curves come in a wide variety of styles; some are shown in Fig. 35.

The skillful use of an irregular curve is part art, part science. Refer to Fig. 36, which illustrates proper use. It is rare that an irregular curve will fit perfectly all points in just one position. The points in Fig. 36 seem to need six positions for a good-fitting curve. Often fewer positions are needed. These suggestions may help you to obtain a smooth curve.

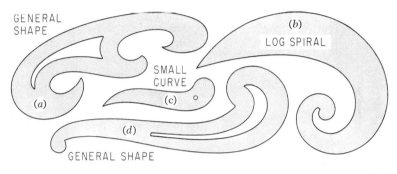

Figure 35
Various irregular curves.

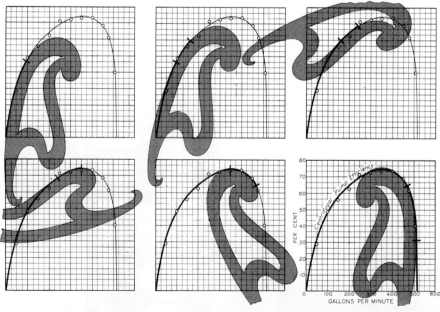

Figure 36
Use of an irregular curve.

■ Place the curve so that the direction of the tightening radius is also that of the points to be fitted.

■ Always stop short (perhaps ½ in) of the maximum arc length that you could fit. This will allow a smooth transition for the next position of the curve.

■ Overlap slightly (perhaps ½ in) a subsequent position of the curve with the previous one. This will maximize a smooth fit.

■ Take advantage of symmetry of points, when possible, by flipping the curve to its mirror-image position. Figure 36 does not offer this advantage.

■ 12. TEMPLATES

Templates are a great time saver for the sketcher and drafter. Holes of various configurations are stamped in plastic which can then be used as the contour of a selected shape. The variety of templates is almost endless. They exist for every aspect of engineering—civil, architectural, electrical, and others.

Everyone can make good use of the most common template, the circle (Fig. 37). Circle templates work well when a compass is not handy or if the circle is very small. With regular compasses you will have difficulty making circles smaller than about 15-mm (⅝-in) diameter.

Ellipses are another common geometric shape. Many varieties of ellipse templates can be purchased. One is seen in Fig. 38. A properly sized ellipse template can save you the trouble of constructing an ellipse. Two other templates are shown in Figs. 39 and 40. These are just representative of the many types available. You should check the listing of templates in the catalog of a major drafting supply manufacturer.

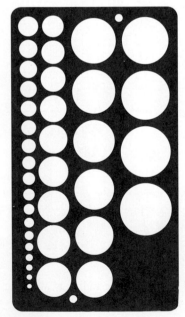

Figure 37
Metric circle template. (Courtesy Koh-I-Noor Rapidograph, Inc.)

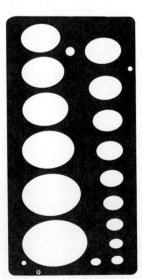

Figure 38
45° ellipse template. (Courtesy Koh-I-Noor Rapidograph, Inc.)

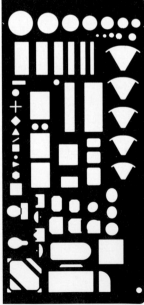

Figure 39
Template for architectural symbols. (Courtesy Koh-I-Noor Rapidograph, Inc.)

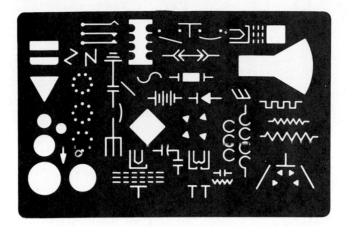

Figure 40
Template for electronic symbols.
(Courtesy Koh-I-Noor Rapidograph,
Inc.)

■ 13. PROTRACTOR

One of the easiest ways to lay off an angle is by using a protractor. A common type is seen in Fig. 41. Many people have used a protractor since grade school days. The one shown in Fig. 41 allows for any angle between 0 and 180°. Better protractors are made of a good-quality transparent plastic with the degree markings etched into the plastic, not painted on the surface. It is advisable to obtain a reasonably large protractor, about 6 in long, to increase the accuracy of your readings.

Figure 41
A protractor of the semicircular type.
(Courtesy Koh-I-Noor Rapidograph,
Inc.)

■ 14. SUMMARY

The instruments discussed in this chapter are basic to sketching and drafting. At low cost they can assist people who want to make initial sketches or drawings before going to the computer for the final form of the design.

It is certainly true that editing can be done with CAD software. Lines can be modified by length changes, rotations, and translations. But there is still a valid need for the basic instruments. These instruments are very compact, fitting easily into a small briefcase (except the T square) for transport to onsite locations where a computer may be inaccessible or impractical (for example, no electric power). Sketches and simply preliminary drawings enable designers to think quickly and cheaply on paper in preparation for the final drawings to be outputted on a pen plotter via a CAD system. Manual efforts and CAD thus complement each other.

PROBLEMS

Problem 1

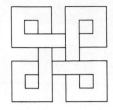

1. An interlacement. For T square, triangle, and dividers. Draw a 100-mm square. Divide the left side and lower side into seven equal parts with dividers. Draw horizontal and vertical lines across the square through these points. Erase the parts not needed.

Problem 2

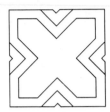

2. A square pattern. For 45° triangle, dividers, and scale. Draw a 4-in square, and divide its sides into three equal parts with dividers. With 45° triangle, draw diagonal lines connecting these points. Measure ⅜ in on each side of these lines, and finish the pattern as shown in the drawing.

Problem 3

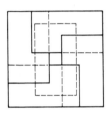

3. Five cards. Visible and hidden lines. Five cards 45 by 75 mm are arranged with the bottom card in the center, the other four overlapping each other and placed so that their outside edges form a 100-mm square. Hidden lines indicate edges covered.

Problem 4

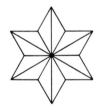

4. A six-point star. For compass and 30°-60° triangle. Draw a 100-mm construction circle, and inscribe the six-point star with the T square and 30°-60° triangle. Accomplish this with four successive changes of position of the triangle.

Problem 5

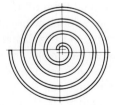

5. A four-centered spiral. For accurate tangents. Draw a 3-mm square and extend its sides as shown. With the upper right corner as center, draw quadrants with 3- and 6-mm radii. Continue with quadrants from each corner in order until four turns have been drawn.

6. Drawing of inner toggle for temperature control. Use decimal scale and draw 10 times size.

Problem 6

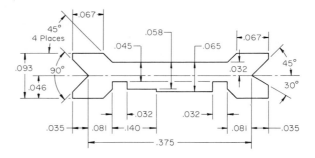

7. Drawing of a mounting leg—O control. Scale, full size.

Problem 7

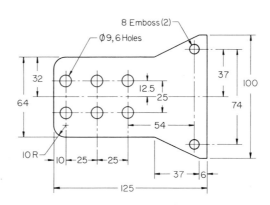

8. Drawing of a brake shoe. Stamped steel. Scale, full size.

Problem 8

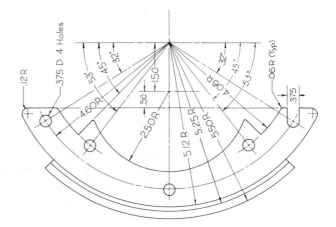

C H A P T E R 3

LETTERING
FOR CAD

■ 1. OVERVIEW

Lettering is an essential component of any design drawing. With lettering, the designer can provide dimensions, notes, and titles. Every design drawing contains some form of lettering. Figure 1 is a sample of a drawing containing a variety of lettering to meet design needs.

The art and science of lettering have been practiced for centuries, in fact, since words were first recorded thousands of years ago. At first, all lettering was done by hand. Certain persons became quite skilled in this area, such as monks who transcribed biblical texts.

More recently, drafters were trained throughout the industrial revolution from 1800 to 1900 to draft the mechanical developments of the time. The drawings were the plans from which the new products could be manufactured. Lettering on the drawings was still done manually, often with great skill and beauty. Manual lettering was necessary well into the twentieth century as an integral part of design drawings. A typical example of a drawing including hand-done lettering is seen in Fig. 2. The part is hand-lettered, although the supporting lettering in the title area is preprinted, to save time and to provide consistency within the company from one drawing to the next.

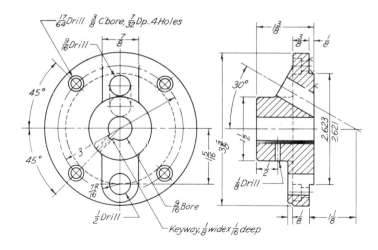

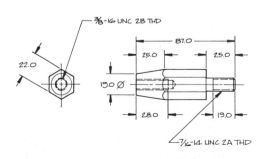

Figure 1
Drawing containing typical lettering.

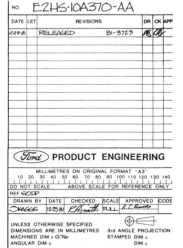

Figure 2
Drawing containing hand lettering and preprinted lettering. (Courtesy Kentucky Truck Plant, Ford Motor Company.)

■ 2. ASSISTANCE IN LETTERING

Drafters have long appreciated aids for their lettering tasks. A number of devices have been used for some time. Two are seen in Fig. 3. Both the Braddock-Rowe triangle and the Ames lettering instrument are traditional devices used to control the spacing within and between lines of lettering. Use of the Ames instrument is shown in Fig. 4. Templates are also available to ease the task of lettering. One simple example is seen in Fig. 5. It provides what is often called ''mechanical'' lettering, for the user inserts the pencil into the selected letter or number and traces the appropriate contour. The scriber of Fig. 6 also creates mechanical letters. A pin traces the selected letter while the pen replicates it on the paper. Dry transfers are another aid for drafters. These press-on letters and symbols, seen in Fig. 7, come in a wide variety of styles.

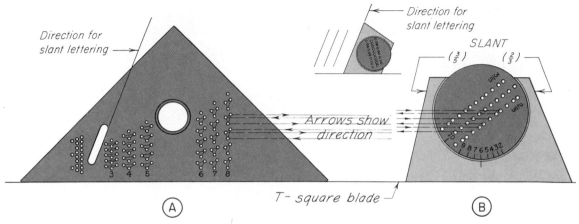

Figure 3
(A) Braddock-Rowe triangle. (B) Ames lettering guide.

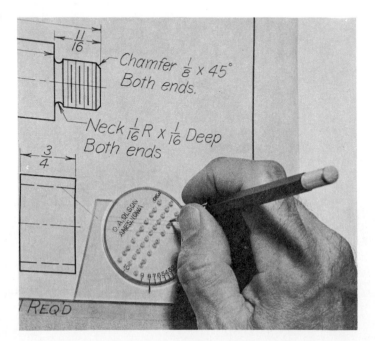

Figure 4
Using the Ames lettering instrument. Lines are drawn as the pencil moves the instrument along the T square (for triangle.)

Figure 5
Lettering template. (Courtesy
Gramercy Corp.)

ABCDEGHJKLMNOP STUVWXYZ
1234567 9&
TIMESAVER   LETTERING GUIDE   NO. 460-V

Figure 6
A scriber set in use. (Courtesy
Koh-I-Noor Rapidograph, Inc.)

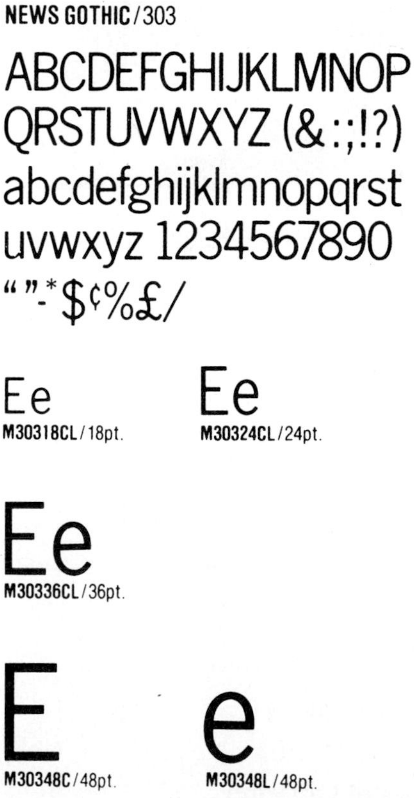

NEWS GOTHIC/303

ABCDEFGHIJKLMNOP
QRSTUVWXYZ (&:;!?)
abcdefghijklmnopqrst
uvwxyz 1234567890
" "-*$¢%£/

Ee
M30318CL/18pt.

Ee
M30324CL/24pt.

Ee
M30336CL/36pt.

E
M30348C/48pt.

e
M30348L/48pt.

Figure 7
Dry transfer letters. (Courtesy
Chartpak Co.)

More recent is the arrival of elegant automated lettering systems, such as in Fig. 8. The user can letter in a variety of styles from preprogrammed modules. The user merely types in the desired notes, which are transferred to the paper via a plotter. This device is as far removed from hand lettering as one can get. It begins to approach techniques used in CAD systems, that is, typing in letters and symbols in a wide variety of available styles.

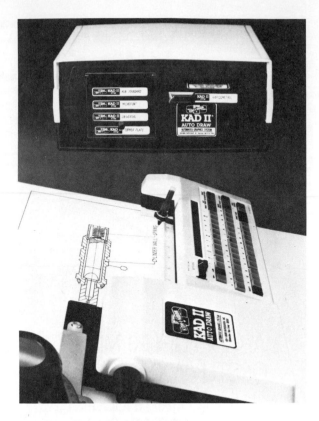

Figure 8
An automated lettering system
controlled by a microprocessor.
(Courtesy Koh-I-Noor Rapidograph,
Inc.)

3. BASIC CONSIDERATIONS IN LETTERING

Next we discuss aspects of lettering that are basic to any mode, manual or computer-generated. Examples of these aspects are illustrated by CAD software, although hand-drawn examples could serve the purpose as well. These aspects of lettering should be considered:

- Styles
- Uppercase vs. lowercase
- Vertical vs. slant
- Size
- Aspect ratio
- Rotation

a. Styles of Lettering

Traditionally lettering styles have been limited only by the imagination of the drafter. Fancy and intricate styles, however, have limited practical use on design drawings because of the time needed to draw them. Users of drawings need only a simple, clear style to facilitate the reading of a drawing. The style shown in Fig. 9, while attractive, is not needed.

TEMPERATURE

Figure 9
A time-consuming lettering style.

However, with the advent of software-driven lettering in CAD systems, the CAD operator is tempted to make use of available styles or fonts. Usually, a simple, quickly drawn style is chosen to minimize plotter time. Figure 10 shows a clear basic style. The pen needs to make only single-stroke motions in the execution of each letter or number, so time is saved. A more ornate style, such as that in Fig. 11, might be used with discretion, such as for a design title only.

TEMPERATURE

Figure 10
An efficient lettering style.

TEMPERATURE

Figure 11
A limited-use lettering style.

The recommended standard for engineering drawings is a simple style. The American National Standards Institute (ANSI) suggests use of single-stroke Gothic characters, as seen in Fig. 12. Such a style ensures good reproducibility and thus good readability.

ABCDEFGHIJKLMNOP
QRSTUVWXYZ&
1234567890
R
abcdefghijklmnopqrstuvwxyz
Height of general drawing lettering
2/3 Height of general drawing lettering

Figure 12
Standardized vertical letters. (ANSI Y14.2M.)

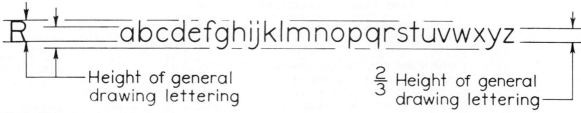

b. Uppercase vs. Lowercase Lettering

Lettering is available in both uppercase (capital-letter) and lowercase (small-letter) formats. When is each format used? You use primarily lowercase lettering almost automatically when you write freehand. A letter written to a relative is invariably done mostly with lowercase lettering (you use capital letters to start sentences). The smaller size of the uppercase letters makes the words flow well and with reasonable speed. Few of us have written a letter in all-uppercase format.

Uppercase lettering, however, is highly readable on a drawing. While one cannot find fault with the lowercase style neatly done in Fig. 4, commercial practice leans toward heavy use of the uppercase format, such as in Fig. 13. Individual letters, numbers, and words can be done by pen plotters in uppercase format about as fast as in lowercase. Because of high readability, uppercase is the preferred format on drawings, as recommended in ANSI Standard Y14.2M.

c. Vertical vs. Slant Lettering

Use of vertical vs. slant lettering is largely a matter of personal or corporate taste. Either format is acceptable, although vertical lettering seems to be more common. Lettering which slants with a 5 : 2 slope ratio, as in Fig. 14, is attractive and recommended. CAD software, however, will permit any slope ratio, as seen in Fig. 15.

d. Size of Lettering

The key element in selecting the size is that the lettering be readable. In practice, lettering is normally at least 0.125 in (3.5 mm) high. Table 1 offers some useful guidelines for which heights are appropriate to various uses.

Table 1   Recommended Minimum Letter Heights

METRIC mm		USE	INCH		DRAWING SIZE
FREEHAND	MECHANICAL		FREEHAND	MECHANICAL	
7	7	DRAWING NUMBER IN TITLE BLOCK	0.312	0.290	LARGER THAN 17 x 22 INCHES
			0.250	0.240	UP TO AND INCLUDING 17 x 22 INCHES
7	7	DRAWING TITLE	0.250	0.240	ALL
7	7	SECTION AND TABULATION LETTERS	0.250	0.240	
5	5	ZONE LETTERS AND NUMERALS IN BORDERS	0.188	0.175	
3.5	3.5	DIMENSION, TOLERANCES, LIMITS, NOTES, SUBTITLES FOR SPECIAL VIEWS, TABLES, REVISIONS, AND ZONE LETTERS FOR THE BODY OF THE DRAWING	0.125	0.120	UP TO AND INCLUDING 17 x 22 INCHES
5	5		0.156	0.140	LARGER THAN 17 x 22 INCHES

BEVEL GEAR DATA	
NUMBER OF TEETH	81
DIAMETRAL PITCH	10.4516
PITCH DIAMETER (THEOR)	7.750
PITCH ANGLE	82° 58'
ROOT ANGLE (BASIC)	80° 56'
PRESSURE ANGLE	20°
ADDENDUM (THEOR)	.042
WHOLE DEPTH (APPROX)	.181
CONE CENTER TO CROWN	.437
CONE DISTANCE	3.9044
BACKLASH WITH MATE	.010/.014
NO OF TEETH IN MATE	10
MATING GEAR PART NO	1620 D 10
DRIVING MEMBER	PINION

NOTES

Ⓑ CARBURIZE AND HARDEN ENCLOSED ZONE TO ROCKWELL "C" 58 MIN - FINISHED CASE DEPTH .020-.025 DP - CORE AND UNCARBURIZED AREAS TO BE ROCKWELL "C" 27 MIN

FINISH UNLESS NOTED TO 100√ ALL OVER

GEAR AND PINION TO BE MATCHED AND LAPPED AS A SET - ETCH GEAR WITH SET NO, MOUNTING DIST, AND BACKLASH

MAGNETIC INSPECT PER MIL-I-6868

STATICALLY BALANCE TO WITHIN 0.06 INCH-OUNCES

PITCH DIAMETER OF GEAR CONCENTRIC TO A WITHIN .002 FIR

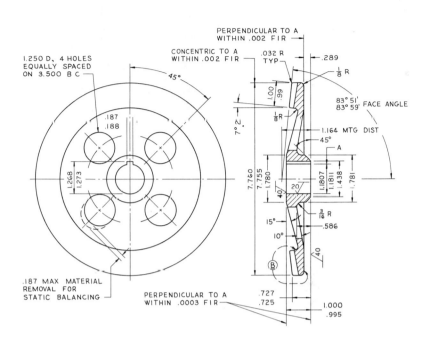

Figure 13
Sample of uppercase lettering.

$ABCDEFGHIJKLMNOP$
$QRSTUVWXYZ\&$
1234567890

Figure 14
Standardized slant lettering. (ANSI Y14.2M.)

MACHINE

Figure 15
Lettering having slope ratio of 2:1.

If a drawing is to be reduced for any reason, the lettering must be sufficiently large to be readable after reduction. The primary constraint in all cases is the legibility of the lettering.

e. Aspect Ratio

The width/height ratio of letters is the *aspect ratio*. The original font style is said to have a 1 : 1 ratio. If all the widths were made 1.3 times the original values, the aspect ratio would be 1.3 : 1. An aspect ratio can be less than 1 : 1, as seen in Fig. 16.

Aspect ratios greater than 1 : 1 create what is called *extended lettering*. Ratios less than 1 : 1 generate *compressed lettering*. Different aspect ratios are easily provided with CAD software. It is up to the drafter or CAD operator to select a pleasing aspect ratio for a particular application.

THIS IS 1:1 ASPECT RATIO

Figure 16
Effect of aspect ratio on lettering.

THIS IS 0.7:1 ASPECT RATIO

f. Rotation of Lettering

Most lettering is presented in a horizontal format. In graphs, however, on some occasions lettering that is other than horizontal may be used. Also lettering can be placed at any angle between horizontal (0°) and vertical (90°). Figure 17 shows various possible angles. Note the different slope for negative angles contrasted to positive angles. Software in CAD packages allows the user to select an appropriate rotation angle for the task at hand.

The discussion above concludes our study of the six basic considerations in lettering. Many options are available to the drafter. The considerations apply equally well to manual and CAD modes of generation. Color variation could be added as an option in the presentation of graphics. However, the physical and psychological effects of color variation will not be discussed now.

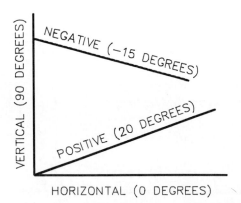

Figure 17
Effect of slope on lettering.

■ 4. COMPOSITION

The drafter has control over the appearance of words, notes, and titles on a drawing. Whether they are done manually or by CAD, careful composition leads to ease of reading and an attractive format. Well-composed material is almost as easy to achieve as a casual unconcerned look. The reward for care taken is a drawing that can be read with accuracy, ease, and confidence. Figure 18 shows a drawing done by a student using CAD software. The drawing contains a simple title and notes. Now we look at some elements of such a drawing, that is, the words, notes, and titles.

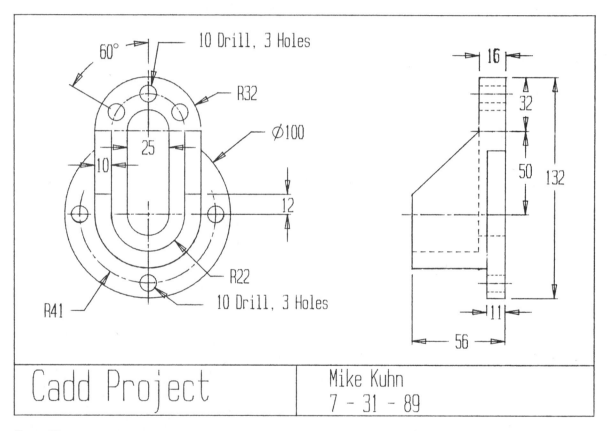

Figure 18
Drawing with notes and title.

a. Words

The composition of words is easily controlled when lettering is done by hand. The main concern is that the style be simple and that the spaces between the letters be close to equal. In Fig. 19 note the difference between the upper and lower lines. In the upper line, the areas between the letters are distinctly unequal. This produces an "accordian" effect, expanded in one place and compressed in another. In the

Figure 19
Effect of letter spacing.

lower line there are approximately equal areas between the letters. The overall effect is much improved. Software in CAD may or may not be able to provide equal areas between letters, depending on the sophistication of a particular package.

b. Notes

Notes are messages consisting usually of two or more words on the same line or multiple lines. Figure 20 features notes to convey information. Capital letters are the preferred style. Notes often have ''leader'' arrows pointing to the feature being described. A note should be as close as feasible to the described feature.

The vertical separation between lines typically may be from one-half letter height to full letter height. Often each line of a note gives its own distinct information, as in the note of Fig. 20: ''ϕ20, ϕ30 C'BORE, 10 DEEP.'' The line ''ϕ20'' indicates that the first, small hole has a diameter of 20 mm. The line ''ϕ30 C'BORE'' says that a 30-mm counterbored hole is provided. The last line, ''10 DEEP,'' reveals that the counterbored hole is 10 mm deep.

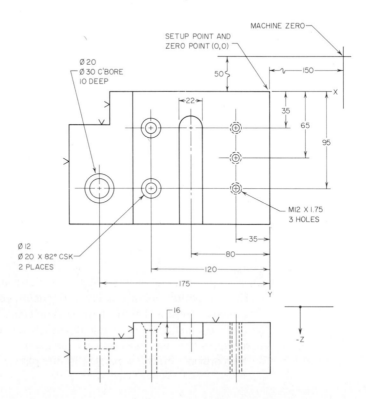

Figure 20
Use of notes in a drawing.

Many commercial drawings contain preprinted notes, as in Fig. 2. The notation "All parts must be individually identified . . ." is typical of a note that is needed from drawing to drawing. Why waste the time of a drafter or a computer-driven pen plotter in creating repetitive notes? Preprinted notes can be very cost-effective.

c. Titles

Titles, like notes, should be clear, concise, and easy to read. Titles convey needed information about a part or assembly and are often contained in a title block. A title block, shown in Fig. 21, is often preprinted. Information within the title block includes the name of the company, part, part number, drafter information, etc. The title block of Fig. 21 is called a *strip block* because it lies along the entirety of one edge. The title block of Fig. 2 occupies a large portion of the right-hand side of the drawing and contains a revision box. Obviously with such complete preprinted title blocks, the drafter has little lettering to do, which saves both time and money.

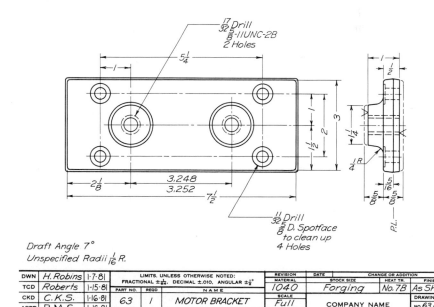

Figure 21
Use of a title block.

Some titles do not require extensive title blocks and may be done entirely by hand or by CAD software. For such titles, good composition is a necessary ingredient. Again, an attractive format can be an aid in readability. Capital letters are usually used, but the letters may be slightly higher than for notes, for emphasis. The style, font, or size of the lettering may differ from that used in notes if the drafter chooses. Good taste should be the rule. Bizarre styles and oversized letters only detract from the rest of the drawing.

Placement of titles can vary. For custom drawings done, for example, by an architect for a client, there is considerable freedom regarding placement. For a company generating a large number of similarly styled drawings, one expects to see the title in the same place on every drawing. The lower right corner of a drawing is a common location for such titles.

d. Title Styles

A number of styles for titles can be generated. Most include some form of justification, that is, placement of words relative to some vertical reference line. One popular style is for the title to be justified symmetrically about a vertical centerline, as in Fig. 22. The length of lines may vary from line to line. The result can be triangular, rectangular, diamond-shaped, or free-form, as in Fig. 22. The rectangular form, seen in Fig. 23, can be created by spacing letters within words so as to force the left- and right-hand edges to align along a vertical line. This style is sometimes called *left-* and *right-hand justification*. The advent of word processors has made this arrangement easier.

One simple style is left-hand justification, shown in Fig. 24. It is certainly easy to do, if not elegant. Another style is to split the justification between the left-hand and right-hand verticals. Figure 25 shows such a style, one which can be an interesting alternative. Also the title could be stretched into one or two lines along the entire lower edge of a drawing.

The structure of titles is limited only by company dictates or individual imagination, whichever has priority for a particular drawing. To a degree, this philosophy applies to all lettering. One advantage to the increasing use of lettering created by CAD software is that many lettering styles, sizes, and manipulations are now available and readily utilized. The need for skilled hand lettering is diminishing in the commercial world as CAD-generated lettering sees wider use. However, the ability to hand-letter well is still an asset in those situations where the human touch is desired or required.

A PROPOSAL
SCHOOL AUDITORIUM
CITY OF KENSINGTON
ADRIAN & ASSOCIATES
JUNE 1989

Figure 22
Title placed symmetrically about a centerline.

ENGINE ASSEMBLY
PORT MACHINE COMPANY
PHOENIX ARIZONA USA

Figure 23
Title of rectangular form.

ANALYSIS
STEERING GEAR
A.J. MILBURGH
CONSULTANT

Figure 24
Title with left-hand justification.

CIRCUIT
LOW POWER TRANSFORMER
FINE—TIME TOY COMPANY
TROY NY

Figure 25
Title with split justification.

PROBLEMS

Copy all notes below in ⅛-in (3-mm) height: Use manual or CAD method.

Problem 1

PAINT WITH METALLIC
SEALER AND TWO COATS
LACQUER AS PER CLIENT
COLOR ORDER.

Problem 2

THIS PRINT IS AMERICAN
THIRD-ANGLE PROJECTION

Problem 3

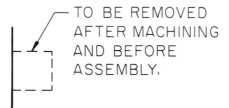

TO BE REMOVED
AFTER MACHINING
AND BEFORE
ASSEMBLY.

Problem 4

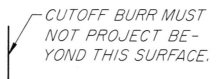

CUTOFF BURR MUST
NOT PROJECT BE-
YOND THIS SURFACE.

Problem 5

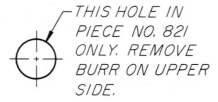

THIS HOLE IN
PIECE NO. 821
ONLY. REMOVE
BURR ON UPPER
SIDE.

Problem 6

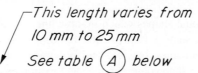

This length varies from
10 mm to 25 mm
See table Ⓐ below

CONSTRUCTION OF GEOMETRIC RELATIONSHIPS

■ 1. OVERVIEW

The way in which geometric elements interact to form patterns is of vital concern to drafters and designers. For example, how do straight lines properly touch arcs to form tangencies? How can one construct a perpendicular to the midpoint of a line? Such interaction of elements is common in design. Figure 1 shows a drawing, done by computer, which includes a number of interactions of geometric features.

You need to recognize how geometric relationships are constructed to better understand how to draft these relationships on the computer. In the following sections, single geometric shapes involving lines are discussed, followed by relationships between lines. Then geometric shapes involving curves are described, followed by a section on relationships involving lines and arcs. A final section highlights the geometry of solids.

■ 2. SINGLE GEOMETRIC SHAPES INVOLVING LINES

Individual shapes which involve lines are discussed early in this chapter because lines are such a fundamental building block of real-life objects. Information is offered on lines, angles, and polygons and how they may be constructed. The geometric shapes are defined, and examples are given of their construction.

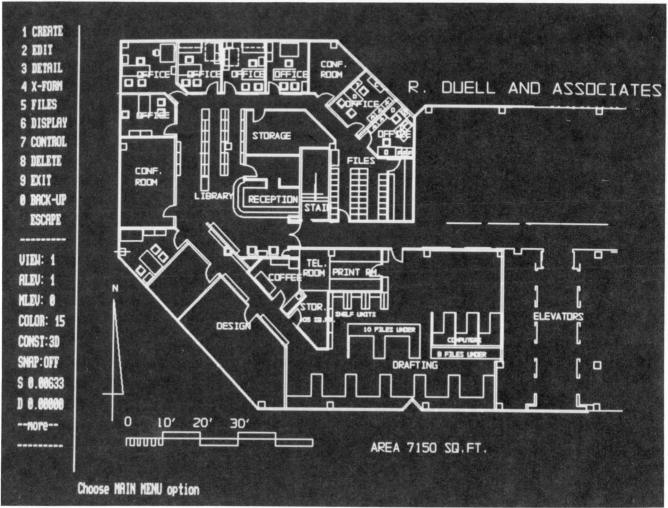

Figure 1
Part having geometric features.

a. The Line

A straight line may be defined by the existence of two points through which it passes. A line may also be determined by one known point, through which it passes, and a subsequent direction for the line. In Fig. 2 the line in case A passes through two given points, 1 and 2. The line may be thought of as infinitely long unless it has been otherwise limited. In case B a line originates at point 1 and moves to the right, an arbitrary choice. A line can also be constructed parallel or perpendicular to another line through some given point. Parallelism and perpendicularity are discussed later.

Figure 2
Defining a line.

b. An Angle

An angle is *acute* if it is less than 90° and *obtuse* if it is greater than 90°. A 90° angle is also called a *right angle*. An angle may be generated in several ways.

1. By subdivision of a circle.   A circle may be divided into equal angles either manually or by using specific CAD software. Figure 3A shows a simple division into eight sectors. The circle is thus divided into angles of 45° each.

2. By rotation of a line.   This method is convenient to use in CAD applications. A computer can be instructed to index or rotate a line about a given point in some incremental amount. In Fig. 3B, a line is being rotated counterclockwise about point *P* in 30° increments, thereby creating 30° angles.

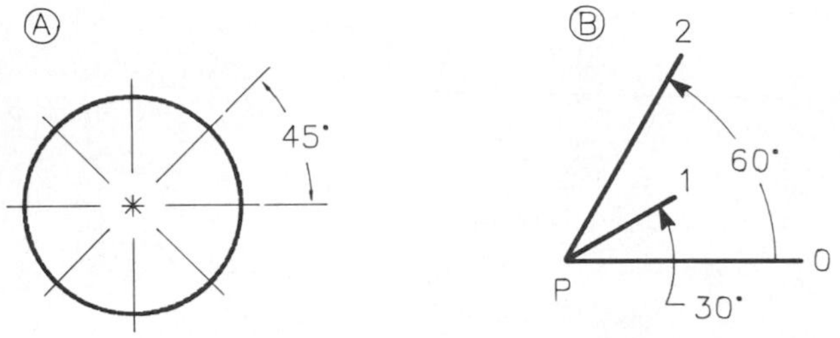

Figure 3
Generation of angles by (A) sub-division of a circle and (B) rotation of a line.

3. By use of the tangent.   Figure 4 shows the tangent method for making an angle. The tangent of angle *A* is *Y/X*. For angle *A* the tangent is found (by tables, calculator, or computer). Knowing the ratio of *Y* to *X,* you can lay out the angle by using some convenient *X* value (for example, 10) and then setting the corresponding *Y* value.

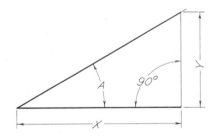

Figure 4
Angle by tangent.

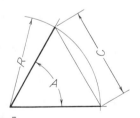

Figure 5
Angle by chord. The proportion of *C* to *R* is obtained from a table of chords.

4. By use of the chord.   A desired angle can be constructed if you know the chord length that corresponds to a given radius. In Fig. 5, you swing some desired radius *R* about a point on a horizontal baseline. The chord length *C* is found in a table of chord lengths for circle arcs (see App. 5). The table gives the chord length for a 1-in radius for any particular angle. Simply multiply the chord length for the 1-in radius by the desired radius. Then swing the obtained *C* as in Fig. 5 to create the angle.

c. Polygons

A *polygon* may be defined as any geometric figure bounded by three or more straight sides. Three-sided polygons are called *triangles*. Four-sided polygons are

Figure 6
Regular polygons.

PENTAGON   HEXAGON   HEPTAGON   OCTAGON   NONAGON   DECAGON   DODECAGON

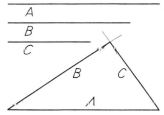

Figure 7
To construct a triangle. The legs are laid off with a compass.

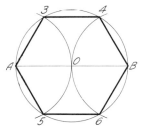

Figure 8
A hexagon. Arcs equal to the radius locate all points.

Figure 9
A hexagon. Tangents drawn with the 30–60° triangle locate all points.

termed *quadrilaterals,* and they include squares, rectangles, parallelograms, and trapezoids. Polygons having more than four sides include pentagons, hexagons, and others, shown in Fig. 6.

Construction of simple squares, rectangles, and parallelograms is self-evident. However, the manner of making triangles and hexagons is worth noting.

1. Triangles. A triangle can be easily created if the length of each side is known. In Fig. 7 lengths *A, B,* and *C* are combined by first laying out *A.* The intersection of arcs *B* and *C* determines that triangle. By way of interest, the construction of an isoceles triangle is seen in Fig. 5, discussed previously. That construction is proper when two equal sides and the included angle are known.

2. Hexagons. A hexagon can be constructed by using the known distance either across the corners or across the flats. Figure 8 shows that if the distance across the corners (the diameter) is known, the radius swung from points *A* and *B* gives corners along the circumference of the circumscribed circle.

The distance across the flats is equal to the diameter of the inscribed circle (see Fig. 9). Tangents to the inscribed circle at a 60° angle define the corners of the hexagon.

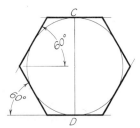

3. Rotation of polygons. Rotation of objects is a common and easily performed function of most CAD software. The general concept that can be applied is seen in Fig. 10. An enclosing box is placed as a boundary around the polygon. The box containing the polygon is then rotated through a desired angle at a selected point. All corners of the polygon retain their respective positions within the enclosing box.

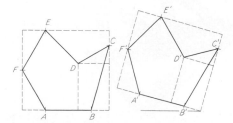

Figure 10
Rotation of a polygon.

■ 3. RELATIONSHIPS BETWEEN LINES

Individual geometric shapes involving lines have been discussed. Now it is important to see how lines can interact with one another. It is necessary to understand such relationships as parallelism and perpendicularity, which exist in abundance in the design world.

a. Parallelism

Generating parallel lines is a basic requirement of many designs. Parallel lines are those which are at a fixed distance from one another.

1. Coordinate system. In a coordinate axis system, such as in Fig. 11, the fixed distance between two lines can be seen. In Fig. 11, line AB has (x, y) coordinates of (50, 50) for point A and (150, 50) for point B. Line AB is 100 units long. Similarly, line CD has (x, y) coordinates of (50, 150) for point C and (150, 150) for point D. Line CD is also 100 units long. The separation between lines AB and CD is a constant 100 units. The lines are therefore parallel. Using parallelism with CAD software often involves the use of coordinates.

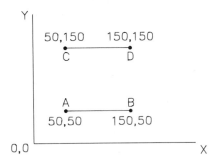

Figure 11
Parallel lines defined by coordinates.

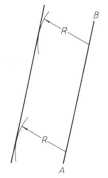

Figure 12
Parallel lines. The parallel is drawn tangent to a pair of arcs.

2. Use of arcs. A constant distance between lines can also be generated by use of a radius R equal in measurement to the desired distance between two lines. Figure 12 indicates how a line is generated parallel to line AB at a distance R away.

3. Use of triangles. Parallel lines can also be made by sliding one triangle along another. Figure 13 shows a line through P which is, by construction, parallel to AB. This is a simple but effective way to create parallels manually.

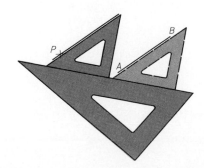

Figure 13
Parallel lines by sliding triangles.

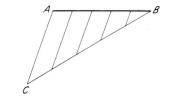

Figure 14
To divide a line.

4. Parallelism to divide a line.

Parallelism serves well to divide a line into equal parts. In Fig. 14 line *AB* has been divided into five equal parts by line *BC*. Line *BC* is at any angle to line *AB*, but its length is sufficient to allow five equal increments to be laid off on some convenient scale. Each increment might be 20 mm, for example. One then joins points *A* and *C* to form line *AC*. Finally, parallels are made to *AC* from the points laid off on *BC*. Line *AB* therefore will be divided in precisely the same proportions as line *BC*.

b. Perpendicularity

Like parallelism, perpendicularity is a primary component of many designs. Establishing the perpendicularity of one line relative to another is a very useful and simple procedure.

1. Coordinate system.

The position of points in an (*x, y*) coordinate system can be used to create a line perpendicular to a given line. In Fig. 15 line *AB* is given with (*x, y*) coordinates of (25, 35) and (75, 35). We want to construct a perpendicular *CD* to *AB*. Let *CD* be 25 units in length, and contact line *AB* at its midpoint.

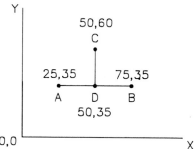

Figure 15
Perpendicular lines defined by coordinates.

The midpoint of line *AB* is at (*x, y*) coordinates of (50, 35). Therefore a perpendicular 25 units long must force point *C* to have coordinates of (50, 60). In effect, we have generated a perpendicular to a line (*AB*) from a point on that line (point *D*). In a similar manner we may construct from a point outside a line a perpendicular to the line (for example, from point *C* to *D* on line *AB*).

2. Use of arcs for perpendicular bisector.

To construct a perpendicular bisector of a line, swing from each end of the line any arc greater than one-half the length of the line. See Fig. 16. The intersections of the arcs establish the perpendicular bisector.

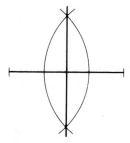

Figure 16
To bisect a line (with compass).

3. Use of triangles. We saw in Fig. 13 how triangles could be used to create parallel lines. Perpendiculars to a line can be created by flipping a triangle to make use of the 90° angle. Figure 17 shows this technique. The process can work for any situation if the base triangle on which the other slides is tilted off the horizontal.

The use of perpendicularity will be greatly extended in subsequent sections, particularly the use involving tangents between lines and arcs.

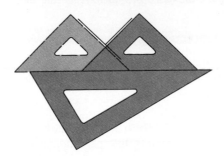

Figure 17
To draw a line perpendicular to another.

c. Use of Diagonals

Diagonals placed inside a shape can have several uses. See Fig. 18. At A the diagonals locate the center of a rectangle. At D the diagonals assist in creating inscribed figures. Cases B and C relate particularly to CAD applications in that they represent scaling of given shapes. Software for CAD normally includes scaling or zoom features to change the size of an object. The percentage change in the length of a diagonal will be reflected in the same percentage change in the size of the object. For example, if a diagonal is doubled and then tripled, the object will double and triple in size, as in case C of Fig. 18.

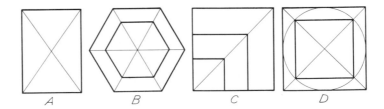

Figure 18
Uses of the diagonal.

A   B   C   D

4. SINGLE GEOMETRIC SHAPES INVOLVING CURVES

It is a rare design indeed that does not include a curve somewhere in its contours. We discuss a variety of the more common curves, such as arcs, circles, ellipses, and parabolas. In addition, we analyze hyperbolas, ogees, cycloids, and others.

a. The Arc

An arc may be considered as a portion of the circumference of a circle. An arc sweeping through 180° creates a semicircle, for example. The center of any arc lies on the perpendicular bisector of the chord of the arc. In Fig. 19 points O and P are to be endpoints of arcs. All created arcs must have their centers along line AB, which is the perpendicular bisector of chord OP. Two centers are shown: center R for the lightly drawn arc and center S for the darker arc.

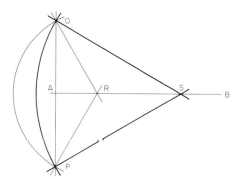

Figure 19
Arc centers.

b. Conic Sections

Figure 20 illustrates the generation of a circle, ellipse, parabola, and hyperbola. A right circular cone contains these sections, depending on the cutting angle.

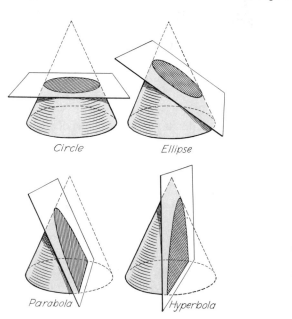

Figure 20
The conic sections.

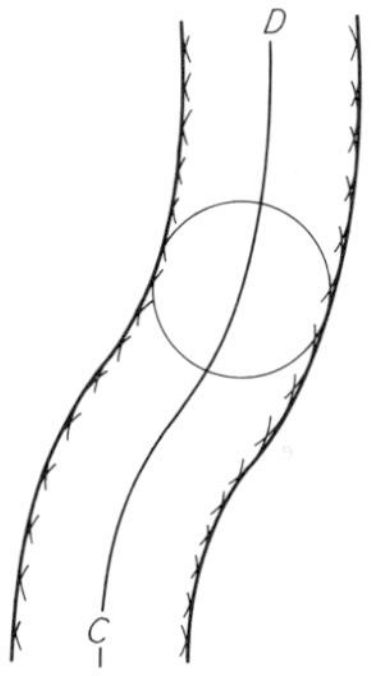

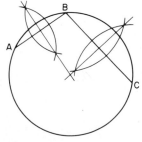

Figure 21
Circle through three points.

Figure 22
Curved parallel lines.

c. The Circle

A circle can be easily created by spinning a radius about a center. On another occasion it may be necessary to pass a circle through three given points. Points *A*, *B*, and *C* of Fig. 21 are given. Through chords *AB* and *BC* perpendicular bisectors are constructed. The intersection of the bisectors occurs at the center of the circle.

Circles can define parallel curves. If one has a given random curve such as curve *CD* in Fig. 22, curves parallel to *CD* can be constructed. The desired separation distance between the new curves becomes the diameter of the circle which generates the curves. Creating a number of circles which all have their centers on original curve *CD* creates the path of the desired curves. This technique is often seen in CAD when circles ''travel'' along a given curve, such as a sine curve. Dynamic animation can be the result.

d. The Ellipse

As a geometric shape the ellipse is both aesthetically attractive and structurally functional. Aside from the circle, the ellipse is probably the most common closed curve. In fact, an ellipse is a circle viewed at an angle. The form of an ellipse is seen in Fig. 23. It is described by the equation $x^2/A^2 + y^2/B^2 = 1$.

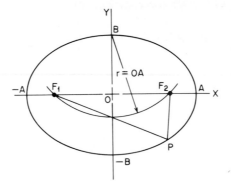

Figure 23
An ellipse by using focuses.

The shape of an ellipse may be generated by referring to Fig. 23. Distance $-AA$ (or $2OA$) is called the *major diameter*. Distance $-BB$ (or $2OB$) is the *minor diameter*. With the major and minor diameters known, the ellipse can be generated. First foci F_1 and F_2 are found by swinging OA (half of the major diameter) from B. Then point P is constrained to follow a path that ensures that distance $F_1P + F_2P$ constantly equals the major diameter $-AA$.

There are many manual ways to construct ellipses, although not all are suited to CAD procedures. One may find software that will generate an ellipse by merely specifying the coordinates of the center along with the desired major and minor diameters. However, there is a concentric-circle method which works well both manually and on a computer screen.

Observe Fig. 24 in which two circles are generated, one by using one-half the major diameter ($R = OA$) and the other by using one-half the minor diameter ($R = OD$). Radial lines are drawn to the large diameter from center O. Lines OP and OQ are two such lines. Points P_1 and Q_1 are thus created on the small diameter. Dropping verticals from points P and Q to intersect horizontals from P_1 and Q_1 gives points on the actual ellipse. This process is repeated sufficiently to generate a smooth ellipse.

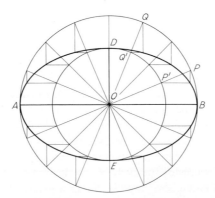

Figure 24
An ellipse by concentric-circle method.

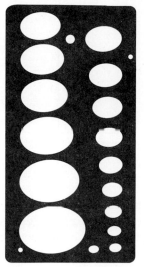

Figure 25
Ellipse template for a 45° ellipse angle. (Courtesy Koh-I-Noor Rapidograph, Inc.)

Ellipse templates are a very convenient tool for laying out an ellipse manually. Templates come in specific ellipse angles. The template in Fig. 25 is for 45°. Just what is the ellipse angle, and how is it found?

The *ellipse angle* is the angle of tilt that an original circle makes with a horizontal plane containing the major axis (the diameter of the circle). Note the ellipse angle in Fig. 26. The minor diameter decreases as the ellipse angle decreases until the original circle becomes a single line (an edge view). Conversely, as the ellipse angle increases, the minor diameter increases up to the limit at 90° ellipse angle, at which point the minor diameter equals the major diameter. That is, the true surface of the original circle would be seen.

To find the ellipse angle for a given ellipse, follow the procedure in Fig. 26. Radius 0-1 is swung from center 0 to intersect line 3-5 projected from 3 parallel to the major axis. A radial line is passed from 0 through the intersection of radius 0-1 and the horizontal 3-5. The ellipse angle is that angle between the major diameter and the radial line.

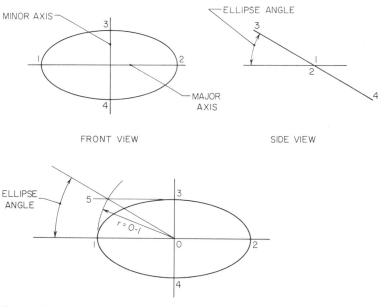

Figure 26
The ellipse angle.

e. The Parabola

Parabolic shapes are seen fairly often, as in optical reflectors and various engineering designs. The form of a parabola is seen in Fig. 27 where OX is the axis. When the vertex is at the origin $(0, 0)$, the equation for a parabola is $y^2 = 4ax$, where a is the distance from the vertex to focus F.

A parabola has the feature that any point P on the curve is always the same distance from the focus F as it is from the directrix. The directrix in Fig. 27 is the vertical line passing through point $(-a, 0)$. Therefore distance FP equals PQ.

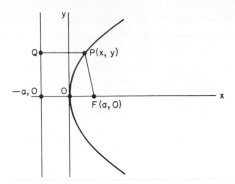

Figure 27
A parabola using focus.

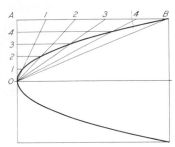

Figure 28
A parabola by parallelogram method.

A general parabola can have its axis parallel to either the x axis or the y axis. For a parabola parallel to the x axis, the general equation is $y^2 + 2gx + 2fy + C = 0$, where $g \neq 0$. For a parabola parallel to the y axis, the equation is $x^2 + 2gx + 2fy + C = 0$, where $f \neq 0$.

One of the easier methods to construct a parabola is the parallelogram method. Refer to Fig. 28. If the ratio of height (y axis) to width (x axis) for a particular parabola is given, the method can be readily applied. A rectangle enclosing the desired maximum height and width is divided into equal parts as shown. From the origin, lines are drawn to the subdivisions along AB. From the divisions along OA lines are drawn parallel to the x axis. The intersections of the constructed lines define points on the parabola. A smooth curve can then be fitted.

f. The Hyperbola

A hyperbola, seen in Fig. 29, is generated by a point P moving such that the difference between PF_1 and PF_2 is a constant. Points F_1 and F_2 are the foci. The equation of the hyperbola is $x^2/a^2 - y^2/b^2 = 1$ for the condition seen in Fig. 29. Note that the lines tangent to the asymptotes intersect at the origin.

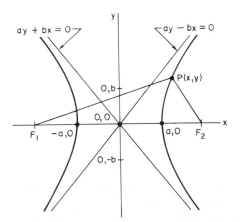

Figure 29
Elements of a hyperbola.

The constant-difference method to construct a hyperbola is seen in Fig. 30. Foci F_1 and F_2 are used as centers. Any radius greater than F_1B is selected, such as F_1P, and is swung from both F_1 and F_2. The radius $F_1P - AB$ is then also swung from F_1 and F_2, creating points on the hyperbola.

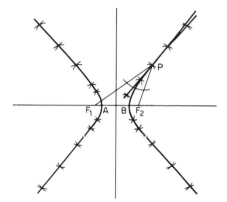

Figure 30
A hyperbola constructed by constant
Difference method.

g. The Cycloid

A *cycloid* is the trace created by a point on the circumference of a circle as the circle rolls along a straight line. In Fig. 31 position P is given in parametric form as $x = r\phi - r \sin \phi$ and $y = r - r \cos \phi$, where ϕ is the swept angle.

One method of constructing a cycloid is shown in Fig. 32. First, an original circle is drawn and divided into equal parts, here eight. The circumference of the circle, $2\pi r$, is laid out on baseline AB. Division points along AB (here eight) are projected perpendicular onto extended centerline CD. The intersections on CD form centers for constructed circles of the same radius as the original circle. Horizontal projections from the division points on the original circle intersect the respective constructed circles to give points on the cycloid.

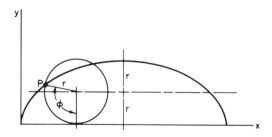

Figure 31
Creating a cycloid.

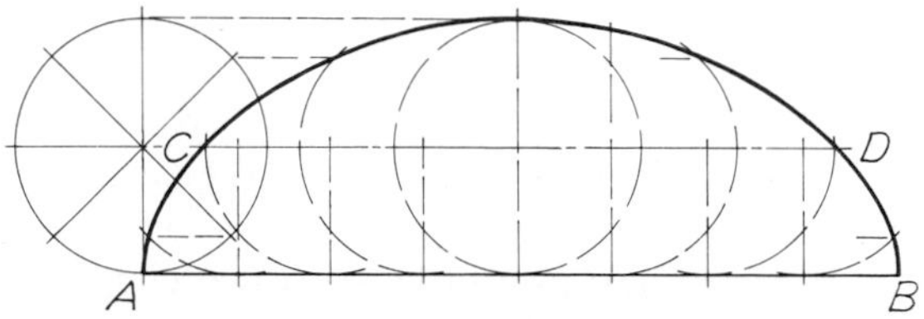

Figure 32
Constructing a cycloid.

h. Additional Specialty Curves

A considerable number of unique curves exist which have mathematical definitions. In this discussion we touched on only a few. Beyond the cycloid are curves such as involutes, logarithmic spirals, and cardioids. The forms of these curves are described in standard handbooks of engineering fundamentals. Computers can execute well these many forms of curves because the curves can be expressed by mathematical equations.

5. TANGENCIES INVOLVING LINES

The condition of tangency is extremely common and very important in design. Scarcely a product exists that does not include a tangency somewhere within its contours. Figure 33 shows but one product having tangencies. It is vital that a designer recognize tangencies and know how they are constructed. Software for CAD systems gives the user the elements needed to build tangencies (lines and arcs), but usually the CAD operator must assemble the elements into proper tangencies.

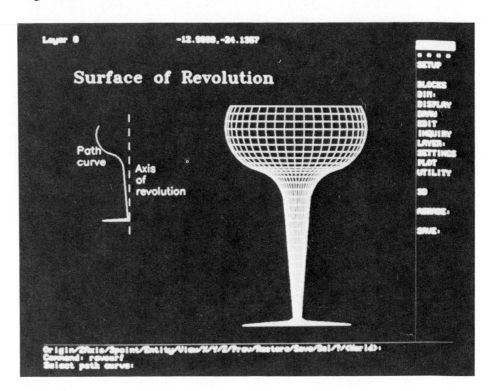

Figure 33
A part having tangencies. (Courtesy of Autodesk, Inc.)

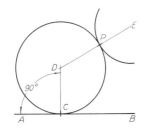

Figure 34
Tangent points.

Eventually we deal with three general categories of tangencies: tangencies between straight lines, between a line and an arc, and between arcs.

First it is necessary to recognize where tangent points exist. A helpful disclosure is seen in Fig. 34, which shows both a tangency between a line and circle and a tangency between two circles. The tangency between a line and a circle occurs at point *C*, where a *perpendicular* to line *AB* is constructed through center *D* of the circle. The tangency between two circles occurs where the line joining the two centers, *D* and *E*, crosses the circumference of both circles, point *P*.

a. Tangent to a Point on a Circle

Suppose in Fig. 35 that we wish to construct a tangent to the circle at point *P*. First we connect center *O* with point *P*. Then a tangent line *AB* at 90° to radius *OP* is needed. We can use the technique of Fig. 17 again, sliding one triangle over another. Side 1 of the triangle in Fig. 35 is aligned with *OP*. Side 2, being at 90° to side 1, will then give line *AB*, the needed tangency.

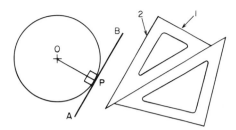

Figure 35
Tangent to a point on a circle.

b. Tangent to a Circle from a Point Outside

Refer to Fig. 36. A circle with a known center passes through points *A* and *B*. A tangency is desired from point *P* to the circle. Align one triangle so that an edge passes through point *P* and the visually estimated tangent point. You can make a good estimation of the tangent point by eye. However, the exact location of tangent point *C* is found by aligning through the circle's center the edge of the triangle which is at 90° to the edge used for the estimated tangent point.

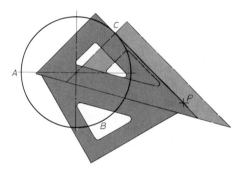

Figure 36
A tangent to a circle from a point outside.

c. Tangent to Two Circles

The process used in Fig. 36 can be employed to construct a tangent line to two circles. In Fig. 37 a T square (or triangle) gives a base on which a triangle can slide. Position 1 sets the estimated tangent points. Positions 2 and 3 give the exact tangent points T_1 and T_2 by utilizing the edge of the triangle at 90° to the edge first used.

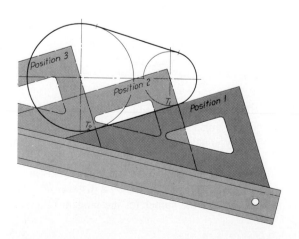

Figure 37
Tangents to two circles (open belt).

d. Tangent by Equations

In CAD work it is frequently convenient to give the form of lines as a mathematical expression. For example, the tangent point between a circle and a line lies on a line whose equation can be expressed. In Fig. 38 the same condition is given as in Fig. 35. A perpendicular is desired from center 0 with coordinates (x_1, y_1) to a given line. The equation of the given line can be expressed as $Ax + By + C = 0$. The equation of a line through (x_1, y_1) perpendicular to the given line is $B(x - x_1) - A(y - y_1) = 0$. The tangent point P will be at the intersection of the two plotted lines.

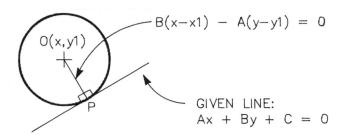

Figure 38
Tangent by use of equations.

e. Arctangent to Two Lines

To place an arc of radius R tangent to two lines, as in Fig. 39, locate point 0 equidistant from both lines, a distance R from each. How can you do this? Point 0 is found at the intersection of two *parallels* to given lines AB and BC. Each parallel must be a distance R from lines AB and BC.

You can construct the needed parallel lines in two ways. (We show both ways for interest.) One way is to swing two randomly located arcs of radius R from line AB, as was done in Fig. 12. Another way is to construct a line perpendicular to BC at any point along BC. On the perpendicular set off a distance R. Then run a parallel line to BC through the set-off point. By sliding triangles you can create this parallel line very easily.

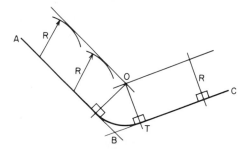

Figure 39
Tangent between lines.

Once the intersection of the constructed parallels provides point 0, you have almost finished. Simply construct perpendiculars from point 0 to both AB and BC. Then you have tangent points T. The arc of radius R is swung from point 0 between the tangent points.

In CAD applications, you might also find the equations of two lines parallel to the given lines, separated by a distance R. The intersection of the two parallel lines again gives the center for the tangent radius.

◼ 6. TANGENCIES INVOLVING LINES AND ARCS

There are two basic cases for tangencies between lines and arcs. One occurs when the center of the tangent arc is located *outside* the original arc. The other occurs when the center is *inside* the original arc.

a. Tangent Center Outside the Arc

Figure 40 illustrates the situation in which the needed tangent center is outside the original arc. We know that the tangent center E must be equidistant from both original arc AB and line CD, a distance R away. We realize that the tangent center E will be along a parallel to line CD at a distance R. Therefore we construct a parallel to CD, as was done in Fig. 39.

Center E must also lie along an arc constructed a constant distance R from original arc AB. This can be easily done if the construction arc to locate E is *concentric* to arc BC, that is, they share the common center 0. We simply *add* the tangent radius R to the original radius r, getting a radius of $R + r$ which is swung from center 0. The intersection of arc $r + R$ with the parallel to line CD gives the center E for the tangent radius R. One tangent point T is found by joining center E and 0. The other is located by dropping a perpendicular from E to line CD.

This construction emphasizes one vital idea. The radius to be made tangent is *added* to the original radius when the tangent center is *outside* the original arc. The result gives a *concave* tangency.

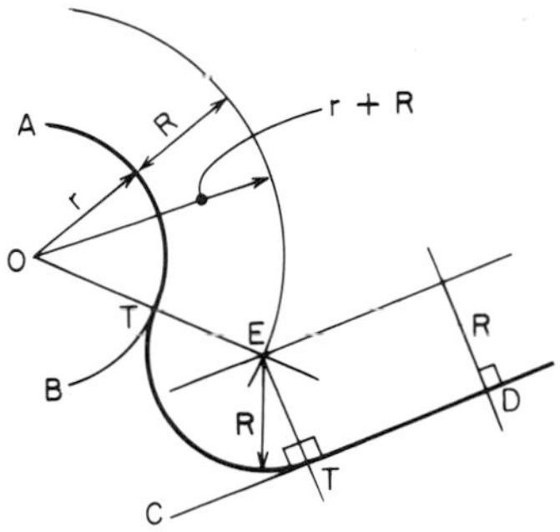

Figure 40
Tangent center outside an arc.

b. Tangent Center Inside the Arc

In Fig. 41 is the construction of a tangent inside an arc. Tangent center E must be a distance R from both arc AB and line CD. Center E is along a parallel to line AB. Therefore a parallel line is constructed to CD a distance R away.

Center E also is a distance R away from arc AB. Therefore an arc is needed that is concentric to arc AB but *inside* the original arc AB. Distance R is *subtracted* from radius r of the original arc. This difference $r - R$ is swung from center O. The intersection of arc $r - R$ with the parallel to CD gives center E. One tangent point T is located by extending a line through centers E and O to intersect arc AB. The other point is found by dropping a perpendicular from E to line CD.

Note the concept involved here. The radius to be made tangent is *subtracted* from the original radius when the tangent center is *inside* the original arc. A *convex* tangency results.

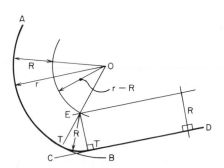

Figure 41
Tangent center inside an arc.

7. TANGENCIES INVOLVING ARCS

Two basic cases are discussed, and each uses concepts covered above. The first case is for the tangent center outside the arcs, and the second is for the tangent center inside the arcs.

a. Tangent Center Outside the Arcs

Refer to Fig. 42. Radius R is to be tangent to arcs AB and CD. Radius R is *added* to original radii r_1 and r_2. Radii $r_1 + R$ and $r_2 + R$ are swung from centers O_1 and O_2, respectively. The intersection at E gives the center for radius R. Note the similarity between this construction and that in Fig. 40. Tangent points T again are found by joining centers O_1 and E and O_2 and E.

The concept seen in Fig. 40 still holds. The tangent radius is *added* to the original radii when the tangent center is to be *outside* the original arcs. A *concave* tangency results.

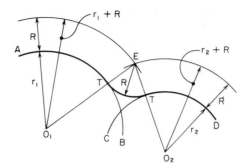

Figure 42
Tangent center outside two arcs.

b. Tangent Center Inside the Arcs

Figure 43 provides the needed information. A large radius R is to be tangent to arcs AB and CD. Radius R is extended from arbitrary points x_1 and x_2 on arcs AB and CD. The extension of R passes through centers O_1 and O_2. Original radii r_1 and r_2 are *subtracted* from R, giving radii $R - r_1$ and $R - r_2$. Radius $R - r_1$ is swung from center O_1 and radius $R - r_2$ from center O_2. The intersection at E gives the center for tangent radius R. The tangent points T are located by extending radial lines from point E through centers O_1 and O_2 to arcs AB and CD.

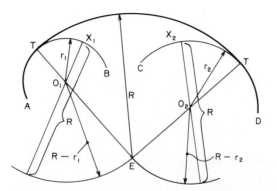

Figure 43
Tangent center inside two arcs.

The concept shown in Fig. 41 still holds. The tangent radius must be *subtracted* from the original radii when the tangent is *inside* the original arcs. A *convex* tangency is created.

c. Reverse Curves

A reverse curve, also known as an *ogee curve,* is shown in Fig. 44. Lines *AB*, *BC*, and *CD* are given plus point *E*, which is to be the inflection point for the reverse curve. Center O_1 is found by extending a perpendicular from point *B* to intersect the perpendicular bisector of *BE*. Center O_1 is therefore a distance R_1 from both point *B* and point *E*. An identical procedure is used to determine center O_2. As a check on construction accuracy, the line joining O_1 and O_2 should pass through *E*.

A variation in reverse curves is shown in Fig. 45. Here line *EF* cuts given lines *AB* and *CD*. Point *P* is to be the inflection point. Arc *EP* is swung to give point *G*. A perpendicular extending from *G* intersects the perpendicular through *P* to give center *H*. Similarly, center *J* is found by the intersection of a perpendicular from *K* and the perpendicular through *P*. The given lines need not be parallel, as seen in the other two examples of Fig. 45.

d. Compound Curves

A compound curve is any curve made up of a series of radii all of which share common tangent points. An example is seen in Fig. 46. Arc *AB* results from radius *R* being swung through angle α. Arc *BC* results when radius *r* is swung through angle β. The common point of tangency is *B*. Note that centers O_1 and O_2 share the same radial line O_1B. A compound curve can result only when centers share a radial line.

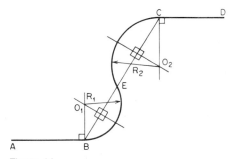

Figure 44
Construction of a reverse curve.

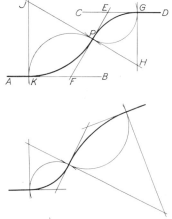

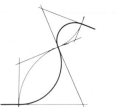

Figure 45
Variations in reverse curves.

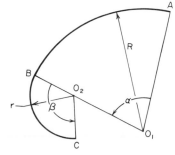

Figure 46
A compound curve.

8. GEOMETRY OF SOLIDS

Geometric figures discussed to this point have been strictly two-dimensional. Three-dimensional geometric solids, however, have a very important place in design. Virtually every object that people use is a 3-D solid. Many solids can be generated by revolving 2-D figures. A sphere, for example, is easily generated by revolving a circle 360° about an axis that is a diameter of the circle.

Software for CAD is increasingly able to handle 3-D shapes in a cost-effective manner. A sample of a CAD-generated solid is seen in Fig. 47. Both wire-frame and solid models are available, with the wire-frame format usually costing much less.

It is important that an overall survey be made of the various forms of solids. Detailed construction procedures will not be offered, but procedures for manual methods can be found in advanced texts and handbooks. Procedures for CAD applications can be studied within specific CAD manuals. Our purpose here is to define and illustrate some of the basic solids that you may encounter in design.

Figure 47
A CAD-generated solid. (Courtesy of Autodesk, Inc.)

a. Classification

Solids consist of closed *surfaces*. A surface may be created by the motion of either a straight or a curved line. In a brief outline we summarize the possible variations:

Surfaces generated by straight lines (ruled surfaces)

- Single-curve surfaces
    Cylinders
    Cones
    Convolutes

■ Warped surfaces
Single-ruled surfaces
Double-ruled surfaces

Double-curve surfaces (surfaces generated by curved lines)
Surfaces of revolution
Surfaces of general form

We survey these surfaces so you can become better acquainted with them. Two definitions are needed for our survey. First, a *generatrix* is a straight line which moves to form a desired surface. Second, a *directrix* is the straight or curved line which the generatrix contacts while forming the desired surface. An example is a right cylinder, seen in Fig. 48. The generatrix follows the path of the directrix (circle) around the axis, generating the cylinder.

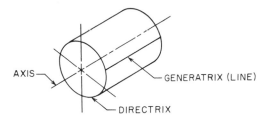

Figure 48
Elements needed to generate a solid.

b. Surfaces Generated by Straight Lines

The term *ruled surfaces* is often used to describe surfaces generated by straight lines, known as *elements*. As outlined, there are two types of such surfaces: single-curve surfaces and warped surfaces. A single-curve surface has curvature in only one direction. A warped surface has on its surface no side-by-side straight lines which either are parallel or intersect.

c. Single-Curve Surfaces

1. Cylinders.   A cylinder is generated by a straight-line generatrix that moves parallel to a straight-line axis while following a curved directrix. A right cylinder is created when the surface elements are perpendicular to the base. In an oblique cylinder, the surface elements are not perpendicular to the base. See Fig. 49. Many everyday cylinders have a circle as the directrix, but any closed curved shape is permitted, such as an ellipse.

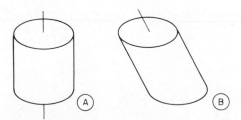

Figure 49
Cylinders. (A) Right cylinder.
(B) Oblique cylinder.

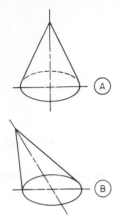

Figure 50
Cones. (A) Right cone. (B) Oblique cone.

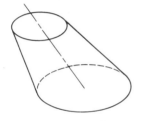

Figure 51
A convolute.

2. Cones. A cone is generated by a straight-line generatrix that moves so that one end is fixed and the other moves along a curved directrix. See Fig. 50. A right cone has its axis perpendicular to the base, intersecting the base at its center. In an oblique cone the axis is not perpendicular to the base.

3. Convolutes. Convolutes are less common than cylinders and cones, but they are not difficult to describe. Basically, a convolute is formed when a straight-line generatrix moves so as to always be in a plane that is tangent to the curved directrices. The simplest form of convolute is the conical convolute, seen in Fig. 51. This convolute becomes a truncated right cone for the special case in which the two directrices are circular and share an axis perpendicular to the base.

d. Warped Surfaces

Warped surfaces are often used as transition pieces between components of a design. Figure 52 illustrates a warped surface. As noted previously, a warped surface has no side-by-side parallel or intersecting elements.

Warped surfaces are seen as both single- and double-ruled surfaces. Single-ruled surfaces include cylindrical, conical, and helicoidal forms. Double-ruled forms generate various hyperboloids such as the circular, elliptical, and parabolic. A limited selection of specific warped surfaces is seen in Fig. 53. Warped surfaces can be expressed mathematically. Therefore CAD software of a sufficiently sophisticated nature can be used to display various warped surfaces in a 3-D mode. One must rely on specific instructions of the particular CAD package being used.

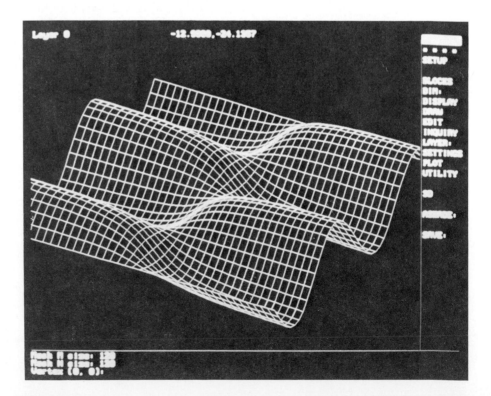

Figure 52
A warped surface.

Figure 53
Various warped surfaces.

e. Double-Curve Surfaces

A double-curve surface contains no straight line. Such surfaces are common in many designs, such as ship hulls, airplane fuselages, and automobile bodies. Double-curve surfaces include the simple and familiar, such as the sphere, as well as the more exotic, such as the annular torus.

There are two categories of double-curve surfaces: surfaces of revolution and surfaces of general form. A surface of revolution is created as a generatrix in the form of a curved line sweeps around a straight-line axis. A surface of general form results from either a variable- or a constant-shape curve sweeping along some noncircular path.

Figure 54 gives a sampling of the more common surfaces. Clearly many of these surfaces are generated by revolving common curves around an axis. In this way, a circle, ellipse, parabola, and hyperbola can all generate their own distinctive double-curve surfaces. Any curve that can be described by a mathematical expression can be created with appropriate CAD software as a 3-D surface.

In this chapter we provide the background for many common geometric constructions and shapes seen in design. A better understanding of these geometric forms can facilitate faster and more confident design, whether done manually or by computer.

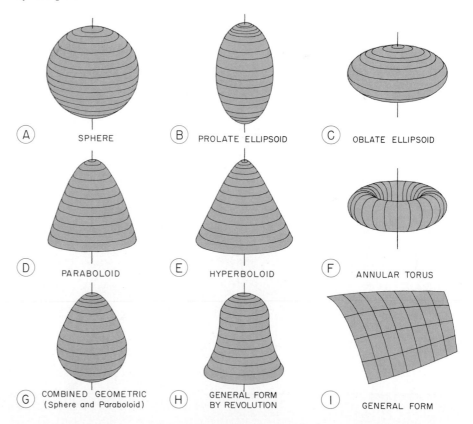

Figure 54
Various double-curved surfaces.

P R O B L E M S

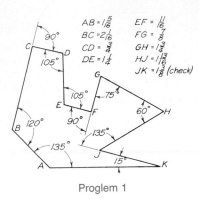

$AB = 1\frac{5}{16}$ $EF = \frac{11}{16}$
$BC = 2\frac{1}{16}$ $FG = \frac{7}{8}$
$CD = \frac{3}{4}$ $GH = 1\frac{3}{4}$
$DE = 1\frac{1}{4}$ $HJ = 1\frac{13}{16}$
$JK = 1\frac{3}{8}$ (check)

Proglem 1

1. Construct a polygon as shown in the illustration, drawing the horizontal line *AK* (of indefinite length) ⅜ in above the bottom of the space. From *A* draw and measure *AB*. Proceed in the same way for the remaining sides. The angles can be obtained by proper combinations of the two triangles.

2. Make a contour view of the bracket. In the upper reverse curve, radii R_1 and R_2 are equal. In the lower one, R_3 is twice R_4. Draw full size.

Problem 2

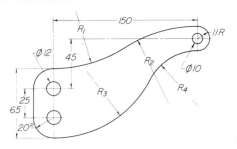

Problems 3 through 6. Draw these objects full size.

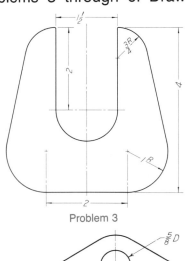

Problem 3

3. Front view of shim.

4. Front view of a level plate.

5. Drawing of heater tube.

6. Front view of an exhaust-port contour.

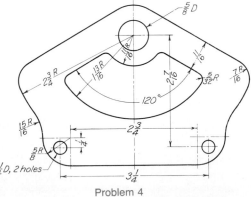

Problem 4

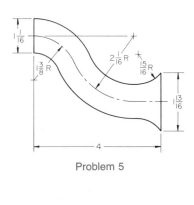

Problem 5

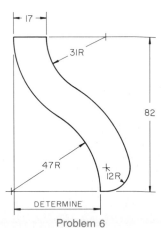

Problem 6

REPRESENTATION OF THE THREE-DIMENSIONAL WORLD

THE THREE-DIMENSIONAL ENVIRONMENT

1. OVERVIEW

We live in a world of three dimensions. It is natural that people express what they see in a 3-D format. People may actually make a 3-D model of an object. They also may draw the object in a 3-D mode on a two-dimensional plane, such as paper or a computer screen. An object seen in three dimensions occupies three axes of direction, typically called the x, y, and z axes. Figure 1 shows a simple object in relation to the three axes.

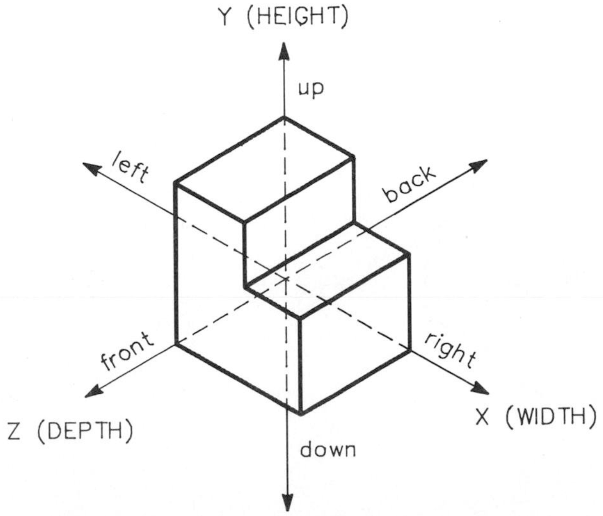

Figure 1
The three axes of space.

The three axes in space are mutually perpendicular. The y axis is the ''up-down'' axis, showing height. The x axis is the right-left axis, showing width. The z axis gives front-back direction, showing depth. The x and y axes define a vertical plane, as do the y and z axes. A horizontal plane is defined by the x and z axes.

The object shown in Fig. 1 can be rotated about any of the axes to show different effects. Notice in Fig. 2 that the object has been rotated 90° about the y axis. In Fig. 3, the object of Fig. 1 has been rotated 90° about the x axis, creating another effect. A final effect is seen in Fig. 4, where the object of Fig. 1 has been rotated 90° about the z axis. Many effects can be used to show various sides of an object. One may move the object through any angle about any axis. Figure 5 shows the original object rotated about the x axis through an angle less than 90°. The effects one may obtain are therefore limitless.

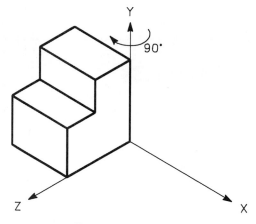

Figure 2
Rotation about Y axis.

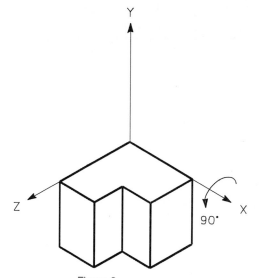

Figure 3
Rotation about X axis.

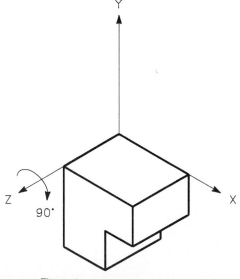

Figure 4
Rotation about Z axis.

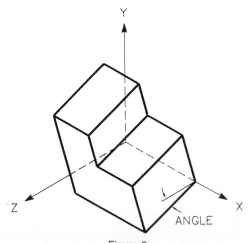

Figure 5
Random angle about X axis.

■ 2. PICTORIAL SYSTEMS

Over the years, people have organized the ways in which objects may be shown in three dimensions. This organization is helpful because we may select what the effect will be. There are three methods to display an object in three dimensions: axonometric, oblique, and perspective. The axonometric method also has three subclasses: trimetric, dimetric, and isometric. See Fig. 6 for an illustration of the various formats. We now look at each format separately to see its advantages and disadvantages.

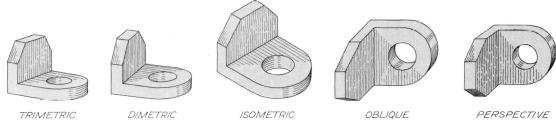

TRIMETRIC   DIMETRIC   ISOMETRIC   OBLIQUE   PERSPECTIVE

Figure 6
Formats for three-dimensional representation.

■ 3. AXONOMETRIC AXES

The system of axonometric axes is set up as in Fig. 1. This system is seen again in Fig. 7 but without the object's being given. Note angles 1, 2, and 3 among the three axes. An essential of axonometric axes is that neither angle 1 nor angle 3 may be drawn 90° on the paper or screen, although each angle *represents* 90° in space. We will see soon that when angle 1 or angle 3 is 90°, another system called the *oblique method* is defined. All three angles summed equal 360°, of course, because a full circle is swept by traveling clockwise from a reference position, such as the *y* axis.

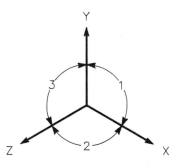

Figure 7
Axonometric axes.

You may select any values desired for the three angles, as long as angles 1 and 3 are not 90° and all values add to 360°. Figure 8A shows one configuration in which none of the three angles are equal. This method is used for *trimetric axes*. It is highly flexible because you have maximum control of the angles. It has few disadvantages, except that you must carefully draw or sketch the axis system desired.

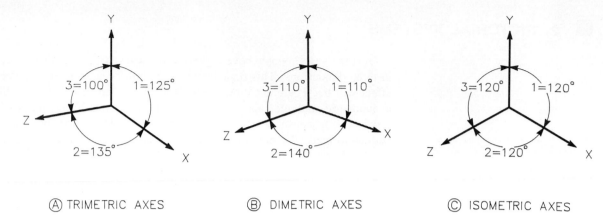

Ⓐ TRIMETRIC AXES   Ⓑ DIMETRIC AXES   Ⓒ ISOMETRIC AXES

Figure 8
Subclasses of axonometric axes.

If angle 1 equals angle 3 (but is not 90° or 120°), the format is used for *dimetric axes,* as in Fig. 8B. This format can have a quite attractive appearance. It can be used to emphasize certain surfaces that you wish to highlight. Alternately, angles 1 and 2 could be made equal for a different effect.

The most specialized method is that shown in Fig. 8C, which shows *isometric* axes. All three angles are equal, and therefore each must equal 120°. This format does not give any better results than the other two, but it is a very convenient method. The axes are easy to lay out since the two nonvertical axes, *x* and *z,* make a 30° angle with the horizontal. Drafters have ready access to 30° triangles, so the task of axis layout is straightforward. Also a 30° angle is not hard to estimate for sketching.

4. OBLIQUE AXES

If angle 1 or angle 3 is 90°, the resulting configuration gives oblique axes, as in Fig. 9. Angle 2 can be any value other than 0, 90, or 180°. Two popular layouts are seen in Fig. 10A. The 30 or 45° axis placement for axis *z* is convenient because drafters have 30 and 45° triangles close at hand. Also sketching these angles is not difficult. A resulting figure is seen in Fig. 10B, where the object is drawn in oblique. Note that planes of the object parallel to the *XY* plane are seen in true shape. Plane *F* is a plane seen in true shape.

The great advantage of oblique axes is that certain planes can remain true to shape, so that drawing them is faster and easier. This advantage will be apparent

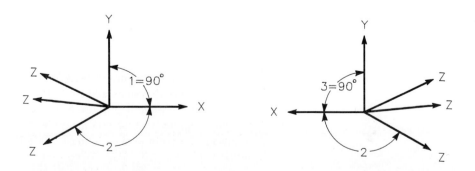

Figure 9
Generalized oblique axes.

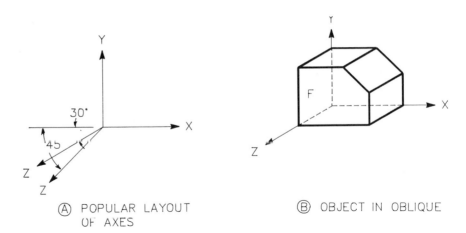

Figure 10
Practical use of oblique axes.

Ⓐ POPULAR LAYOUT OF AXES

Ⓑ OBJECT IN OBLIQUE

when we discuss the actual construction of oblique drawings and sketches. The only major disadvantage of oblique axes is that objects can look distorted along the z axis overall, an aspect we will see later.

5. PERSPECTIVE AXES

So far we have been dealing with axis systems that have one major assumption: parallel lines stay parallel along any given axis. For example, in Fig. 11A, any lines drawn along the x direction stay parallel, and likewise along the z direction. Such parallelism makes objects easy to draw, but it does introduce distortion. For real objects having parallel edges, those edges *appear* to converge as the edges go farther and farther away from us. The edges of a highway converge at a distant horizon, for example. This effect is called *perspective*. We will study perspective in a later section.

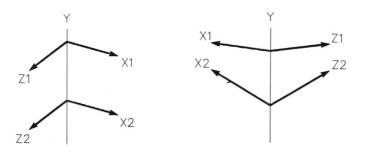

Figure 11
Nonperspective vs. perspective axes.

Ⓐ NON−PERSPECTIVE AXES

Ⓑ PERSPECTIVE AXES

The axes for a 3-D perspective method converge at a distance from us, as in Fig. 11B. If extended, the x and z axes would eventually come together at a vanishing point VP on the horizon. Axes in the y direction could also be nonparallel, if desired. The object seen in the other systems is shown in Fig. 12 in perspective. Perspective can give very attractive results. It is a system much used by architects and others who develop drawings to present to clients and the public.

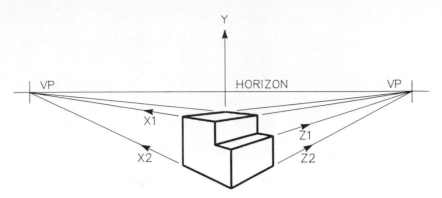

Figure 12
Use of perspective axes.

Perspective is more difficult to draw than axonometric or oblique, but the results may be well worth the effort. Sketching a perspective, however, need not be any more difficult than using the axonometric or oblique method.

6. FREEHAND SKETCHING OF PICTORIALS

Ideas for shapes of objects are seen first in the human mind as 3-D shapes. Shapes for parts to be designed evolve from the 3-D conceptualization. Whether the design is for a chair, an electronic chassis, or a car steering mechanism, ideas are often first realized as freehand 3-D sketches. To be able to sketch in three dimensions is a great asset. Sketching allows your mind to express ideas freely and with a good representation of what you are considering for a design.

There are three choices of method for showing objects in three dimensions. These relate directly to the three axis systems already discussed: axonometric, oblique, and perspective. The choice depends partly on the sketcher's personal tastes. Some like to sketch in axonometric, others in oblique. The choice also depends on how you wish to highlight features of an object.

Perspective gives the most realistic appearance of an object but has the problem that parallel lines do not stay parallel in most cases. The isometric method (in the axonometric classification) is easy to use but may make some objects look odd. The oblique method is excellent if you wish to keep a forward-face true shape. It is a popular format because of its simplicity.

7. SELECTION OF PENCIL AND PAPER FOR SKETCHING

Three variables affect the appearance of a sketched line: the pressure exerted on the lead, the grade of lead, and the texture of the paper. Naturally, the harder you press on the lead, the darker the line you will get, up to the limit where the lead breaks! Also the harder the lead, the lighter the line for the same pressure exerted. Finally, the texture of the paper will affect the darkness of the line, given the same grade of lead and pressure exerted.

Figure 13A and B shows the effects on both pressure and grade of lead. The combination of softest lead (6B) and greater pressure produces the darkest line. Figure 14A and B shows the effect of paper texture. The smooth paper gives a more solid, close-grained line than the rough paper for the same applied pressure.

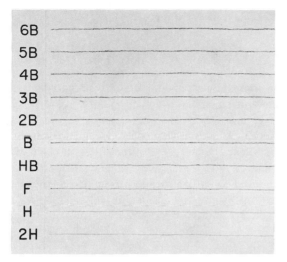

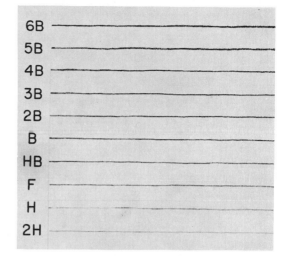

Figure 13
Effects of lead pressure and grade.

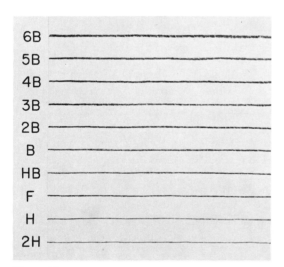

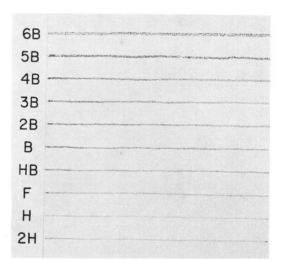

Figure 14
Effects of paper roughness and lead grade.

8. STYLES OF PAPER FOR SKETCHING

Sketchers may choose from a wide selection of paper styles and forms. Some sketchers like to work on plain white paper having a texture (smoothness) that pleases them. Others prefer a colored paper, with light green, buff, and blue papers being popular. In addition to plain paper, gridded paper can be used effectively. Gridded paper is subdivided evenly by a number of grids per inch or centimeter. Grid lines can serve as guidelines to the sketcher to help keep lines straight and parallel to each other. Special paper with isometric grids is helpful for sketching in that mode.

■ 9. TECHNIQUES OF SKETCHING

Figure 15
Sketching a vertical line.

Figure 16
Sketching a horizontal line.

Beginning sketchers sometimes worry that their lines will be too "sketchy" or wiggly. This worry should not be a major concern. The two most important rules of sketching are that lines should have good directional stability as well as uniform darkness, sharpness, and thickness.

Hold the pencil loosely and well away from the point. Figures 15 and 16 show the positions for creating vertical and horizontal lines, respectively. To ensure directional stability, keep your eye on the endpoint of the line being drawn. Make short strokes rather than try to draw a long line with one sweep. Inclined lines may be made as in Fig. 17A and B. It is also good technique to rotate the paper to various positions so that you can make lines comfortably and accurately.

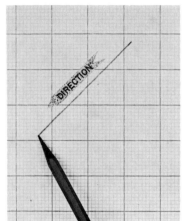

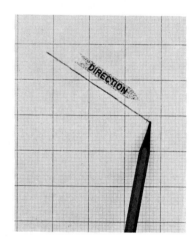

Figure 17
Sketching inclined lines.

Circles can be sketched best by marking the radius along radial lines placed at about 45° intervals. See Fig. 18. Sketch a circle a bit at a time, to increase your accuracy.

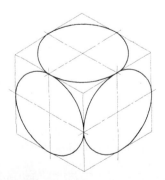

Figure 19
Sketching isometric circles.

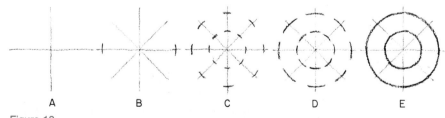

Figure 18
Method of sketching freehand circles. (A) Draw center lines; (B) draw diagonals; (C) space points on the circle with *light*, short lines (by eye); (D) correct and begin filling in; (E) finish.

Ellipses are best done by boxing in the enclosing squares. Then blend in a smooth curve which is tangent at each midpoint of a square. Figure 19 shows the process for an isometric sketch.

10. SELECTION OF AXES FOR SKETCHING

a. Isometric

The axes must contain a vertical line and two lines at 30° to the horizontal (Fig. 8C). No 30° triangle is available if you are going to sketch freehand, so you must estimate the 30° angles. One good way to estimate angles is seen in Fig. 20A. The human eye can estimate thirds of a quadrant fairly well.

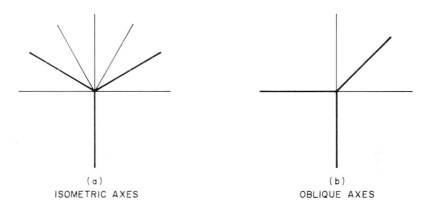

Figure 20
Selection of axes.

(a)
ISOMETRIC AXES

(b)
OBLIQUE AXES

b. Dimetric and Trimetric

As seen in Fig. 8A and B, there is great flexibility in these methods, so that the angle layout is at the discretion of the sketcher. However, in dimetric be sure that angle 1 equals angle 3 or that angles 1 and 2 are equal. You may experiment with various angles to see which looks best for an object.

c. Oblique

Figure 10 indicates that 30 or 45° is a common angle, although any angle can be used. However, objects become excessively distorted if a 45° angle is exceeded. The z axis can go in the direction shown in Fig. 10 or in the reverse (negative) direction, seen in Fig. 20.

d. Perspective

Refer to Fig. 12. The most natural effects are obtained if the two vanishing points (VPs) are placed as far apart as practical. Be sure that the vanishing points for horizontal lines are on the horizon, not elsewhere. By sketching in the upper and lower edges, you can soon tell if the effect will be pleasant. If not, you can adjust the vanishing points.

11. HINTS FOR SKETCHING OBJECTS: AXONOMETRIC AND OBLIQUE

A few suggestions can help the sketcher to obtain attractive sketches. Suggestions are based on common sense, but are worth listing.

1. Always keep parallel lines of an object parallel in the sketch. This includes vertical lines, too. The obvious result of not following this advice is seen in Fig. 21. Note the use of negative axis directions compared to Fig. 1. This is a common and useful technique. Case B looks ugly and distorted compared to case A.

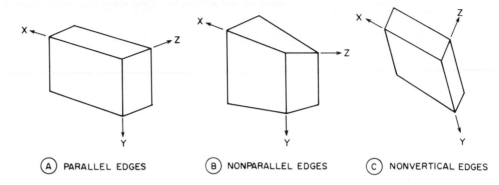

Figure 21
Effects of edge orientations.

(A) PARALLEL EDGES   (B) NONPARALLEL EDGES   (C) NONVERTICAL EDGES

2. Keep the x, y, and z axes close to their ideal positions. Figure 21C shows the effect of nonideal axis positions. Axis y is nonvertical, giving a poor effect. Axes x and z are too far off the horizontal, creating distortion. It is better to be too close to the horizontal than too far from it.

3. Block in all portions of the object within rectangular prisms. Then modify the prisms to create the final shape. Note the process in Fig. 22, done in isometric. The cylinder becomes elliptical with tangents to the midpoints of the enclosing isometric square. One side contains rounded corners.

   The same object sketched in oblique is seen in Fig. 23. Note that the object has been aligned so that its circular and rounded features face forward. This alignment retains the true circular shapes which can be a distinct advantage to both the sketcher and the sketch user.

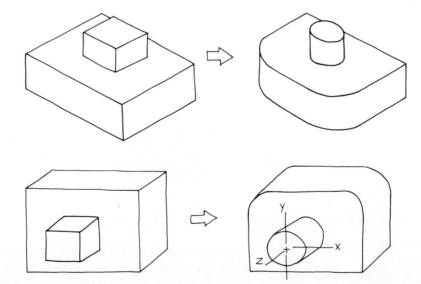

Figure 22
Block-in technique for sketching isometrics.

Figure 23
Block-in technique for sketching obliques.

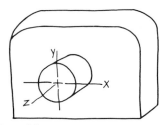

Figure 24
A cabinet oblique sketch.

The same scale has been used in all three directions in Fig. 23. Such treatment is called *cavalier oblique*. A treatment is called *cabinet oblique* when the scale along the z axis is made *one-half* that along the x and y axes. See Fig. 24. Many sketchers find that cabinet oblique is more attractive than cavalier oblique. We will see more of both later when we convert 2-D drawings to 3-D drawings.

12. HINTS FOR SKETCHING IN PERSPECTIVE

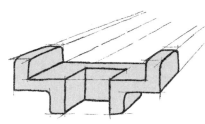

Figure 25
A one-point perspective sketch.

To construct perspective drawings with instruments is a slow process. However, you can sketch objects in perspective with relative ease if you keep in mind a few concepts.

Realize that all parallel horizontal lines will converge to the same vanishing point on the horizon. Refer again to Fig. 12. The horizontal lines on the right-hand side converge to the vanishing point on the right. Similarly, the horizontal lines on the left-hand side converge to the VP on the left.

A special case exists when a face of the object is aligned in oblique. Recall that in oblique (Fig. 23) one face will show as a true shape. This can also occur in perspective, as in Fig. 25. If the front face is true shape, the perspective is called a *one-point perspective* because there is only one vanishing point for the receding horizontal lines.

The sketcher must decide how to best align the object to emphasize the desired features. In Fig. 26, we see an object of fairly complicated shape but which looks good in perspective. This object is oriented much as the simple object of Fig. 12, in which there are two principal receding directions. There are two vanishing points for horizontal lines, even though the actual vanishing points are off the paper. When two vanishing points exist, the perspective is sometimes called a *two-point perspective*.

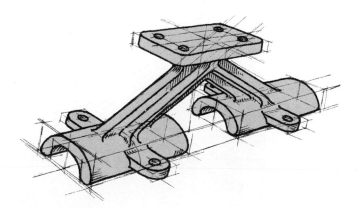

Figure 26
A two-point perspective sketch.

13. MODELING REPRESENTATIONS FOR 3-D SHAPES

The objects illustrated so far look pretty much as we see them. That is, the objects are opaque. We cannot see through them. However, there are several ways to represent objects, and these ways relate directly to how CAD programs may display objects. We take a brief look at three forms of representation: wire frame, wire frame with hidden-line removal, and solid modeling.

a. Wire Frame

This form of representation is the easiest for a computer to handle in terms of power needed. An object is shown such that all edges are visible. In Fig. 27 we have a CAD-done wire frame. It appears to be made of wires, hence the name *wire frame*. It is up to your eye to determine which edges are closest and which are farthest away. The effect is rather odd, but the object is still very much a 3-D one. Much CAD software gives results in this form because the value per dollar is excellent. A maximum 3-D effect is provided with the minimum computer memory and time needed to generate the output. An example of another output is seen in Fig. 28.

For objects containing curved surfaces, you can use the worthwhile technique of ruled surfaces. In Fig. 29 note that elements on the surface are placed at regular intervals, thereby generating the shape of the part. This technique is employed often for complex shapes, such as ship and plane contours. The automotive industry also finds many applications for this technique.

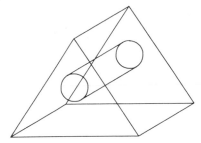

Figure 27
A wire-frame 3-D via CAD.

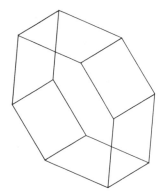

Figure 28
Another wire frame via CAD.

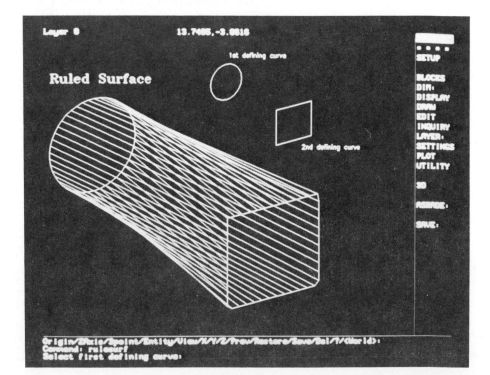

Figure 29
Wire frame by ruled surface.
(Courtesy of AutoDesk, Inc.)

b. Wire Frame with Hidden-Line Removal

The unrealistic effect of Figs. 27 and 28 could be eliminated if you could get rid of the edges which are supposed to be hidden. CAD software is available that enables only visible lines to be seen. Figure 30 is an example of that. The effect is much more attractive than that of Fig. 28. There is a price for this extra sophistication, however. The computer power needed is roughly double that for a simple wire-frame configuration. Extra power means extra money. Someone must weigh whether the potential results are worth the cost.

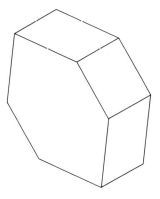

Figure 30
Figure 28 with hidden line removal.

c. Solid Modeling

This format represents the most elegant form of display. An object is shown in its most realistic form, complete with shading of surfaces. The results can be impressive. The object in Fig. 31 looks almost like a photograph of the genuine object. There is a real need in industry and business for such capability from software and computers. Presentations of potential designs to clients have maximum impact when solid modeling can be offered. Another example is shown in Fig. 32. While everyone can admire the realism of solid modeling, the present high cost of software and hard work required to provide this effect must be considered.

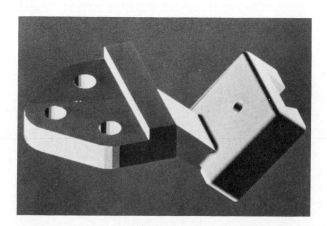

Figure 31
A solid model with shading.

Generating solid models may cost 10 times more than simple wire-frame modeling of the same object. Again, it becomes an economic decision as to what a particular effect is worth.

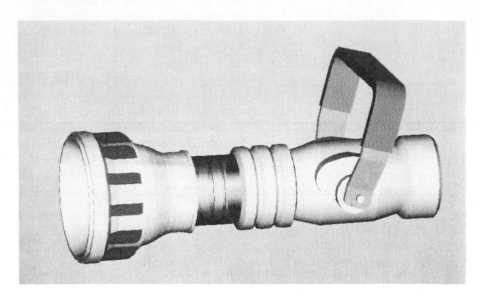

Figure 32
Fire hose nozzle done in solid modeling. (Courtesy of AutoDesk, Inc.)

14. SOLIDS BUILT FROM COMPONENT PARTS

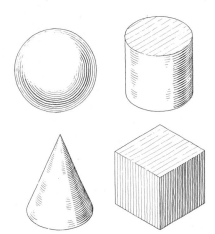

Figure 33
Components parts used in modeling.

It is useful to think of the total object as a summation or subtraction of individual components. The value of this approach to visualizing parts is that solids created on CAD systems are often easiest to produce if you can add or subtract component parts. Component parts themselves are units of simple shape, such as cubes, cylinders, and cones. A few component parts are seen in Fig. 33.

An example of utilizing component parts is given in Fig. 34. Here the object can be thought of as comprising one rectangular prism (1A) laid beside another of equal shape (1B) with a cylinder (3) subtracted from prism 1B. A triangular wedge (2) has been added to prism 1A.

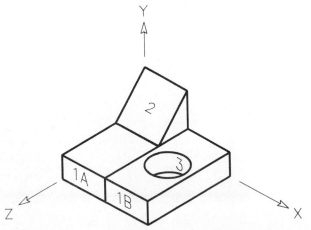

Figure 34
Object made up of component parts.

A computer can store a library or file of component parts to be added or subtracted at axial positions of choice. If prism 1A and wedge 2 were subtracted, the object in Fig. 35 would result. Users of CAD software can speed creation of drawings through replication and translation of shapes in an axis system. Techniques particular to a specific software package can be learned from the instruction manual. Note that both Fig. 34 and Fig. 35 are displayed in the wire-frame mode with hidden-line removal.

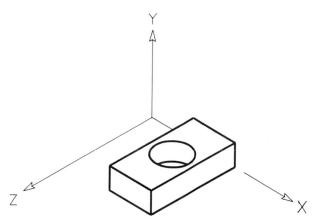

Figure 35
Deletion of component parts to give new object.

A further example of the use of component shapes is given in Fig. 36. Here the object of Fig. 35 has been modified so that it is a hollow box with a lid. Cylinder 3 has been deleted. The upper surface of the rectangular prism is now thought to be a lid, which can rotate about a horizontal axis or hinge that is parallel to the z axis. Rotation is available in many CAD software packages. In Fig. 36 the lid has been rotated in 45° increments until the lid is opened parallel to the xz plane. This simple example is a mere introduction to what sophisticated CAD processes can do.

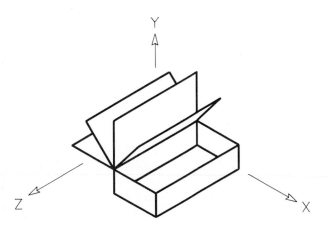

Figure 36
Modification of Figure 35 to include rotation.

P R O B L E M S

A number of objects are shown in Probs. 1 through 9. The objects are shown with isometric axes. Sketch the various objects on 8½ × 11 in paper, two objects per sheet. Sketch as shown in isometric or with oblique axes. Or you may sketch the objects in one- or two-point perspective.

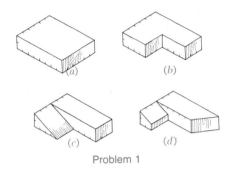

Problem 1

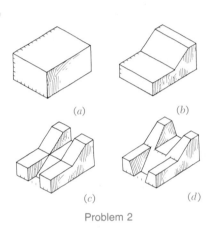

Problem 2

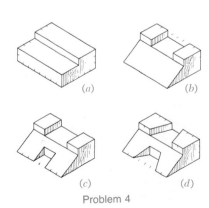

Problem 4

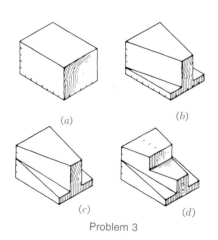

Problem 3

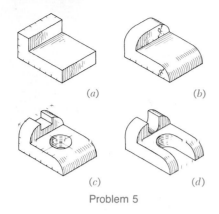

(a) (b)

(c) (d)

Problem 5

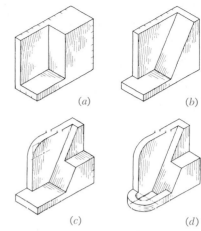

(a) (b)

(c) (d)

Problem 6

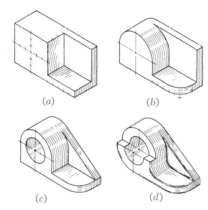

(a) (b)

(c) (d)

Problem 7

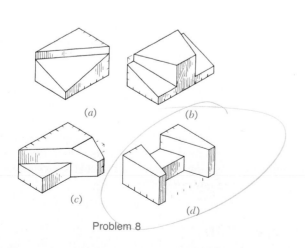

(a) (b)

(c) (d)

Problem 8

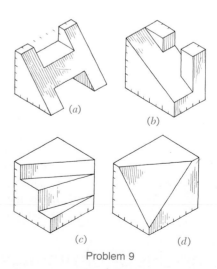

(a) (b)

(c) (d)

Problem 9

C H A P T E R 6

ORTHOGRAPHIC PROJECTION: A CONVERSION FROM THREE DIMENSIONS TO TWO DIMENSIONS

1. A LIMITATION OF PICTORIAL VIEWS

It is a fact that a three-dimensional pictorial drawing or sketch of an object can reveal the object's shape very well. All three axial directions (x, y, and z) are seen. The eye can scan the total shape in one view. Seeing a total shape in one view is a valuable asset in defining an object's shape. One problem can arise, however. How can the shape or part be best described so that it can be easily manufactured?

Showing a complicated part in a 3-D mode may lead to real difficulties in manufacture. Look at the object in Fig. 1. To expect this product to be produced from this illustration alone is asking for trouble. The dimensions are crowded and confusing. Shapes may be unclear to many viewers. Some way is needed to show this object in a simpler format that can give more than one view. Then each view contributes its own information. The total of all views then constitutes a description of the object.

Our work in this chapter focuses on a useful alternative method besides pictorials to show the shapes of objects. This method is known as *orthographic projection*. It has the great advantage of showing separate, individual views of faces of an object to clarify exact shapes and positions of features.

2. ORIGINS OF ORTHOGRAPHIC PROJECTION

Orthographic projection can provide a 2-D representation of a 3-D object. Orthographic projection originates in the box seen in Fig. 2A. The box contains

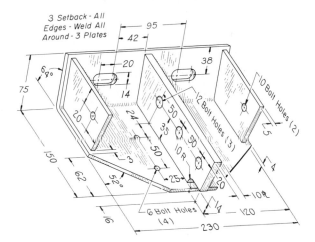

Figure 1
A possibly confusing 3-D.

eight sectors, or *octants*. Three mutually perpendicular planes intersect at the very center of the box, at the origin of the *X, Y,* and *Z* axes. In Fig. 2B the darkened octant of Fig. 2A is cut open to reveal three mutually perpendicular planes. One of the planes is the *F,* or frontal, plane. Another plane is the *P,* or profile, plane. Both plane *F* and plane *P* are vertical. The third plane is the *H,* or horizontal, plane.

A simple sphere has been inserted in the open octant of Fig. 2B. The sphere is then projected onto the *F, H,* and *P* planes. The sphere has been "captured" on the *F, H,* and *P* planes. This case is known as *first-angle projection*. It is widely used in Europe, Asia, and other areas, but not in the United States.

Note that three elements are needed to capture or project an object onto a plane: an object, projectors, and a projection plane. These three elements are crucial to further study.

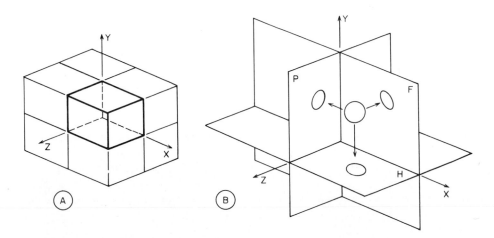

Figure 2
Position of octant for first angle projection.

In Fig. 3A a different octant of the possible eight is used. This octant is at the lower left back portion of the box. It is shown enlarged in Fig. 3B. Again we have the same three mutually perpendicular planes: *F, H,* and *P.* A sphere is again projected on the *F, H,* and *P* planes. Projection in this particular octant is known

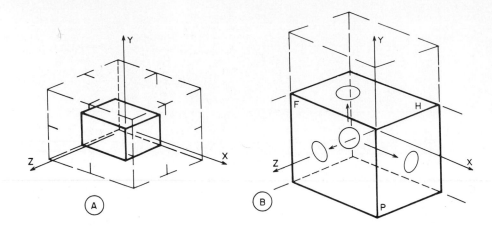

Figure 3
Position of octant for third angle
projection.

as *third-angle projection*. This form of projection is used in the United States, although both the first- and third-angle projections are equally valid. However, all future reference to projection in this book is to third-angle projection only.

3. DEVELOPMENT OF ORTHOGRAPHIC VIEWS

Let us concentrate on the three variables previously mentioned: the object, projectors, and picture plane. If the projectors converge to a single viewing point, or station point, one has a perspective system, as in Fig. 4. The resulting view of the object captured in the picture plane changes size. This may lead to interesting artistic effects, but the changing size can be a handicap to someone trying to read exact shapes and sizes.

Figure 4
Perspective projection.

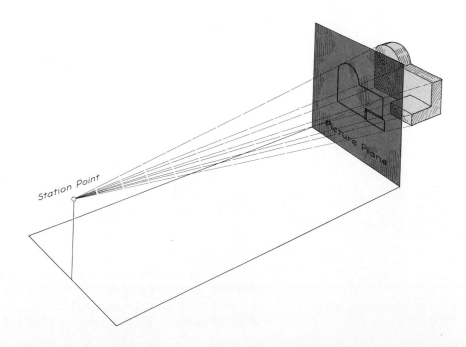

If the station point were moved to infinity, the projectors would become parallel. See Fig. 5. Note that the projectors are shown *perpendicular* to the picture plane. When the parallel projectors are perpendicular to the picture plane, the method is called *orthographic projection*.

Orthographic projection has two subdivisions: *multiview* and *axonometric*. When a principal face of the object is parallel to the picture place, as in Fig. 5A, the result is a multiview projection. We study multiview projection in detail in this chapter. When the object is randomly rotated relative to the picture plane, the result is called axonometric projection, as in Fig. 5B. Axonometric pictorials were seen in Chap. 5 and are studied further later. Orthographic projection, therefore, can yield both a 2-D multiview result and a 3-D axonometric result. We concentrate on the 2-D multiview for the remainder of this chapter.

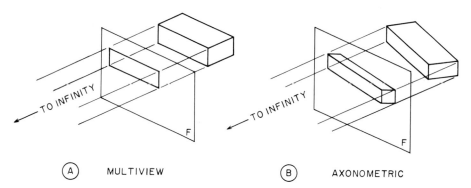

Figure 5
Forms of orthographic projection.

Ⓐ MULTIVIEW

Ⓑ AXONOMETRIC

■ 4. THE PROJECTION BOX

Figure 3 shows a projection "box" consisting of frontal, horizontal, and profile planes. This projection box is shown isolated in Fig. 6. Note that there are actually six projection faces, or picture planes. There are front and back frontal planes, upper and lower horizontal planes, and left and right profile planes. For convenience, the *X, Y,* and *Z* axes of Fig. 3 have been relocated at the hidden corner in Fig. 6. Also given are the three components of space: width, height, and depth.

An object has been placed inside the projection box in Fig. 7. The object has been projected onto all three planes. This 3-D picture of the various projections is fairly clear, but not ideally so. We want to convert from the 3-D version to a 2-D version in order to use the multiview method.

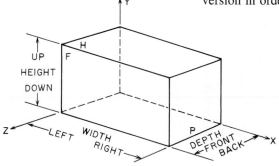

Figure 6
Third quadrant projection box.

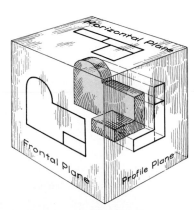

Figure 7
Object of Figure 4 inside the projection box.

■ 5. CREATING MULTIVIEW PROJECTIONS

A breakthrough occurs in Fig. 8. The projections on the 3-D box of Fig. 7 are forced into a 2-D plane when the box is cut open along its edges and the *H* and *P* planes are each swung out 90°. The *H* and *P* planes become part of a continuous plane which includes the frontal plane.

We can go a step further and move all six planes of the projection box into a single plane. We see this happening in Fig. 9. Here all six possible projections of the object are swung outward. The final result is seen in Fig. 10 where the positions of all six projections are shown. This configuration provides six views of the object with all views in the proper position.

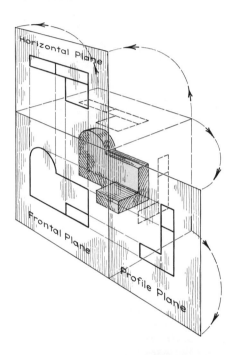

Figure 8
Eight rotating projection plane, 90°.

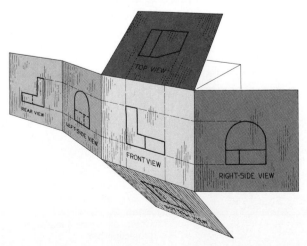

Figure 9
Rotating all six projection planes.

TOP VIEW

REAR VIEW   LEFT-SIDE VIEW   FRONT VIEW   RIGHT-SIDE VIEW

BOTTOM VIEW

Figure 10
The six principal projection views.

The right-side (profile) view is to the right of the front (frontal) view. The left-side view is to the left of the front view. The top (horizontal) view is above the front view, and the bottom view is below the front view. The rear view ends up beside the left-side view. Note one interesting and important result: Corresponding *F, H,* and *P* views are *mirror images* of each other in outline. That is, the top and bottom horizontal views are mirror images of each other. The left- and right-side profile views are mirror images, as are the front and rear frontal views. This feature of mirror imaging can be very helpful for both drawing and reading objects.

The six possible projections just seen in Fig. 10 are known as the six *principal views.* Any view attached to another is perpendicular to that view. For example, the top view is perpendicular to the front view; the right-side view is also perpendicular to the front view. This perpendicularity between any two adjacent (attached) views is a characteristic of orthographic projection which never varies.

■ 6. NUMBER OF NEEDED VIEWS

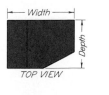

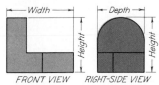

Figure 11
The sufficient views of the object of Figure 8.

The purpose of multiviews is to provide as many views as necessary to describe the shape and location of all features of an object. How many views are actually needed depends on the object to be described. One would certainly not need all six views of the object in Fig. 10 to describe its shape. That figure has redundancies in that the bottom view offers nothing more than the top view. Also the left-side and rear views simply repeat information in the right-side and front views. The three views of top, front, and right side are quite sufficient to reveal the shape of the object, as given in Fig. 11.

Notice in Fig. 11 that width is seen in both the top view and the front view, height in the front and right-side views, and depth in the top and right-side views. This repetition of directions among the views is a strength of multiview because a width feature on the top view, say, will be located directly in alignment in the front view, thereby helping the reader to check the shape and position of a feature. Similarly, all height features are in alignment as well as all depth features.

Does the discussion so far imply that all objects are best served by having three views? No. Some objects can be described well with just two views. The tin can in Fig. 12A proves this point in that the top and front views given fully describe the shape. Adding a right-side view, for instance, as in Fig. 12B, does nothing to further the understanding of shape.

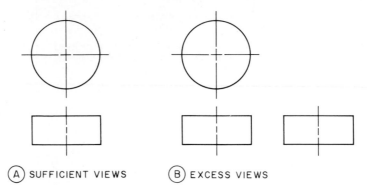

Figure 12
Views of a tin can.

Can just one view ever be sufficient? One view can indeed be enough to describe a shape if the object has a simple shape and an accompanying note accounts for the missing direction. We see in Fig. 13 the top view of a washer. The inside and outside diameters are dimensioned as well as the thickness which would normally occur in the front view as a height. Not very many objects, however, can be described in just one view. A few more objects can be expressed with only two views, but most objects require three views.

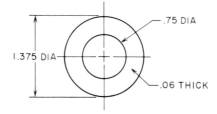

Figure 13
A one-view drawing.

To indicate why three views, not two, are needed, examine Fig. 14. You may think, based on the top and front views alone, that the object is a simple rectangular prism, which it could be if the right-side view were that corresponding to RS-1.

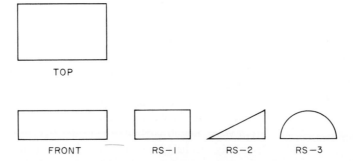

Figure 14
Object needing three views.

Still, right-side views RS-2 and RS-3 are just as valid as RS-1. Therefore, for this object a side view is needed to show the shape. It is quite common to need three views to describe shapes.

7. ORIENTATION OF THE OBJECT

To help interpret the shape of a drawing, it is important to properly orient an object relative to the projection planes. For ease of reading of a drawing, it is vital to place the object with a major face parallel to a principal plane. Also the maximum measurement is usually chosen as the width of the object, rather than its height or depth. In Fig. 15, the object is oriented so that the maximum measurement appears as width in the front view. The same effect is achieved in Fig. 16 where the longest measurement shows in the front view. This is an object for which the top, front, and right-side views are quite sufficient to show the shape of all features.

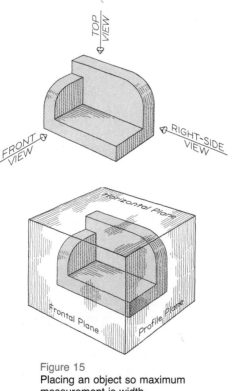

Figure 15
Placing an object so maximum measurement is width.

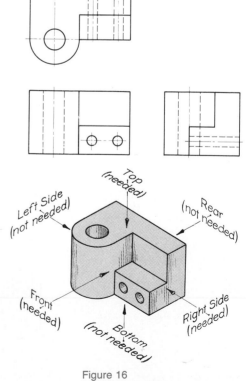

Figure 16
Selection of views.

◼ 8. MEANING AND USE OF LINE TYPES

It is important to focus briefly on what the various line types mean and how they interact with each other. In Chap. 2 we presented the alphabet of lines which defines all types of lines used in technical drawing. (See Fig. 10 in Chap. 2.)

So far we have used the three most common line types: visible lines, hidden lines, and centerlines. These line types are well named. The line is the most basic of all object elements, save for the single point. A line may represent the edge of a surface, the intersection of two surfaces, or the limit of a surface. Figure 17 illustrates these three representations made by a line.

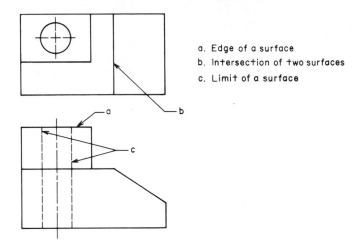

a. Edge of a surface
b. Intersection of two surfaces
c. Limit of a surface

Figure 17
Various meanings of lines.

Visible lines are needed, not surprisingly, when a feature is visible. One simple example is that the outline lines or boundary of *any* object is always visible. Hidden lines must be used when a feature is buried inside an object or is hidden from sight by another feature. For example, the vertical hole in Fig. 17 is hidden in the front view. Centerlines are used for axes of symmetry, whether for a cylindrical hole or for a part having symmetry.

The way in which hidden lines intersect with visible surfaces and edges is seen in Fig. 18. Note that no space exists when a hidden line begins at a surface. However, if a surface continues, a space is used. Also hidden corners require the

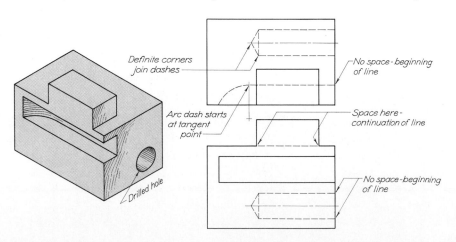

Definite corners
join dashes

Arc dash starts
at tangent
point

Drilled hole

No space - beginning
of line

Space here -
continuation of line

No space - beginning
of line

Figure 18
Proper use of hidden lines.

intersection of dashes. Careful attention to these details will create a drawing with maximum readability.

One important use of lines involves the *precedence of lines*. Certain types of lines have precedence over others, or "cover" other lines. The precedence of lines, in descending order, is visible lines, hidden lines, and centerlines. That is, a visible line will cover a hidden line coincident with it, but a hidden line will cover a centerline. Note in the top view of Fig. 19 that a visible edge covers the right-hand surface limit of the hole.

Also note that the corner seen in the front view is hidden in the right-side view and covers the centerline coincident with it. The protrusion of the centerline beyond the object is still evident, however.

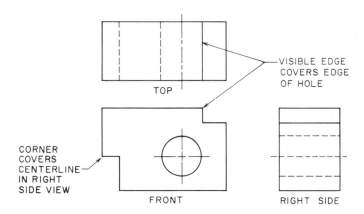

Figure 19
Precedence of lines.

9. VISUALIZING MISSING VIEWS

It is extremely useful to be able to visualize the missing views of an object. A person skilled in the technique of determining such views can communicate to others information that clarifies the exact shape of objects. To help you determine missing views, we explain useful techniques by using a series of guidelines in conjunction with selected objects. It could be argued that a designer knows what shape is desired before creating multiviews of an object. This is partly true, but even experienced designers and drafters often must show views of an object that are perhaps not entirely known.

We use the following guidelines in visualizing missing views:

1. Use alignment of width, height, and depth features.
2. Sketch a supplemental 3-D pictorial of the object.
3. Consider the meanings of the lines.
4. Look for the repetition of basic contours among views.
5. Be aware of which surfaces are true shape and which are not.
6. Know which features are holes and which are not.
7. Number the corners of areas so that respective corners can be aligned among views.
8. Acknowledge that an alternative missing view may be possible for the same given views.

Let us begin to visualize a missing view by looking at Fig. 20A. Given the front and right-side views, what would the top view look like? More basically, what is the shape of the object?

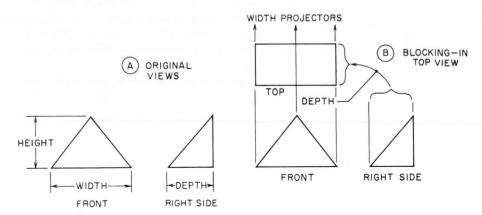

Figure 20
Building a missing view.

By guideline 1 the top view must contain information about width projected from the front view and information about depth obtained from the side view. Therefore the top view can be blocked in as in Fig. 20B. At this point, guideline 2 pertains to the creation of a 3-D sketch (see Fig. 21). The maximum height H, width W, and depth D are transposed from the 2-D multiview to the 3-D pictorial. Also the tent shape in the front view of the 2-D multiview is carried into the 3-D pictorial.

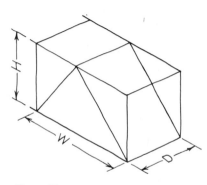

Figure 21
Initial 3-D sketch.

Guideline 3 says that you must be aware of the meaning of lines. All lines are visible lines so far. Therefore, hidden features are not present in the front and side views. By guideline 4, we note that there is a triangle in both front and side views. It is highly likely that triangle(s) will be seen in the top view. Numbering at least one triangle (guideline 7) can be helpful. Numbering a triangle 1-2-3 in Fig. 22A brings us closer to the final solution. Since point 2 is at the top center rear position,

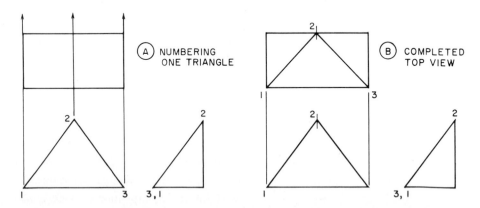

Figure 22
Completion of the missing view.

as seen in the front and side views, point 2 must be similarly located in the top view. See Fig. 22B. The solution is complete, with the 3-D version given in Fig. 23.

For interest's sake, note that the object determined above is actually a pyramid with a rectangular base which shows its true shape in the top view. Of the four

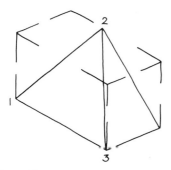

Figure 23
Final 3-D sketch.

triangular sides, three are inclined and one, the rear, is vertical. The vertical triangle is true shape in the front view and is seen as an edge (line) in the top and side views. This analysis is done to satisfy guideline 5, which alerts you to which surfaces are true shape. There are no holes in this object (guideline 6). An alternative solution does not appear to exist (guideline 8).

A variation of Fig. 22 is seen in Fig. 24. The top view is desired, given the boundary of the front view and the right-side view in Fig. 24A. By an analysis identical to that of Fig. 22, we develop the solution shown in Fig. 24B. You may wish to sketch a 3-D pictorial of this object.

A case with the top and front views given is shown in Fig. 25A. Here guideline 7 has been heavily used. (What other guidelines are relevant?) All corners of the inclined surface of the upper portion of the object have been numbered. The numbers are aligned according to width between the top and front views. Note that

Figure 24
Another missing-view problem.

Figure 25
Building a missing left-side view.

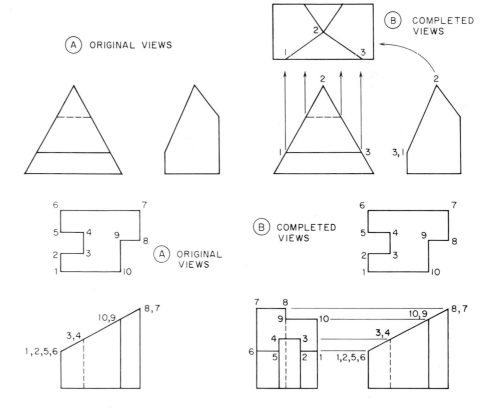

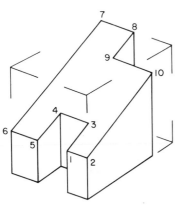

Figure 26
Pictorial of the object of Figure 25.

numbers seen first in the front view are noted first. That is, 1 precedes 2, 5, and 6. Also 3 precedes 4. However, 10 precedes 9, and 8 precedes 7. It is common practice to label a corner by placing numbers first that are seen first in that view. An axonometric pictorial of this object is shown in Fig. 26 with the object oriented so that the left-hand side shows well.

Another example of labeling corners is given in Fig. 27. Here, for variety, we have an oblique pictorial with lettered rather than numbered corners. For the sake of completeness, every corner has been labeled. Complete labeling is not a necessity, but it can be worthwhile if the shapes are difficult to analyze.

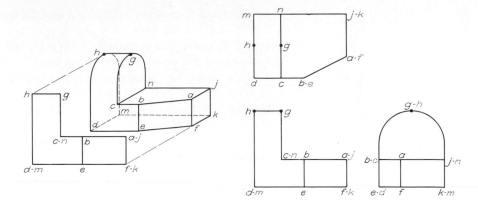

Figure 27
Another example using identified corners.

10. SURFACE CONDITIONS

It is important at this point to summarize the conditions that may apply to surfaces among multiviews. Figure 28 will help in this regard. Four conditions are shown. Figure 28A reveals the common case of a surface in true shape, seen here in the top view. Another common case in which a surface is foreshortened is shown in Fig. 28B. The surface shows as an edge (or line) in the front view, and its area is less than the true area in the top and right-side views. A curved surface is given in Fig. 28C which is an edge in the front view. A more specialized case is that of Fig. 28D where a curved surface has tangencies to other surfaces.

A surface which shows as an area in all principal views (*H*, *F*, and *P*) is called an *oblique surface*. Such a surface is seen in Fig. 29. The triangular surface is always seen as a triangle but never as a true-area triangle. We will learn later how to find the true area of such oblique surfaces.

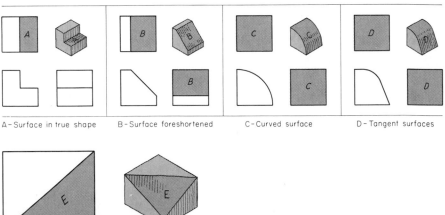

Figure 28
The meaning of areas.

A–Surface in true shape   B–Surface foreshortened   C–Curved surface   D–Tangent surfaces

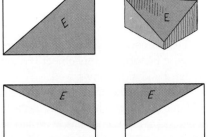

Figure 29
Oblique surface.

■ 11. ALTERNATIVE SOLUTIONS

Part of the task of visualizing views involves the realization that alternative solutions may exist. If the given views are insufficient in number or are ambiguous, a reader of the multiviews of the part may be confused. For example, if we were to say that the part shown in Fig. 30A is "essentially a rectangular block," then the role of the circle would be unclear. The circle could represent a hole, as in Fig. 30B. The hole could go all the way through as shown, or it could go partway through. The circle could also represent a raised protrusion, as in Fig. 30C. We are reminded here of guideline 6: Know which features are holes and which are not.

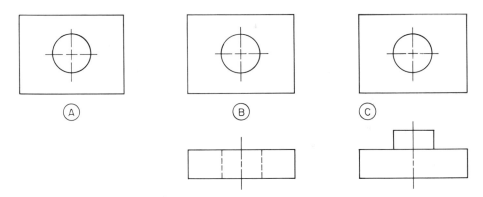

Figure 30
Alternate solutions.

Alternative solutions frequently arise when the given views are ambiguous. Note the top and front views given in Fig. 31A. The exact shape is confusing; in fact, it is unknown. Two possible solutions are seen in Fig. 31B and 31C. To avoid alternative solutions, the designer or drafter must give sufficient views to fully clarify the desired shape. This reminds us of guideline 8 (Sec. 9): Acknowledge that an alternative missing view may be possible for the same given views. You should avoid, however, alternative solutions. A particular part to be manufactured should have one and only one shape, as shown in sufficient and proper multiviews.

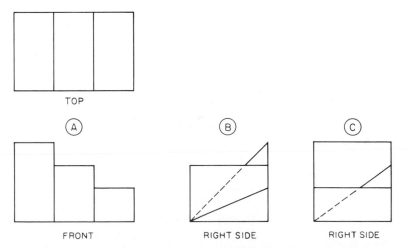

Figure 31
Ambiguous top and front views.

12. PRACTICAL HINTS IN PROJECTING MULTIVIEWS

You should be comfortable now with the concepts underlying multiview projections. The alignment of views and the meaning of lines have been discussed and examples given. A few practical hints on setting up and projecting multiviews may be helpful. These hints in one sense are common sense, but mentioning them may facilitate faster, more accurate work.

When you are using a T square and triangle, it is important that the paper be taped down. When a sheet of paper is floating loose, accuracy suffers in the creation of parallel and perpendicular lines. Also recall that the T square is used for the projection of horizontal lines and the triangle for vertical lines, as in Fig. 32. Do not swing the T square around to make vertical lines.

The best method to transfer depths between views involves use of the dividers. Figure 33 illustrates this technique as used between the top and side views. Some persons prefer the alternative method of using a 45° miter line, shown in Fig. 34. This method is definitely slower than using dividers. In addition, a miter line works only if the two views involving distance transfers are perpendicular to each other. Later we will see a case of auxiliary views for which dividers must be used because a miter line will not work. Alternatively, some people try to use a scale to move distances from one view to another. Use of scales is not recommended because errors are easily made as the brain tries to memorize the reading during the transition between views. Dividers are the best method for the transfer of distance under all circumstances.

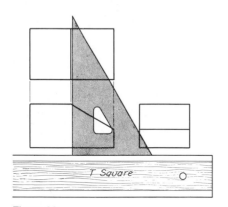

Figure 32
Use of a triangle and T square for vertical and horizontal lines.

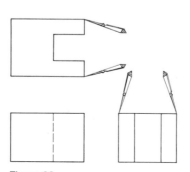

Figure 33
Transferring depth by dividers.

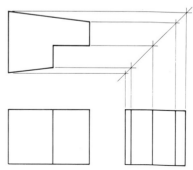

Figure 34
Transferring depth by miter line.

13. PROJECTING CURVED FEATURES

The idea of projecting curved features within multiviews is no different from that for straight-line features. The practical variation between the two types of features is simply that a curve must often be approximated by a number of selected points. Take the general case shown in Fig. 35. The shape of the curve is generated by selecting random points in one view and then locating them in another view. Observe that points 1 and 2 have been chosen in the top view. Their location in

Figure 35
Projection of a curved boundary.

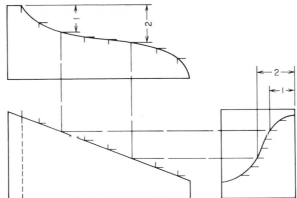

Figure 36
Projection of an elliptical boundary.

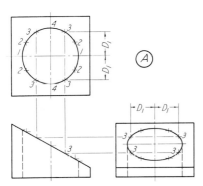

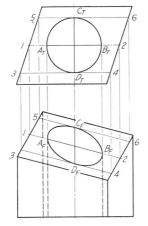

Figure 37
Projection by points on common lines.

the front view is easily found by direct projection from the top view. Points 1 and 2 are then located in the right-side view. Use of dividers is recommended. Additional points are added to provide a sufficient number to fit a smooth curve through the points, by using an irregular curve.

A more specialized case is that of a common geometric shape such as a circular hole. In Fig. 36, the hole of the top view is projected most easily onto the side view by using the centerline. Symmetry about the centerline allows us to pick up two points at the same time. Point 3, for example, is equally positioned on both sides of the centerline. Therefore, using dividers, we can locate positions with one setting of the dividers. Additional points are located by symmetry about the centerline until we have a sufficient number to draw the ellipse.

Another case of interest is shown in Fig. 37. Points are generated on the hole seen in the top view by running lines through the hole and attaching the lines to the edges of the object. The lines containing points of interest on the hole are projected directly onto the front view. The points on these lines drop onto the same respective lines in the front view. That is, points A and B are located on line 1-2 in the top view. They stay on line 1-2 in the front view. Note that points A, B, C, and D are located in the top view at particularly useful positions. Points A and B are at the extreme width positions; C and D are at the extreme depth positions.

14. USING MULTIVIEWS TO CREATE PICTORIALS

It is a valuable skill to be able to sketch or draw 3-D pictorials from 2-D multiviews. You can take an object's multiviews, which may be unclear to someone who is not technically trained, and create for that person a 3-D pictorial which reveals the shapes of all important features. We have discussed desired 3-D pictorials and given 2-D multiviews separately. Now let us bridge the gap between the two.

We start with the given 2-D multiview, as in Fig. 38. A rather basic example is illustrated with given top, front, and right-side views. The overall shape is a rectangular block. In step A an axis system is selected, here an isometric system with equal angles between any two axes. An oblique system could have been chosen just as well.

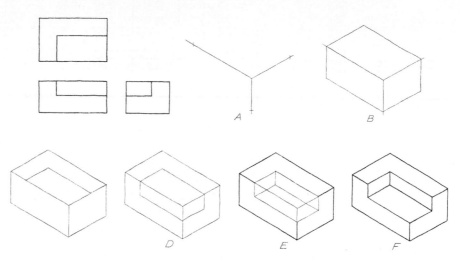

Figure 38
Stages in making a pictorial sketch.

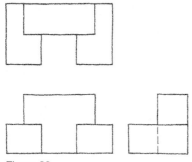

Figure 39
A drawing to be read. This is the object modeled in Figure 40.

Next, in step B, the overall height, width, and depth of the total block are sketched in lightly. In steps C, D, and E the notch is sketched in. The final form is seen in step F where unnecessary construction lines are removed.

Another example is given in Figs. 39 and 40. This example utilizes the modeling technique of removing or subtracting geometric shapes from a basic block to obtain the final desired form of the object. In Fig. 38 shapes were removed by erasing sketched lines. This example shows the physical act of cutting away actual shapes from the basic block. What is done here with the modeling knife is conceptually identical to the subtraction process in computer-aided drafting with editing techniques used to delete portions of the total shape. The solid block in step A of Fig. 40 becomes the shape in step F. Step F corresponds to the multiviews of the same object in Fig. 39.

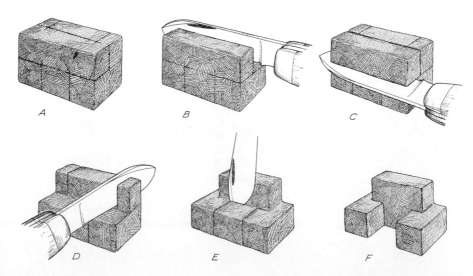

Figure 40
Stages in modeling.

15. SUMMATION STUDIES

A goal of this chapter has been to learn to express 3-D shapes in orthographic projection, that is, 2-D multiviews. Numerous designs require that the product be displayed in 2-D multiview to aid in dimensioning and ultimately production of the design as a finished product. To be able to visualize a 3-D shape in 2-D format is very helpful for a designer. The converse is also true. To construct a 3-D pictorial from a 2-D multiview is very helpful, whether on paper, on a computer monitor screen, or by the creation of a physical model.

To help you develop the ability to visualize objects in both 2-D and 3-D formats, two figures (Figs. 41 and 42) are provided. In Fig. 41 are shown complete multiviews along with the accompanying pictorials. Study each object carefully so that you understand each surface.

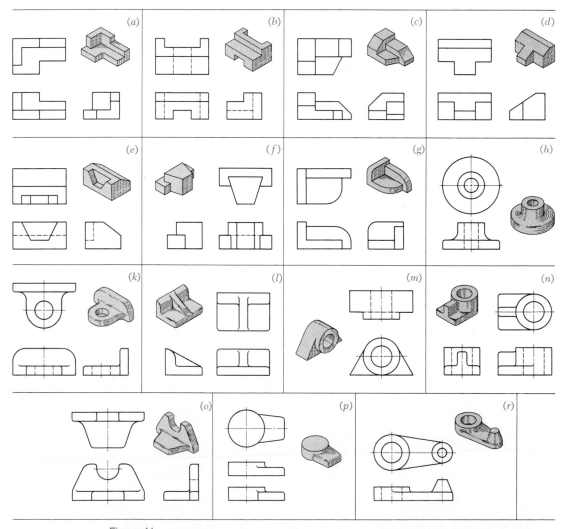

Figure 41
Projection studies. Study each picture and the accompanying orthographic views and note the projection of all features.

Figure 42 is somewhat more difficult. Here you are to sketch the pictorial that corresponds to each multiview layout. Top and front views are always given, along with either a right-side view or a left-side view. One exception is case B in which front, bottom, and right-side views are given. Sketching the desired pictorials will develop skill in the art and science of converting from multiview to 3-D format. This skill will serve well the needs of both manual drafters and CAD users.

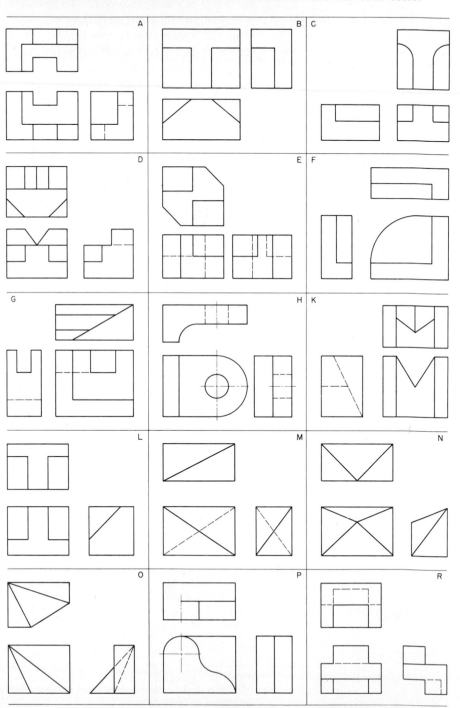

Figure 42
Reading exercises. Read each drawing (A) to (R). Make pictorial sketches or models if necessary for understanding.

PROBLEMS

Problem 1

1. Draw three views of the pivot block.

2. Draw three views of the bearing rest.

3. Draw three views of the sliding-pin hanger.

4. Draw three views of the hanger jaw.

5. Draw the top, front, and left-side views of the aileron tab-rod servo fitting.

6. Make an orthographic drawing of the rigging yoke.

7. Make an orthographic drawing of the missile release pawl.

Problem 2

Problem 3

Problem 4

Problem 5

Problem 6

Problem 7

C H A P T E R 7

MORE ON THREE-DIMENSIONAL OBJECTS

1. INTRODUCTION

You may need to know more about the creation of pictorials than previous discussion has provided. You may wish to learn how to accurately place any line or curve within a 3-D pictorial. Such knowledge can help you create pictorials by hand or work with pictorials generated by computer software. Knowing correct procedures can only help you make effective pictorials.

In this chapter we emphasize the use of scale factors, generation of straight lines of all types, and creation of curves. These elements are applied to both axonometric and oblique systems. Finally, we offer a practical overview of perspective, giving insight into the manipulation of various variables of perspective.

2. THE SCALING FACTOR

The discussion of the sketching of pictorials in Chap. 5 stressed the proper use of axes. However, little was said concerning the scale used along the three x, y, and z axes. Figures 23 and 24 of Chap. 5 did use the terms *cavalier oblique* and *cabinet oblique,* but the subject of scaling was not discussed in depth. It is appropriate now to probe a little deeper into scaling theory for pictorial axes.

a. Scaling for Axonometric Pictorials

We realize from the discussion in Chap. 6 that orthographic projection can yield both axonometric and multiview projections. Figure 5 of Chap. 6 displayed an axonometric projection on a vertical (frontal) projection plane. A more thorough illustration of the generation of an axonometric projection is seen in Fig. 1. The simple rectangular block of Fig. 1A has been rotated and tilted, as seen in the horizontal and right-side profile views of Fig. 1B. The view projected onto the front view of Fig. 1B has created an axonometric projection with its *x*, *y*, and *z* axes. Note the relocation of frontal face 1-2-3-4 from Fig. 1A to Fig. 1B. Also note the relocation of the *x*, *y*, and *z* axes for convenience compared to Fig. 1 of Chap. 5.

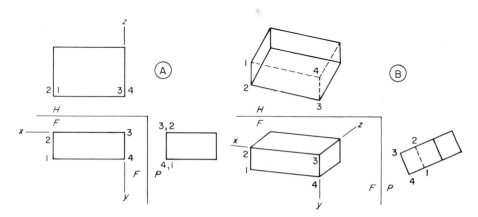

Figure 1
Generation of anoxometric projection.

Recall that if all three angles between the *x*, *y*, and *z* axes are equal, we have an isometric system. If two of the three angles are equal, the system is dimetric. If no angles are equal, the system is trimetric. The particular angles generated are the direct result of how much rotation and tilting occurred within the horizontal and profile views. Regardless of the angles between axes, one important event has occurred: the true height, width, and depth of the original block of Fig. 1A have all been *foreshortened* through the act of axonometric projection in Fig. 1B. The amount of foreshortening varies with the particular angles between the *x*, *y*, and *z* axes, but some foreshortening is unavoidable.

Is this foreshortening going to cause a major problem for drawing or sketching an axonometric pictorial? No. The sole purpose of pictorials is to give the user an overall idea of the shape of an object. The relative proportions of the sizes of features are very important. However, the actual scale or size of the total object is not critical. The object need only be sufficiently large to reveal small details clearly.

Therefore, the amount of foreshortening due to the process of axonometric projection can be effectively ignored. The lengths of the heights, widths, and depths can be to any arbitrary scale of convenience. Not surprisingly, full size or some easy multiple of full size is usually selected. Objects may be made full size, double size, triple size, half size, quarter size, or whatever suits the person creating the pictorial. There is only one rule for axonometric pictorials: The *same* scale must be used on all three *x, y,* and *z* axes. If the *x* scale is to be 4 times size, for example, so must the *y* and *z* scales be 4 times size. Figure 2 shows an object in which the original full size of the multiview (A) has been laid out on isometric axes (B) to produce an isometric pictorial (C).

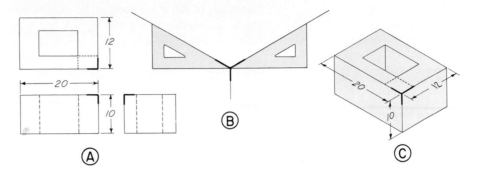

Figure 2
Layout of an isometric pictorial

b. Scaling for Oblique Pictorials

The manner by which oblique projections are generated determines the scaling factor. We observe in Figs. 9 and 10 of Chap. 5 that the oblique system always features a 90° angle between the *x* and *y* axes. Theoretically the *z* axis may be at any angle to the horizontal. How do these axis angles actually occur?

The process of oblique projection is revealed in Fig. 3. A rectangular block, similar to that of Fig. 1, is projected into the front view from given horizontal and right-side profile views. However, the *position* of the block relative to the frontal plane is very different from that in the axonometric case. Whereas for axonometric projection the object was rotated and tilted; for oblique projection the object has a major face that is kept parallel to the frontal plane. Note that plane 1-2-3-4 is parallel to the frontal plane.

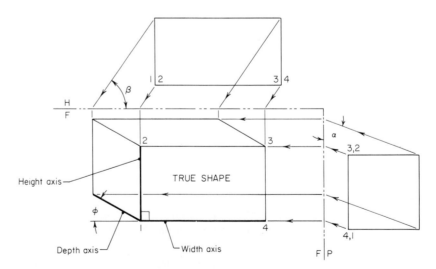

Figure 3
Generation of an oblique projection.

Note a second difference between axonometric and oblique projections. The object for axonometric projection is viewed in the orthographic mode. That is, we look perpendicularly through the projection plane (plane *F*) to view the object. In oblique projection, the object is not viewed orthographically. It is viewed at any arbitrary angle other than the 90° of the orthographic mode, hence the name *oblique*. In Fig. 3, the viewing angle looks at the object in a downward direction from the left, giving the projected angle β in the horizontal view and angle α in the right-side profile view.

The resulting front view in Fig. 3 is the oblique projection. The view shows a vertical height axis *y*, a horizontal width axis *x*, and a depth axis *z* seen at angle φ to the horizontal. Especially notice that plane 1-2-3-4 keeps its true shape. It is an important fact that *any* plane of an object which is parallel to the front keeps its true shape. This fact is seen in Fig. 4 where planes 1 and 2 are each parallel to the front view and where each plane keeps its true shape, a circle. Planes parallel to the frontal plane therefore *keep the same scale* as they had prior to projection. If, for example, plane 1-2-3-4 of Fig. 3 were full size, it would remain full size in the oblique projection; if half size, then half size. The scale along the *x* and *y* axes remains unchanged.

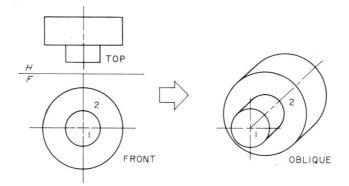

Figure 4
Example that planes parallel to the front view keep their true shapes.

What about the scaling factor along the *z* axis? Unlike that along the *x* and *y* axes, scaling along the *z* axis can vary widely, depending on the resultant angles α and β of Fig. 3. The scale along the *z* axis can be less than, equal to, or even greater than the scale along the *x* and *y* axes. This highly variable scaling along the *z* axis may seem distressing, but it need not be so. Recall that the value of a pictorial is to show overall shape. So we are free to make the scaling factor along the *z* axis anything we please, as long as an attractive pictorial results.

The angle φ of the receding axis in Fig. 3 may be any convenient angle, although 30 or 45° is most commonly used. The drafter or sketcher is free to make angle φ any angle that gives a pleasant effect, although steep angles such as 60° seldom create a good effect.

1. Scaling for cavalier oblique. One convenient scaling factor for the *z* axis is that which makes it equal to those of the *x* and *y* axes, that is, *true size*. Then all three axes have the same scale, as in axonometric projection. The ratio of scaling for *x* to *y* to *z* will be 1 : 1 : 1. Such an oblique system is called *cavalier*. We may multiply the 1 : 1 : 1 ratio by any single factor (2, 3, 4, ½, ¼, etc.), and cavalier oblique is still retained. We may have double-size cavaliers or half-size cavaliers or any other.

A cavalier oblique of simple shape can be easily drawn. Figure 5 shows the conversion of a 2-D multiview of an object to a cavalier oblique. The scale of the oblique is that of the multiview. The receding z axis appears to have a 45° angle with the horizontal. The front and rear faces maintain their true shapes, and therefore the semicircular arc retains a true radius. The overall effect of this cavalier oblique is reasonably pleasing.

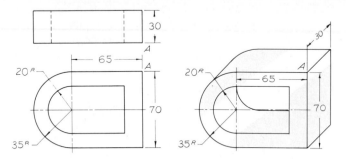

Figure 5
A cavalier oblique.

2. Scaling for cabinet oblique. A distorted unpleasant effect can be created in oblique pictorials if the distance along the z axis is long relative to the distances along the x and y axes. One effective way to decrease distortion is to decrease the distance along the z axis relative to those along the x and y axes. A format called *cabinet oblique* results if the ratio of scaling for x to y to z is made $1 : 1 : \frac{1}{2}$ rather than the $1 : 1 : 1$ of cavalier oblique. The effect of halving the z scaling is seen in Fig. 6. The object drawn in cavalier oblique in case B looks bulky. The use of cabinet oblique in case A gives a trimmer-looking object.

Realize that any multiplier may be applied to the $1 : 1 : \frac{1}{2}$ ratio of cabinet oblique. For example, multiplying by 2 gives $2 : 2 : 1$, which would make distances on the x and y axes double-size and distances on the z axis full-size. Other combinations include $4 : 4 : 2$, $10 : 10 : 5$, $\frac{1}{2} : \frac{1}{2} : \frac{1}{4}$, or whatever is desired to space the object well on a sheet of paper or a computer screen.

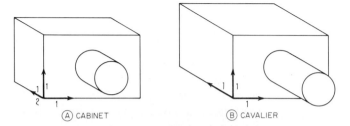

Figure 6
Obliques: cabinet vs. cavalier.

■ 3. PLACEMENT OF THE OBJECT

Careful use of scaling along x, y, and z axes can increase the attractiveness of an oblique pictorial, as discussed previously. Proper placement of the object relative to its contours can also help to create a reasonable-looking oblique. Note in Fig. 7 the three possibilities for placement of the figure. The characteristic shape involves arcs and curves. In case A, these arcs are placed parallel to the front. The result is attractive and fairly easy to draw. In cases B and C, the arcs appear distorted. The effect is less satisfactory, and the generation of the oblique would be harder than in case A.

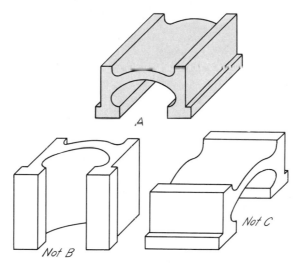

Figure 7
Effect of placement of object.

We also recommend that the longest dimension of an object be placed along the *x* axis. This technique gives a good sense of proportion to the oblique pictorial. Ideally, the face of the object containing the most distinctive contours (case A in Fig. 7) will also be the face containing the longest dimension. If you are not so fortunate as to have the distinctive contour *and* longest dimension in the frontal face, then keep the contoured face facing front and simply cut down on the receding *z* axis by using cabinet oblique.

4. CREATING STRAIGHT LINES

What could be easier than producing straight lines in pictorials? Just draw them in, right? The response is yes and no. Yes is the response for any line *parallel* to an *x, y,* or *z* axis. Notice in Figs. 2 and 5 that all straight lines parallel to axes did indeed keep the same length in the pictorials as in the multiviews. Alternatively, we could have decided to change the scale in the pictorial to some convenient multiple of the multiview scale. For example, the lengths in the pictorials could have been double those of the multiviews. The ease of drawing the pictorial would not be affected.

a. Nonisometric and Nonoblique Lines

Let us consider lines *not* parallel to axes. In Fig. 8 there is a simple block with diagonals 1-2 and 3-4 on the top surface. In the multiview (A), the two diagonals are equal in length because the boundary of the object is a square. Notice that the diagonals do *not* retain their true lengths in either the isometric (B) or the cavalier oblique (C). This fact occurs because the original 90° angles of the enclosing square of the multiview do not remain 90° in the pictorials. Diagonal 1-2 has become shorter than true length; diagonal 3-4, longer. These diagonals are examples of

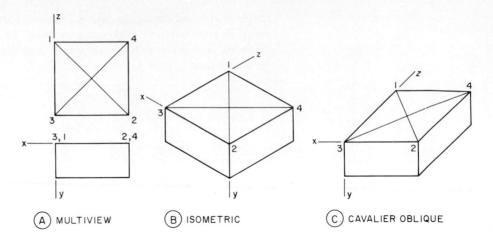

Figure 8
Lines not parallel to axes.

(A) MULTIVIEW   (B) ISOMETRIC   (C) CAVALIER OBLIQUE

nonisometric lines (at B) and nonoblique lines (at C). Any lines not parallel to axes are known as *nonisometric* or *nonoblique* lines, depending on the type of pictorial.

The way to construct a line that is not parallel to an axis is actually straightforward. Simply locate the endpoints of the line, and then join the line between the endpoints. This method works in every case.

b. Example with Nonisometric Lines

Figure 9 shows a multiview (A) of a five-cornered pyramid. The x, y, and z axes have been labeled and the five corners numbered. To construct an isometric pictorial, lay out the axes as usual, 120° apart. Then box in the maximum height, width, and depth of the pyramid as at B.

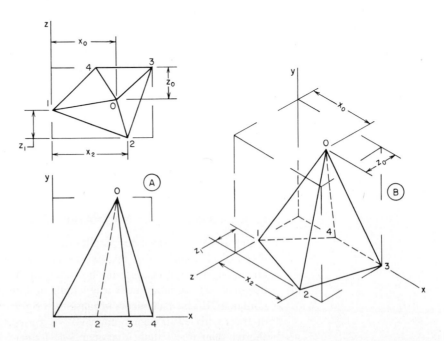

Figure 9
An isometric pictorial with nonisometric lines.

Each corner of the pyramid is located by moving *parallel* to an axis. Point 1 is located by moving on the base along the z axis a distance z_1. Point 2 is located by using distance x_2 along a direction parallel to the x axis. Points 3 and 4 are found similarly along the x axis. Point 0 is found on the upper surface at the intersection of coordinates x_0 and z_0. Next make the various nonisometric lines which make up the edges of the pyramid by joining the endpoints already located. Hidden corner 4 is included, even though pictorials often do not contain hidden lines. The result is an isometric pictorial of the pyramid.

c. Example with Nonoblique Lines

The process of constructing a pictorial containing nonoblique lines is identical to that for pictorials having nonisometric lines. Figure 10 shows an object in a three-view multiview consisting of top, front, and right-side views. The x, y, and z axes are labeled as is the inclined face 1-2-3-4-5. The axes are placed at B in a cavalier oblique pictorial. A 45° depth axis z has been chosen. Other angles could have been used. The maximum height, width, and depth of the object as seen in the multiview have been transferred to the oblique, to form an enclosing box. The same scale has been selected for the pictorial as for the multiview.

Any point can be located by moving along a direction parallel to an axis, as for axonometric views. Points 1 and 5 are already at given corners. Point 4 is located by using distance z_4 from the multiview. Point 2 shares this distance also. Point 3 is found by dropping down distance y_3 and then moving forward from the back distance z_3. Then all lines are joined between proper corners. You can see that the process is not difficult as long as you move parallel to the axes in both the multiview and pictorial.

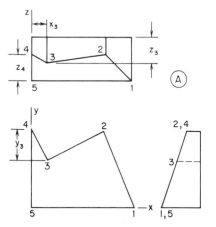
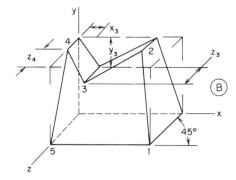

Figure 10
An oblique pictorial with nonoblique lines.

5. CURVES IN PICTORIALS

You must understand the concept of constructing any curve in a pictorial. Curves occur commonly in many objects and parts. You should be comfortable placing curves in any type of pictorial. From previous discussion, we know that any line can be found if its endpoints are located. Two points define a line. Points also define a curve, but more than two points are needed. The number of points needed

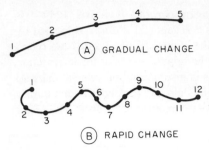

Figure 11
Number of points needed to define a curve.

to define a curve varies. Ideally, the more points obtained, the better the fit of the curve. An infinite number of points would define a curve perfectly, but we must settle for less than an infinite number.

If a curve changes shape very gradually, points used to define it can be farther apart than if a curve changes shape rapidly. Figure 11 shows that fewer points are needed to define case A than case B. We could easily fit a smooth curve through the five points of case A, but perhaps 12 points would be a minimum number for case B. A drafter must exercise reasonable judgment as to how many points are needed to define a particular curve.

Fortunately, the process of generating proper curves is identical for both axonometric and oblique pictorials. We discuss curves for both types of pictorials in the same narrative. First, we explain a general method which works for *any* curve, including circles. Then we discuss a technique to handle only circles.

a. Gridding: A Method for Any Curve

The power of the gridding method lies in its complete versatility. Any curve can be generated by gridding. In Fig. 12 a multiview (A) and two solutions are given. Solution B is for an axonometric drawing, which could thus be an isometric, dimetric, or trimetric. The solution at B happens to be an isometric one. Solution C shows a cavalier oblique, although a cabinet oblique pictorial could just as well be provided.

We begin in the multiview by placing parallel construction lines randomly through the upper surface of the object in the top view. The lines must be parallel to an axis, here the x axis. Recall that only when you move parallel to an axis is the true distance retained.

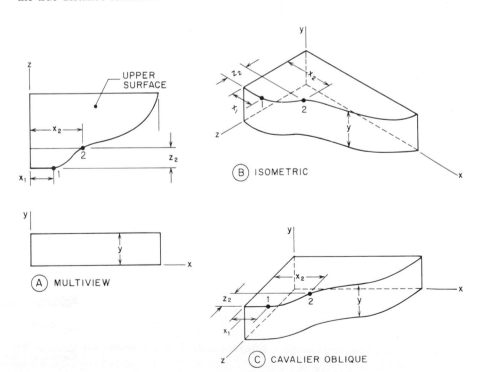

Figure 12
Constructing curves by the gridding method.

One point is located on the forward face at distance x_1 from the left-hand edge of the object. The z distance for this point is zero. A second point is found at the intersection of x_2 and z_2. This process can be repeated many times to obtain as many points as necessary to define the curve well. In Fig. 12 an insufficient number are shown, in order to keep the illustration uncluttered. An additional three or four points would probably be needed.

Each point located on the multiview is transposed to the pictorials. You must be careful to move only in directions parallel to axes, as was done in the multiview. After a sufficient number of points have been selected, a smooth curve is fitted through the points. An irregular curve is recommended to assist in the curve fitting if an instrument drawing is being made. If the object is being sketched freehand, blend in a smooth curve by eye.

You must describe the manner in which the curve on the lower surface is made. From the multiview, note that the lower surface is parallel to the upper. Every point on the lower curve is a fixed distance y from a corresponding point on the upper curve. Once the upper curve is complete, you simply lower the points of the upper curve the distance y. The upper curve is thereby reproduced as the lower curve. This convenient situation can arise because parallels stay parallel in both axonometric and oblique pictorials. Whether straight lines or curves are used, parallelism can be a distinct advantage in constructing such pictorials.

The object in Fig. 12 has a rather random curve for which gridding works well. Will gridding work also for circles? Yes, as seen in Fig. 13. Here a vertical plane containing a circle is converted to an isometric by using grid points, such as $a'b$ and ab'. The method is not rapid, but the circle is converted effectively to an ellipse in the isometric pictorial.

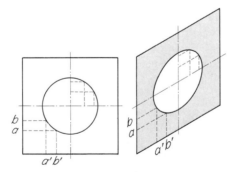

Figure 13
Gridding a circle for an isometric pictorial.

Circles are, of course, a common geometric shape. Templates which contain isometric circles are available to speed the creation of many sizes of isometric circles. Figure 14 shows one such template which provides necessary ellipses representing circles of specific diameters. Templates to fit circles in oblique are also available. Templates can be excellent time savers whose initial costs are quickly repaid.

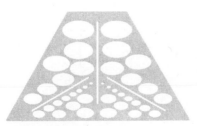

Figure 14
An isometric ellipse template.
(Courtesy Kon-I-Noor Rapidograph, Inc.)

b. Four-Center Method for Pictorial Circles

You are encouraged to use templates whenever possible to make pictorial circles. However, often just the right size ellipse cannot be found on a template, especially for large ellipses. In this case, the four-center method is very useful.

The four-center method creates what appears to the eye as an ellipse, by using two different-size radii. The fact that the resulting construction is not an exact ellipse does not lessen its value. The purpose of a pictorial is to show the overall appearance of an object. By this criterion, the four-center method is quite convincing.

The process consists of placing an enclosing square around the circle to be converted to a pictorial. Follow the steps in Fig. 15, which happens to be for an isometric. In step A, the enclosing square *ABCD* is drawn. Then in steps B, C, and D the enclosing square is oriented in three different ways, one for each of the three principal planes in isometric.

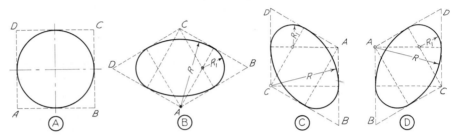

Figure 15
Isometric circles, four-centered method.

From the midpoint of each side of the enclosing square, a perpendicular is constructed. These four perpendicular lines intersect at four positions: one at each of the two obtuse angles (>90°) of the enclosing square and two in the open area within the boundary of the square. These intersections form *centers* for the compass. Two different radii are used. The larger radius is set at the intersection of the obtuse angle. The smaller is set at the intersection in the open area. The size of the radii is that needed to reach from the center to the midpoint of the enclosing square. Note that the large radius is actually larger than the original radius, seen in step A. Also the smaller radius will be smaller than the original radius. Therefore, the original radius is never used.

If less than a full circle is needed in a pictorial, the process remains the same. The only difference is that fewer intersections of perpendiculars are needed. Observe the object in Fig. 16. The enclosing squares of the multiview are placed in

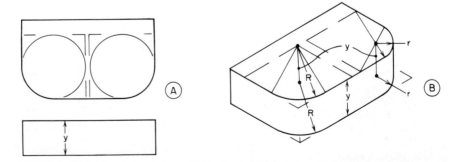

Figure 16
Using one center for a quarter isometric circle.

the pictorial, here an isometric one. Since only a quarter circle is needed at each of the two rounded corners, only one of the four intersections is needed at each corner. View B shows the needed intersection at each corner. One corner requires the smaller radius; the other, the larger radius. The rounded corners on the lower surface are made by simply dropping a distance y the centers used on the upper surface. The same two radii are used again. A vertical tangency line is placed by eye between the smaller rounded corners to complete the pictorial.

The examples above were for isometric pictorials, but the four-center method works for cavalier oblique pictorials, too. The method is valid regardless of the angle of the receding axis, be it 30, 45°, or any other angle. Figure 17 demonstrates the process. Perpendiculars are constructed from midpoints of the enclosing squares.

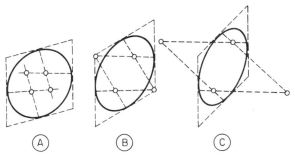

Figure 17
Cavalier oblique centers, four-centered method.

An angle less than 30°, as in case A, has all intersection points within the open area of the enclosing square. An angle of 30°, as in case B, is actually identical to the isometric case in that the isometric pictorial features a 30° angle with the horizontal. Case C shows the intersection points when the angle is greater than 30°. Note that two of the intersection points are *outside* the enclosing square.

We may also construct less than full oblique circles by the same process as for isometric pictorials (Fig. 16). Note, however, that the four-center method works only for cavalier oblique, not cabinet oblique pictorials. The four-center method requires an enclosing square with equal sides, a condition not met in the cabinet oblique pictorial which cuts the size in half in the direction of the receding axis.

c. Circles Not in a Principal Plane

The previous examples of the four-center method were for circles in a principal plane, that is, a horizontal, frontal, or profile plane. If a circle is not on a principal plane, the four-center method will not work. We must return to the method of gridding, discussed previously in relation to Figs. 12 and 13.

Recall that any point can be located if distances are taken parallel to the x, y, and z axes. A sufficient number of points can define a curve. Figure 18 shows a front view and a left-side view of an object having two inclined faces. A round hole and curved upper surface are shown in the front view. Cavalier oblique has been selected as the pictorial type. Cabinet oblique would be acceptable also.

A vertical plane has been placed midway in the left-side view. Distances are then taken parallel to the receding axis to selected points where the hole and curved upper surface intersect the inclined planes. An irregular curve or ellipse template then can be used to fit the finished curves.

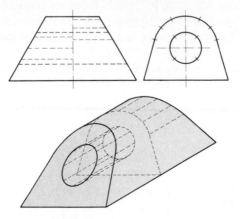

Figure 18
Curves not in a principal plane.

6. CONCEPTS OF PERSPECTIVE

Perspective is by far the most realistic of all pictorial systems. It most nearly represents what we see daily. Figure 19 is a drawing done in perspective. The result is a convincing portrayal of what many people see every day. A perspective generated by computer is shown in Fig. 20. It, too, looks realistic.

a. Characteristics of Perspectives

Everyday observation of life around us reveals some of the more easily noticed features of perspective:

1. Objects become smaller as their distances from the observer increase.
2. Parallel lines no longer remain parallel as they recede into the distance.
3. Horizontal parallel lines converge to a single point on the distant horizon.

These casual observations are apparent to anyone. However, we need to make an orderly study of all variables which control perspective. Only in this way can we learn well the concepts of perspective. We will see that there is a true logic to interaction among the variables.

b. Variables Involved in Perspective

We discuss variables on an as-needed basis, beginning with the primary ones. Refer to Fig. 21. Here a person is looking at a pole. Immediately four vital variables are apparent: the object (OB), the projection plane (PP), and the projectors (P), which converge at the person who is the station point (SP). We need an object to observe, a projection plane to capture the object, projectors to transfer the object to the projection plane, and a station point to which the projectors converge. This initial discussion has therefore provided variables OB, PP, P, and SP.

Figure 19
A manually created perspective drawing.

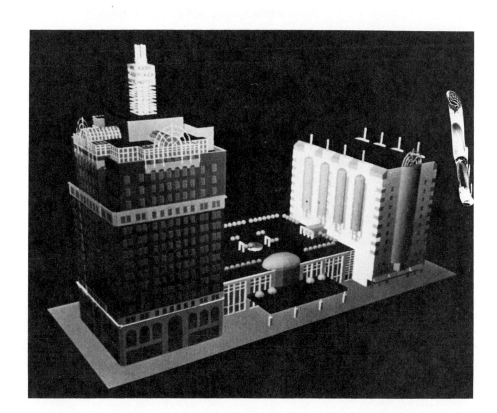

Figure 20
A computer-generated perspective.

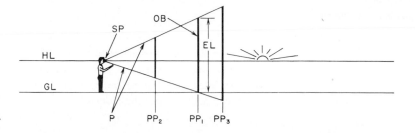

Figure 21
Variables within a perspective system.

Additional variables can be identified. The elevation EL of the object represents the true height (in scale) of the pole. The ground line GL represents the earth on which the observer stands. The horizon line HL is that place in nature where earth and sky join. In perspective HL is assumed to be infinitely far away. Three more variables are therefore added: EL, GL, and HL.

Figure 21 has two more characteristics. First, the station point SP is exactly aligned heightwise with the horizon line HL. That is, a person looking straight ahead would see the horizon. This is true in actual life.

Second, Fig. 21 shows three projection planes, not just one. They are labeled PP_1, PP_2, and PP_3. These are deliberately included to highlight an important concept. Notice that PP_1 is placed directly on the object OB. The resulting "picture" of the pole will show the pole to be exactly *true height*. If PP_2 is used as the projection plane, the resulting picture captured between the projectors will give a result *smaller* than the original pole in PP_1. Finally, if PP_3 is used, the result will be a picture of the pole *larger* than the original. To summarize:

■ An object is true height when the object and projection plane coincide.

■ An object is less than true height when the projection plane is in front of the object.

■ An object is greater than true height when the projection plane is behind the object.

The creator of perspective therefore can control the height of an object by controlling the position of the projection plane relative to the object.

One last variable, the vanishing point, waits to be introduced. Earlier we stated that horizontal parallel lines converge to a single point on the horizon. Figure 22 shows this fact. The edges of the two highways are, in reality, parallel and horizontal. However, in perspective, each highway converges to a point on the horizon. Each convergence point is called a *vanishing point* (VP). This illustration shows two vanishing points. In other perspectives there could be as few as one VP or as many as the creator of the perspective wants.

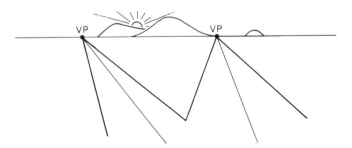

Figure 22
Vanishing points for horizontal lines.

All parallel lines converge to their own vanishing point, just as horizontal lines do. This holds for vertical lines, too, as seen in Fig. 23. Vanishing points for vertical lines turn out to be difficult to construct. Therefore most drafters and sketchers simply taper the sides of tall buildings, etc., to give an attractive effect.

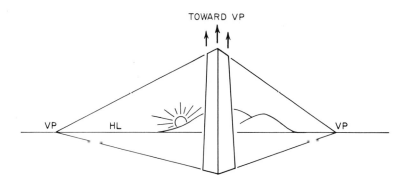

Figure 23
Perspective with a vertical vanishing point.

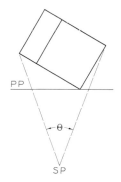

Figure 24
Lateral angle of view.

c. Effects of the Viewing Angle

We may create different effects in a perspective by viewing an object at assorted angles. Note Figs. 24 and 25. Figure 24 shows a top view of an L-shaped block with angle θ between the extreme left and right projectors. The object happens to have one corner in the projection plane (PP), an arbitrary condition. In Fig. 25, we see the effect of changing angle θ. Angles of perhaps 20 or 30° give the most pleasant effect.

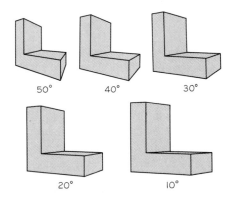

Figure 25
Comparative lateral angles of view.

Another viewing angle that affects perspective is angle Ω in Fig. 26. This angle involves height conditions, whereas angle θ involves horizontal conditions. The L-shaped object is seen in a right-side view relative to Fig. 24, a top view. Note the ground plane (or GL) and position of the horizon plane (or HL) in Fig. 26. Angle Ω is changed by holding the ground plane fixed and lowering the horizon.

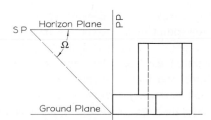

Figure 26
Elevation angle of view.

Figure 27 shows that for the high angle of 50°, we are looking down on the object. At 10°, the horizon has dropped below the top of the object so that the top cannot be seen. The effects of lowering the horizon are very distinct. An angle Ω of about 20 or 30° gives an attractive effect.

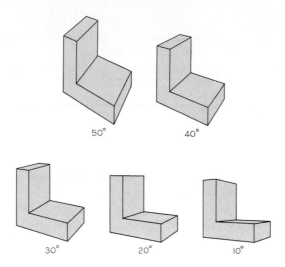

Figure 27
Comparative elevation angles of view.

7. CONSTRUCTING A PERSPECTIVE

It is time now to actually construct a perspective pictorial. The principles of making a perspective are explored first for the most basic object, a point. We use Fig. 28. Do not confuse yourself by trying to understand the whole illustration at once. We will explain it piece by piece.

Note that there are two views in Fig. 28, a top view and a front view. The top view includes the station point (SP), the object (OB) at position 3, and various projectors, to be explained later. The top view also contains the projection plane (PP), which is effectively the transparent sheet of glass on which is "etched" the actual perspective.

The front view features the perspective itself, built from projected points on PP in the top view and from information contained in the front view. Such information includes SP, ground line (GL), horizon line (HL), and the elevation (EL) of the true scaled height of the object above HL. The determination of the vanishing point (VP) on HL is discussed shortly.

a. The Key to All Perspectives: Placing a Point on a Horizontal Line

All perspectives can be constructed by using one basic, critically important concept: Any point of an object can be located by placing some horizontal line through the point, locating that horizontal line in perspective, and putting the desired point on the line. This concept is sound because it enables us to readily find any horizontal line in perspective.

Two points define any straight line. Two points which always define a horizontal line in perspective are the vanishing point of the horizontal line and the true elevation point, where the horizontal line coincides with (crosses) the projection plane.

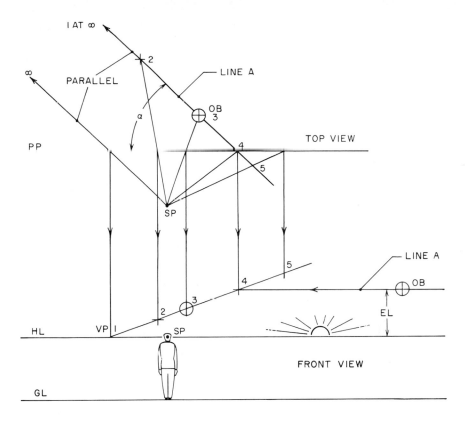

Figure 28
Construction of the perspective of a point.

We know that a horizontal line reaches the horizon at a vanishing point. (See Fig. 22.) We also know that true elevation is shown only in the projection plane. (See Fig. 21.) By combining both facts, we can put any horizontal line into perspective and with it any point on that horizontal line.

Return to Fig. 28. We want to put the object, a point at position 3, into perspective. To begin, we must place a horizontal line through the point. This line is called line *A*. Line *A* may be at any convenient angle α to the projection plane (PP). Line *A* is thought to be infinitely long. It reaches from in front of PP all the way back to infinity. We know that infinity for a horizontal line must be on the horizon (HL). We also know that line *A* is at true elevation as it crosses the projection plane (PP).

The different variables can now come together to produce a perspective. Line *A* (and then the point on line *A*) can be put into perspective by finding where it crosses the horizon and where it crosses the projection plane PP. It is relatively easy to find where it crosses PP. In the top view, it crosses PP at position 4. Therefore we project position 4 into the front view and align it heightwise with the true elevation (EL). Position 4 of line *A* is now shown in perspective.

The vanishing point is now needed as the second point to define line *A*. We know that VP is on the horizon for horizontal line *A*, but where? We need only look in the direction which will show line *A* crossing the horizon infinitely far away. We look *parallel* to an infinitely long line to see its end. If we stand on a long, straight highway, for example, and look at the highway disappearing as a point on the horizontal, we are looking parallel to the edge of the highway.

Therefore, we look parallel to line A in the top view. Where the line of sight crosses PP is where we see in the projection plane the vanishing point at position 1 on the horizon. The vanishing point is therefore on the horizon in the front view in direct projection from the top view.

Line A is now known in perspective in the front view. It passes between VP and position 4 at true elevation. Now we can quickly get the original point at position 3. We simply sight position 3 in the top view from SP. We see position 3 in PP and project that information into the front view *onto* line A. The original object, a point at position 3, is now in perspective.

Three other positions—2, 4, and 5—have been included as a point of interest. Once line A is in perspective, any number of points may be placed on it. Points 2, 4, and 5 are representative points. All points are found by sighting them from SP in the top view, locating their crossing of PP, and projecting these crossings onto line A in the front view.

Notice the relative positions of all the points. Imagine line A as the path of a satellite streaking across the horizon toward us. Point 1 is on HL at an infinite distance. Point 2 is somewhat closer to the observer. Point 3, the original point, is closer still. At point 4 the object is coincident with PP and is at true-scale elevation. By point 5, the object has passed in front of PP and is at an elevation greater than true elevation. In contrast, points 1, 2, and 3 which are all behind PP and therefore at less than true elevation.

You now have the concepts of constructing perspective in hand. You can master any object, whether it be a simple line or block or some complex part. In the next sections, perspectives of planes and solids are discussed.

b. Perspective of Planes

Planes are created in perspective by using exactly the same concepts as for a point, just described. In Fig. 29, three parallel planes are put into perspective. All have the same height. All have two vertical and two horizontal sides. Plane 1 is entirely behind the projection plane (PP). Plane 2 has its forward vertical edge in PP. Plane 3 straddles PP, part behind and part forward of PP.

Again, any point can be found in perspective if it is placed on a horizontal line having two known points, a vanishing point and the true elevation at PP. Convenient horizontal lines already exist in Fig. 29. They are the upper and lower edges of the rectangular planes.

The upper and lower edges are thought to be extended to infinity on the horizon. Again we look parallel to a line to see its end infinitely far away. Since all horizontal edges of the three planes are parallel, all edges share the same VP. The specific VP is found by sighting from SP in the top view parallel to the edges of the planes. The crossing of PP by the sighting projector is projected to HL in the front view and becomes VP.

True elevations of the edges are picked up in the front view. True elevation y can be used only where each plane touches PP in the top view. Plane 1 must be extended to reach PP. That position where extended plane 1 touches PP is projected into the front view and is given true elevation y.

Plane 2 already touches PP. That position also is given true elevation in the front view. The position where plane 3 crosses PP is projected in the front view and is given true elevation y.

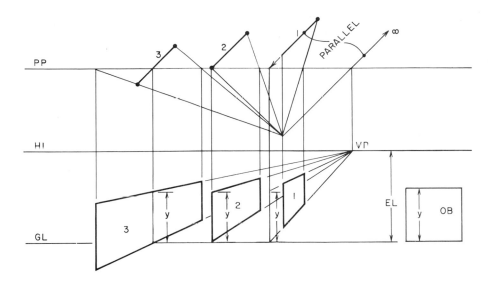

Figure 29
Planes in perspective.

The upper and lower edges of all planes are extended from true elevation to VP. The planes become, in effect, infinitely long ''fences.'' The forward and back vertical lines of each plane are now clipped off by using the projectors sighted from SP in the top view.

Note that *all* projectors to the corners of planes must be projected from the projection plane (PP). Notice for plane 3 that we must sight the forward corner past itself and into PP. This causes the forward vertical to be larger than true elevation *y*. All other vertical lines become shorter than *y*, except for the forward corner of plane 2 which is actually true height *y* because it sits in PP.

c. Perspective of a Solid

Let us continue to use the same concepts to build a solid in perspective. Refer to Fig. 30. While the object may look different from the planes of Fig. 29, the process of construction is really identical. The object is a shed with a pitched roof. A pole stands nearby. The top view shows that one corner of the shed stands in PP. The pole is behind PP.

Two vanishing points have been selected. The reasoning is that there are two principal directions for horizontal lines. However, one VP could have been used— the one on the right side of the perspective. The SP has been chosen to offer a view of the right-hand side of the shed. The horizon (HL) is above the shed, so the perspective will look down on the shed. (Refer to Fig. 27.)

Begin with an easy corner, 1-2. It sits in PP, so it can be placed immediately in perspective by having its true elevation align with 1-2 projected from PP. Line 2-4 is horizontal. A VP for line 2-4 is found by sighting from SP parallel to 2-4. The crossing of PP by the sighting projector is projected to HL as VP. Line 2-4 is then put into perspective, just as the lower edge of plane 3 of Fig. 29 was. Point 3 is actually part of horizontal line 1-3, parallel to line 2-4. Line 1-3 uses the VP of line 2-4. Therefore point 3 can be easily found. Realize that we must sight from SP past points 3 and 4 to get them into the projection plane before we project them into the front view.

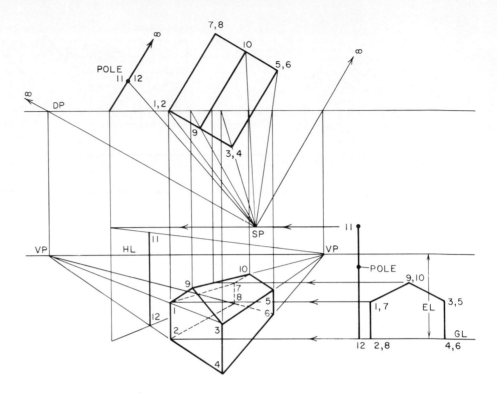

Figure 30
A solid in perspective.

Let us now obtain plane 3-4-5-6 in perspective. Happily, corner 3-4 is already in perspective. Simply extend horizontals 3-5 and 4-6 to their own VP in order to clip off the actual points 5 and 6. For points 7 and 8 we can make use of existing corners 1 and 5 as well as 2 and 6.

Send the horizontal line from 5 to its left-hand VP. Send the line from 1 to its right-hand VP. The intersection of lines 5-7 and 1-7 gives point 7. An identical condition occurs for point 8 (intersection of lines 6-8 and 2-8). Alternately, plane 1-2-7-8 could be completed by extending the total plane to its right-hand VP and clipping off points 7 and 8.

All that remains is the pitched roof and pole. The roof is taken care of by sending the horizontal line containing points 9 and 10 to the right-hand VP. The exact spot where the line crosses PP in the top view is sent to the front view, to be aligned with true elevation. Points 9 and 10 are sighted from SP and projected to its proper line in the front view. Note that point 9 is in front of PP.

The roof is finished by joining the inclined edges, that is, lines 1-9, 3-9, 5-10, and 7-10. Endpoints define a line, and all endpoints are available for these inclined edges. The inclined edges are *not* horizontal and therefore cannot use VPs on the horizon. A powerful technique has been used for these inclined edges: Find their endpoints by allowing these points to be located on horizontal lines.

The pole is put into perspective by placing horizontal lines through points 11 and 12. If the horizontal lines are parallel to those used previously, they can use a previous VP. The horizontal lines are arbitrarily made parallel to lines using the right-hand VP. Therefore that VP is used. The upper and lower horizontal lines are extended into PP to utilize true elevation. Points 11 and 12 are then sighted from SP to complete the pole.

The overall discussion has given the conceptual framework to complete any perspective having straight lines. The concepts are constant. The process becomes repetitive since all points are found by placing them on horizontal lines.

8. PERSPECTIVE FOR OBJECTS PARALLEL TO THE PROJECTION PLANE

On some occasions we may wish to place a face of an object parallel to the projection plane. In so doing, any face parallel to PP will keep its original *shape* but not size, unless the face is actually in PP. Keeping the original shape can be useful if the face contains circles or other features that could be tedious to do in a nonparallel face.

Figure 31 is a basic example of an object having a face parallel to PP. This object in fact has two planes parallel to PP, planes 1-2-3-4 and 5-6-7-8. The method of constructing the perspective is the same as in earlier examples. Let us see how these concepts apply.

The vanishing point is found as before by looking parallel to the direction of convenient horizontal lines. In this case, the view from station point is parallel to line 4-8 (or any of the other parallel horizontal lines: 3-7, 1-5, 2-6). The sight projector parallel to 4-8 crosses PP, and this point is projected directly into the front view as VP onto the horizon (HL). Note that since the sight projector is perpendicular to PP, VP will lie directly below SP.

True elevation again must be used in conjunction with VP to find the perspective of horizontal lines. The object sits behind PP. Therefore face 1-2-3-4 is projected forward into PP in the top view. In this position face 1-2-3-4 is true size. The

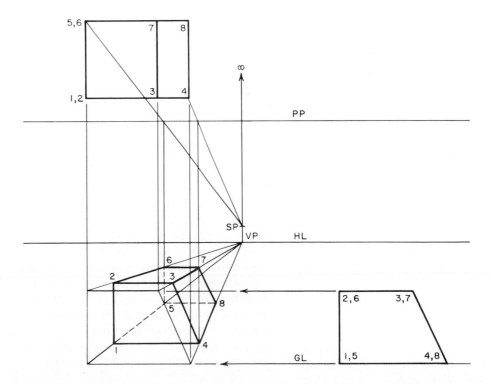

Figure 31
Perspective of an object parallel to projection plane.

elevation information in the front view is aligned with the projectors of 1-2-3-4 from the top view. The true-size shape is outlined lightly as a construction reference.

Horizontal lines are then extended from the true-elevation position of face 1-2-3-4 all the way to VP on the horizon. All that remains is to clip off the actual positions of faces 1-2-3-4 and 5-6-7-8. The perspective can be finished quickly by realizing that faces 1-2-3-4 and 5-6-7-8 keep their shapes. Therefore all edges remain parallel to the same respective edges of the true elevation existing in PP. This means, for example, that edges 1-4 and 2-3 remain parallel to the horizon. Edges 1-2 and 5-6 remain vertical. Therefore only points 4 and 5 are sighted from SP in the top view. The rest of the perspective is built by keeping faces 1-2-3-4 and 5-6-7-8 in true shape. The sizes of both faces are smaller, of course, than true size because they both lie behind PP.

Clearly having one face of an object parallel to PP can make a perspective faster to construct. Whether the result looks better or worse than for a different orientation of the object is for the drafter to decide. Notice how similar in appearance the example just discussed (Fig. 31) is to obliques. The obvious difference lies in the tapered effect of receding edges. Clearly the perspective version looks better than the oblique version. However, more effort is required for the perspective.

9. CURVES IN PERSPECTIVE

Creating curves in perspective is a variation on the same theme: Any point can be located by finding the perspective of a horizontal line placed through the point. Figure 32 shows a random curve which is part of a horizontal plane. Random curves can be generated by the gridding method seen earlier in Fig. 12. A series of parallel lines placed on the object defines points on the curve. The lines, and subsequently the points, need only to be placed in perspective.

In Fig. 32 lines are placed parallel to the projection plane. Five have been used, including the back edge of the object. More parallels are recommended for a more accurate solution, but the five given are sufficient to illustrate the technique. The enclosing rectangle around the curve is put into perspective in the normal manner. Note that line 3 lies in PP and so is used at true elevation, which is given as the position of the edge view of the plane. The vanishing point is found by sighting from SP parallel to edge 1-5.

Lines 2, 3, and 4 are established in perspective by sighting from SP the various ''hook-on'' points 2, 3, and 4 and projecting them into the front view. The points on the curve of interest are A, B, and C. Since points A, B, and C sit on lines already in perspective, the points are easily placed in perspective by sighting each one from SP. The final curve is fitted through the located points.

The gridding process used in Fig. 32 works for *any* curve, including circles or other common geometric shapes such as ellipses or parabolas. The gridding method can be a shortcut for a circle, however. Figure 33 shows a circle in a vertical plane. First the vertical enclosing square is put into perspective; the techniques are not shown here because they are identical to those in earlier examples. Then diagonals are put into the perspective square. Next midpoints of the sides of the square are located. An additional point is found, perhaps by using distance x. Finally, a smooth curve is fitted through the points.

Any object whatsoever can be put into perspective by using the concepts and techniques discussed in the last several pages. The concepts should be useful when a perspective is constructed in any mode, be it a hand drawing, a freehand sketch, or manipulation of a software program in CAD. The realism of perspective is unsurpassed. The effort expended to use this form of pictorial will be well worth it.

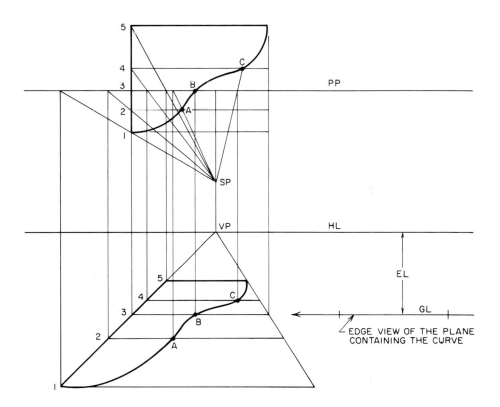

Figure 32
Perspective of a curve.

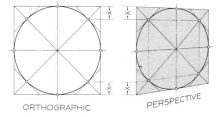

ORTHOGRAPHIC   PERSPECTIVE

Figure 33
Perspective of a circle.

P R O B L E M S

ISOMETRICS   Construct isometric drawings for
Problems 1, 2, and 3.

1. Guide block.

2. METRIC. Hopper.

3. METRIC. Forming punch.

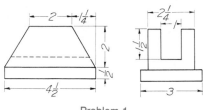

Problem 1

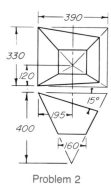

Problem 2

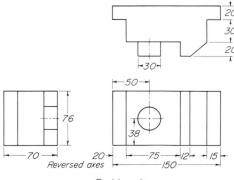

Problem 3

OBLIQUES Construct oblique drawings for Problems 4, 5, and 6.

4. METRIC. Slotted link.

5. Hook brace.

6. METRIC. Slotted guide.

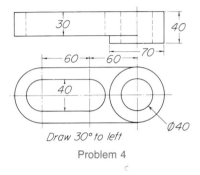

Draw 30° to left

Problem 4

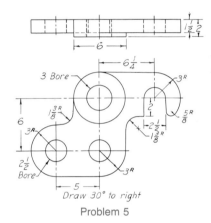

Draw 30° to right

Problem 5

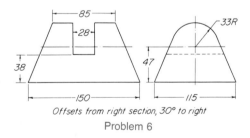

Offsets from right section, 30° to right

Problem 6

PERSPECTIVES Perspective drawings may be made by using Probs. 1 through 6 or other problems from other chapters.

PICTORIAL SKETCHING The following problems are planned to develop skill in both pictorial sketching and reading orthographic drawings. Make the sketches to suitable size on 8½ × 11 in paper, choosing the most appropriate form of representation—isometric, oblique, or perspective.

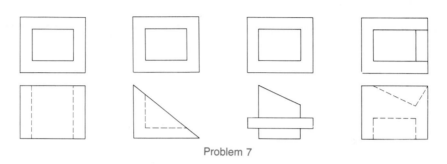

Problem 7

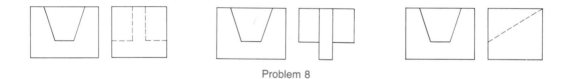

Problem 8

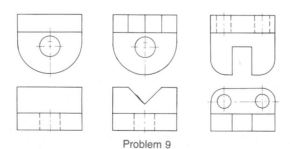

Problem 9

CLARIFICATION OF SHAPES AND SIZES

C H A P T E R 8

TECHNIQUES
OF
SECTIONING

1. REASON FOR SECTIONING

Anyone involved in technical representation of parts often sees the technique shown in Fig. 1. Note the use of fine parallel lines within a visible-line-bounded perimeter. These parallel lines indicate that the part has been cut open. An imaginary "saw" has cut across the part to reveal the internal details. *Sectioning* is the name given to this technique of cutting into a part to show features that would otherwise remain hidden.

Sectioning is a powerful technique that clarifies interior portions of an object that would be difficult to understand otherwise. The power of sectioning is evident in Fig. 2. A top view with round features can be seen. A regular nonsectioned front view is shown in view A. Note the maze of hidden lines which almost totally confuse the viewer. Anyone trying to understand the interior details of the object would become easily frustrated.

View B, however, provides good clarity of interior shapes. View B is known as a *fully sectioned* front view. The object has been cut open along its left-to-right centerline. The fact of sectioning is documented by use of the thin, parallel lines known as *section lining,* or *crosshatching*. Section lining is used where solid material has been cut. Holes and open spaces are not given section lining because they are not cut. Other cases in which section lining is not used are discussed later. Note that view C is a special removed section of the part cut along cutting plane *C-C*. Such special cases are discussed later as well.

141

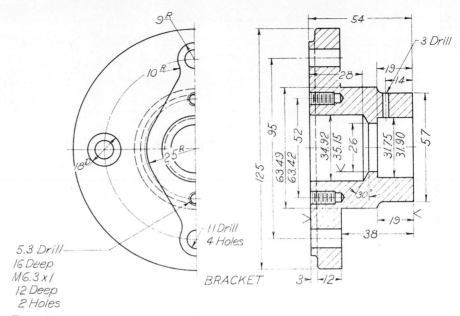

Figure 1
Example of sectioning.

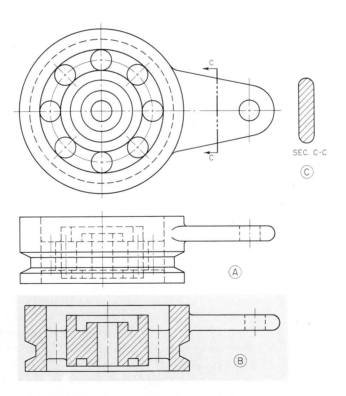

Figure 2
Clarity of hidden features by
sectioning.

2. SYMBOLS USED IN SECTIONING

a. Material Symbols

Through the years an attempt has been made to define actual materials by the use of particular symbols. Figure 3 lists many of these symbols. Naturally, this list is not exhaustive. There are hundreds of alloys and compounds having no symbol to designate them. How do we differentiate between the metals of tin and nickel, for example?

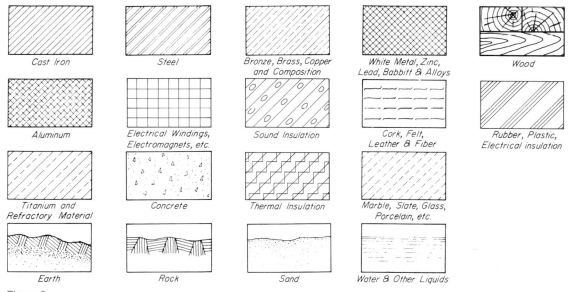

Figure 3
Symbols for material in section.

Fortunately the problem of insufficient symbols is solved by using specific material designation in informational blocks on drawings. Figure 4 shows material information in the lower right area of the title block: "ES2-MIA100-BA steel." This very specific steel could not easily be represented by a symbol. Therefore, symbols used in sectioning are of a general type. In fact, the symbol for cast iron is used frequently because it is the easiest to draw. The cast-iron symbol may be used even if the material is not cast iron. It is only important that the exact material be specified in an informational block on the drawing.

Drawing sectioning symbols is relatively easy, if not especially fast. A moderately hard lead is suggested, such as 2H or 3H. Keep the lead sharp. Parallel lines within section lining normally should be at some angle other than horizontal or vertical. Angles of 30, 45, and 60° are usual. Section lining is thinner and lighter than other visible lines. Space parallel lines as far apart as feasible. If you space section lining too tightly, it is time-consuming and difficult to control. Figure 5 illustrates typical section lining with the cast-iron symbol.

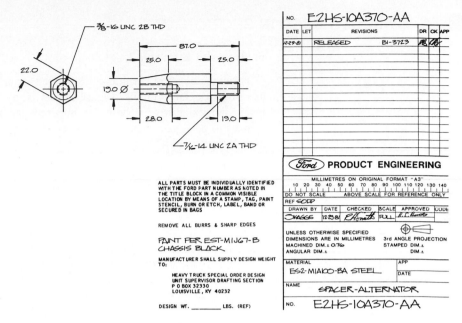

Figure 4
A drawing listing a particular material within the title block: ES 2-MIA100-BA steel.

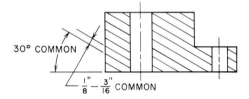

Figure 5
Typical section lining.

The direction of the parallel lines of material symbols can be reversed for effective representation of different parts of an assembly. Figure 6 illustrates the relative positions of three different parts within one assembly. The cast-iron symbol is used throughout, but by changing the spacing and angle of the section lining we can easily tell which part is which. Note that for the same part the section lining maintains the same spacing and angle.

Another example of sectioning within an assembly is seen in Fig. 7. There appear to be a total of five parts: a body, a cap, two screws, and a thin gasket. Again, the same spacing and angle are used for the same respective parts, cap, and body. The gasket, being thin, is shown solid. The screws are left unsectioned, a useful convention we will see more of later.

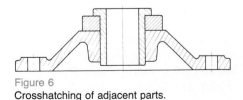

Figure 6
Crosshatching of adjacent parts.

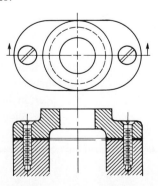

Figure 7
Additional example of sectioning within an assembly.

b. Cutting-Plane Symbol

It is often helpful to indicate *where* the part has been cut open. A cutting-plane symbol can tell the viewer exactly where the cut has been made. A cutting-plane symbol has already been included in two figures. Figure 2 shows cutting-plane *C-C* for the removed section. Figure 7 shows a cutting plane in the top view. In both cases, the arrows on the cutting plane point in the direction of viewing which produces the particular section. That is, in Fig. 2 we are looking toward the circular features of the part. In Fig. 7 our view is toward the rear of the assembly.

The cutting-plane symbol has two forms, both given in Fig. 8. Case A uses heavy long dashes of uniform length. Case B uses a long-short-short format for the dashes, but again they are heavy. The symbols must be sufficiently dark and thick to stand out well on a drawing.

A drafter may elect not to use any cutting-plane symbols. The assumption then is that the cutting plane passes directly along the main centerline of the object. For example, in Fig. 2 the front view does not have a corresponding cutting plane indicated in the top view. The assumption is that the cut has been made along the central right-to-left centerline. In general, it is a good idea to insert cutting-plane symbols. Then there is no doubt as to where the cut has been made.

Figure 8
Cutting plane symbols.

3. SECTION TYPES

Specific types of section are available in sufficient variety to allow the drafter to show any sectioned portions desired. We review the major types. A drawing may contain any or all types of sectioning. Each type has its advantages.

a. Full Section

This type of section is used when an object is cut fully across from one side to the other. Figure 9 shows a full section in the front view. All interior detail is revealed, including the hollow cavity and two small holes, one vertical and one horizontal. The cutting plane is shown in top view as *A-A*. Notice that all visible lines in the background are drawn. It is important to show background lines, as

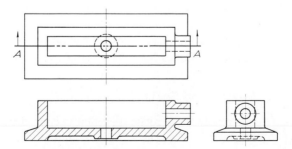

Figure 9
A full section.

demonstrated in Fig. 10. Omission of background lines creates the incomplete effect in case A. Clarity is improved by providing all visible background lines, as in case B.

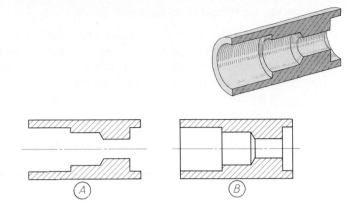

Figure 10
The need for background lines.

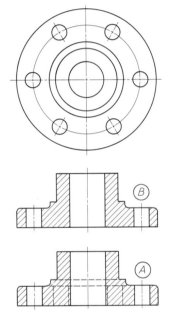

Figure 11
Omission of hidden lines to improve clarity.

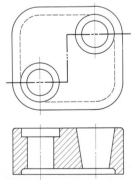

Figure 12
An offset section.

Hidden lines in sections are usually omitted. Note in Fig. 11 that case B is clear as to interior detail, but that the inclusion of hidden lines in case A only clutters the sectioned view. Hidden lines are necessary only if the shape is unusual and requires hidden lines to clarify the shape.

Any view may be sectioned. The example in Fig. 9 was a sectioned front view, but top and side views are just as valid for sectioning. The drafter chooses the view(s) for sectioning.

A full section need not be cut along one continuous plane, but may zigzag to pick up hidden features. Figure 12 gives us an example. The cutting plane zigzags in the top view to make both holes visible in the sectioned front. A section incorporating a zigzag path for the cutting plane is called an *offset section*. Note that the position where the cutting plane turns 90° (about halfway across the object) is really an arbitrary one. The 90° turn is *not* shown as a line (edge) in the front view. Any line on an object is always a feature of the object itself, not part of some cutting plane.

b. Half Section

Half sections are so named because only half of the object is sectioned. This situation thus leaves one-half of the object unsectioned. Note the position of the cutting plane in Fig. 13. A half section allows the viewer to see both the inside and outside of the object, having the best of both worlds. Not only can the interior details be revealed, but also the outside contours remain. Half sections are used generally with objects having symmetry, such as those based on a series of diameters. Hidden lines are optional on the unsectioned portion of the object.

c. Revolved Section

A revolved (or rotated) section is created by revolving a selected cross section 90° about its axis. The revolved section is then seen as a cross section superimposed on the regular view. In Fig. 14 a position is selected in the top view for rotation of the cross section. Any position may be chosen along the central centerline of the object. In each case, the rotation is for 90° and only 90°, either clockwise or counterclockwise. If an object is symmetric in the front and rear halves, the direction of rotation makes no difference because the resulting cross section is identical

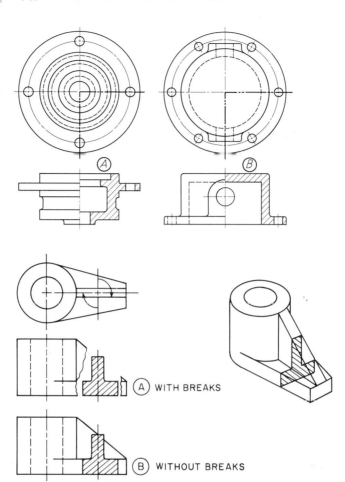

Figure 13
Half sections.

Figure 14
Revolved sections.

in the displayed view. A 3-D view of the object is given in Fig. 14, to aid in identifying the chosen cross section. Note that the cross section arbitrarily is shown in its original position prior to a 90° rotation.

The front view of Fig. 14 shows the resultant revolved section. There are, in truth, two front views: case A and case B. The only difference is that in case A the revolved section is shown *with breaks*. In case B it is shown *without breaks*. Both forms are acceptable. A revolved section with breaks merely isolates the cross section more fully and draws attention to the cross section.

Why use a revolved section? The primary purpose of a revolved section is to *save space*. A cross section is normally seen in some kind of end or side view. By superimposing the cross section on an existing view, we no longer need an additional view.

d. Removed Section

A revolved section becomes a *removed section* by the simple technique of removing the revolved section from the object. At times leaving a revolved section in place could cause the detail of the object to be covered up. Look at Fig. 15. This figure, which shows the same object as Fig. 14, includes two forms of removed

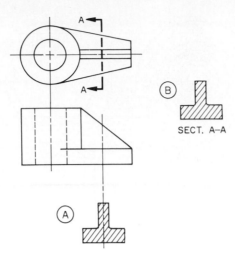

Figure 15
Removed sections.

sections. In case A, the centerline of the cross section has been extended, and just the cross section is shown. If a removed section is to be used, then a regular front view (without a revolved section) is appropriate.

Alternatively, in Fig. 15 we have the option of placing the removed section *anywhere* by adding a selected cutting plane *A-A* in the top view and then placing the cross section where desired. The cross section has to be labeled *A-A* to tie in with cutting plane *A-A*. Features of the object in the background behind the cutting plane are usually not given in removed sections. However, we may change the scale of the removed section relative to the main views to increase clarity. In such a case, the changed scale of the section must be noted beside the removed section.

Removed sections are a powerful device to show contours of complicated shapes. An excellent use of removed sections is seen in Fig. 16. The intricate shape of the propeller is revealed in a manner almost impossible to achieve graphically in any other way. The process of removed sections is also useful in shapes such as jet-engine turbine blades, airplane fuselages, and other objects of continually varying shape. A series of such cross sections for a given part defines an "envelope" of the entire external surface.

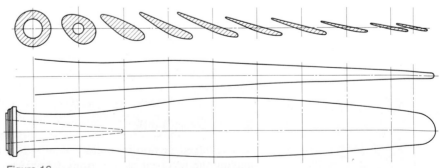

Figure 16
Value of removed sections for a complicated shape.

Figure 17
Complex surface generated by
numerical controlled machining.

Such an envelope can be programmed into a computer to permit numerical control (NC) machining. A complex part can be machined without being touched by human hands. Figure 17 shows a part of a complex external surface which is produced by computer-driven machining. This is an illustration of the broad, vital area of computer-aided manufacturing (CAM) which has been expanding rapidly within the last decade.

e. Broken-out Section

This simple but very useful type of sectioning is shown in Fig. 18. Sometimes called a *partial section,* it offers maximum flexibility to the drafter. As much or as little of a part is cut open as is desired. In Fig. 18, sufficient sectioning is done to fully reveal the interior holes.

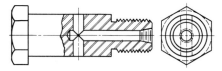

Figure 18
A broken-out section.

A broken-out section can always be spotted by the break between sectioned and nonsectioned portions, shown as a freehand wavy line. Also no cutting-plane symbol appears on the drawing. However, we assume that the cut goes along the centerline of the object.

f. Assembly Section

As the name implies, assembly sections are used for drawings which show parts put together into their operational positions. Figure 19 shows a gearbox which has been fully sectioned in the front view. A partial left-side view is given, too. This figure shows a more complicated assembly than that in Fig. 6.

Note that all materials have been given the cast-iron symbol. It is highly unlikely that each part is made of cast iron, but time is saved by using this symbol. Again,

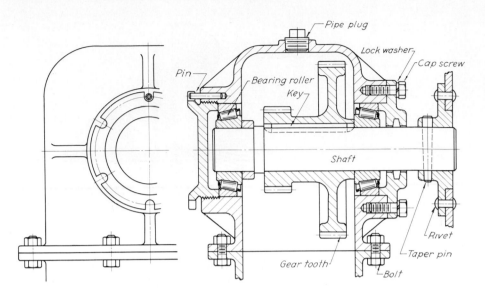

Figure 19
A sectional assembly.

some informational block on the drawing will indicate true materials. Normally such materials appear in a parts list accompanying the drawing.

Note in Fig. 19 the reversal of direction for section lining from one part to the next, but yet the *same* part keeps the *same* direction. Also smaller parts have more closely spaced section lining than larger parts do. This technique creates good visual impact.

We must look at an additional important technique in an assembly drawing. Solid (nonhollow) parts lying on the centerline are *not* sectioned. In Fig. 19 all the bolts, screws, pins, rivets, and plugs are left as external, nonsectioned parts. Why? The reason is simply that the characteristic appearance of each solid piece would not be improved if it were sectioned. The purpose of sectioning is to show interior detail. If a part is solid, there is no point in sectioning it. Also the outside view of a part sometimes is highly revealing of what that part is. A nut and bolt, for example, are best recognized by outside views.

Overall, a sectioned assembly is a good demonstration of the considerable utility of sectioning. How else could we look inside a product so effectively to see the types and positions of parts? Whether done by hand or by computer, the purpose of sectioning is to clarify parts and their functions.

4. CONVENTIONS USED IN SECTIONING

a. Nonsectioned Features

We know that sectioning is used to increase the clarity of interior features of a part. The need for clarity is primary. Any technique that can improve clarity should be used. Clarity is so important that we are allowed to distort literal truth in projection to promote clarity. We are allowed ''graphic license'' to change true projections to permit greater understanding of shapes.

Look at the example in Fig. 20. Two different objects have identical outlines. Case A has four triangular fins and a vertical hole. Case B is entirely solid except for the vertical hole. Strictly speaking, a full section of each object will give the

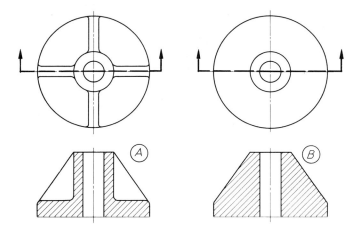

Figure 20
Fins in section.

same result. Each has the front view seen for case B. However, the shape of the fins in case A will be hard to detect because the front view of A is that of B. After all, the cutting plane passes through solid material, except for the hole, in each case.

To enhance understanding and clarity, we decide to leave the triangular fins *unsectioned,* even though the cutting plane theoretically passes through them. Now we can see the presence of the fins. This technique of not sectioning the fins violates the truth, but is permitted to increase clarity.

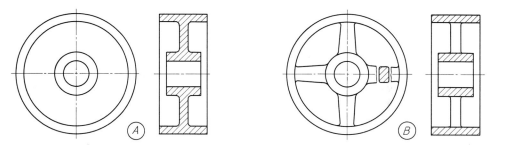

Figure 21
Spokes in section.

Figure 21 shows another example. The solid web between the rim and the hub is sectioned in case A. However, the spokes in case B are left unsectioned, to avoid giving the impression of a solid web, as in A. Notice incidentally the small revolved section of the spoke in case B which reveals the spoke's cross-sectional area. A final example is shown in Fig. 22. Decide for yourself why the front view is best sectioned as given.

Let us summarize the conventions relating to nonsectioned features:

1. Leave unsectioned any feature through which a cutting plane passes if:
   a. The shape of the feature would be lost if sectioned.
   b. The feature is a fin, spoke, or other aspect not solid throughout the entire object.
2. Leave unsectioned solid objects on the centerline of any assembly of parts. Refer to Fig. 19 and the corresponding discussion.

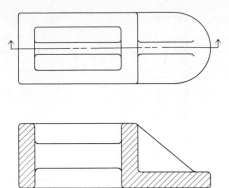

Figure 22
Ribs in section.

b. Alignment

Alignment is very helpful in clarifying the shape of an object. See Fig. 23. The true projection as given is not very useful in showing clearly the shape of the spokes. The true projection may allow the drafter to demonstrate skills of the trade, but the actual value of such true projection is not great. It is far better to place the spokes exactly opposite one another. Then the shape of the spokes is distinctly clear. The spokes have been "aligned," that is, rotated to be 180° apart. The three-part symmetry of the spokes now appears to be two-part symmetry.

Note also in Fig. 23 the use of nonsectioned features. In the true projection, the cutting plane has passed through the spoke, and section lining was provided. In the view having aligned spokes, the spokes were properly left unsectioned. Thus two conventions have been used in a single view.

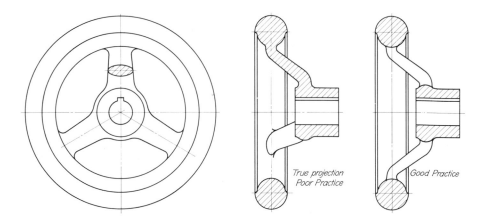

Figure 23
Aligned spokes.

Another example of alignment is given in Fig. 24. In this case, the three-part symmetry of both the fins and the holes is aligned to become two-part symmetry. True projection is avoided, but the true *relationship* of the features to the total object is enhanced. The true shape of the fins is seen, and the true radial distance of the holes from the center is given.

A final example is shown in Fig. 25. The relationship of the features in this moderately complex part is made clear by use of alignment. The cutting plane

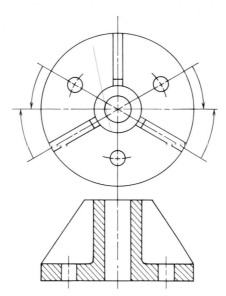

Figure 24
Fins and holes in alignment.

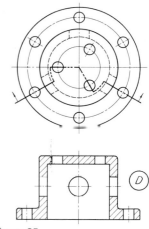

Figure 25
Use of zigzag cutting plane in alignment.

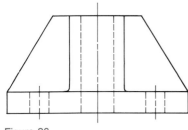

Figure 26
Figure 24 without sectioning.

zigzags through the various holes to create an offset section. All holes are rotated (aligned) to the central right-left centerline and then projected to the front view. The true radial positions of all holes are now available. Such information is valuable to the user of the drawing.

The convention of alignment may be used for features of an object, *whether sectioned or not.* Alignment is seen often in conjunction with sectioning, but we may still align features of an object which is not sectioned. Look again at Fig. 24. Try to visualize the front view without sectioning, but still involving alignment. The view should be that of Fig. 26. In fact, Fig. 24 did not require sectioning to be understood. Sectioning was used to illustrate a concept. Actually, complicated parts (such as in Fig. 2) benefit most from sectioning.

5. MISCELLANEOUS TECHNIQUES

To conclude our discussion of sections and conventions, a few common techniques deserve mention. These techniques, like others, help make drawings easier to understand or allows them to be made faster or both. Space saving can also be a consideration.

a. Half Views

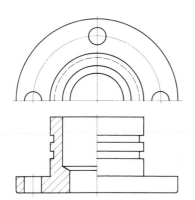

Figure 27
Use of a half view in sectioning.

Half views of objects save space and are faster to make than full views. Consider Fig. 27, in which only half of the top view is given. The part is assumed to be symmetric about the centerline, with four equally spaced holes. There is really no reason to show the forward half of the top view. A centerline forms the boundary at the forward edge. A centerline boundary is a firm indicator that a half view exists. Notice that the front view is a half section, showing both external and interior features. The front view could also have been fully sectioned or could have been left unsectioned.

To reaffirm the use of a centerline as a boundary, see Fig. 28. Two simple objects are shown. Case A has a centerline boundary on the forward side. Case A is therefore a full circular disk of 360° having two holes 180° apart. Case B, however, has a solid-line boundary, indicating that this object is a semicircular disk with just one hole. No sectioning is done on either disk because there is no real need to reveal interior detail.

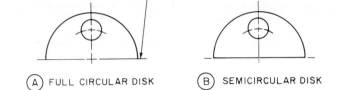

Figure 28
Centerline boundary to denote a half view.

b. Alternate Section Lining

An alternative to not sectioning noncontinuous members such as fins, webs, and spokes is to use alternate sectioning. We have already discussed the reasons for not using regular section lining (see Fig. 20), in that the feature could be totally obscured. It may bother some people to not see sectioning lining across various noncontinuous features. But there is the option, seen in Fig. 29, of alternating every other section line across the noncontinuous feature. Note that the boundary of the feature, here a web, is drawn as a dashed line, not a solid line, which is done when the feature is left unsectioned.

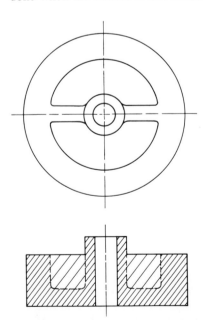

Figure 29
Alternate section lining.

c. Breaks

Sometimes a part is too long relative to its cross-sectional area to be drawn clearly. An example is a 20-ft-long tube of 1-in diameter. On any normal-size paper, the diameter will appear very small compared to the length. Using a break as in Fig. 30 can help clarify a drawing. The pipe of Fig. 30 has been drawn at full size, but other scales are quite acceptable. The excessive length has been collapsed into one of convenience by use of the break. However, the *actual* true length must be given when the part is dimensioned.

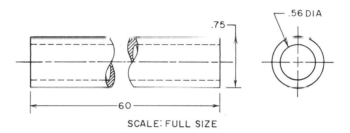

Figure 30
Use of a break.

Breaks may be used as long as no detail of interest would be lost in the shortening of the part. Various symbols may be used for breaks (see Fig. 31). The symbols for rectangular and wood sections are sketched freehand. Round and pipe sections may be done carefully freehand or with help from an irregular curve or template.

The purpose of this chapter has been to stress the value of sectioning techniques. They are easy to apply in manual drafting. In CAD work most software packages have sectioning routines from which the user may select one or more appropriate treatments. Based on knowledge gained from this chapter, the user can proceed with confidence as sectioning is applied in CAD.

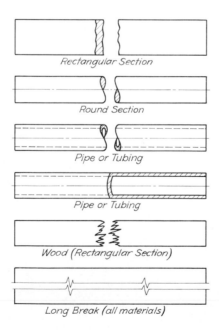

Figure 31
Conventional breaks.

P R O B L E M S

1. Change the right-side view to a full section.

2. Change the right-side view to a full section.

3. Change the right-side view to a sectional view as indicated.

4. Draw the top view as illustrated and the front view in half section on *A-A*.

5. Draw the top view and front view in section.

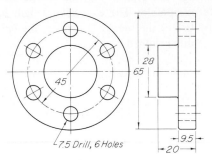

Problem 1

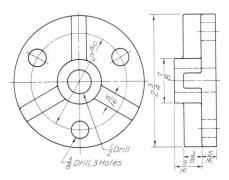

Problem 2

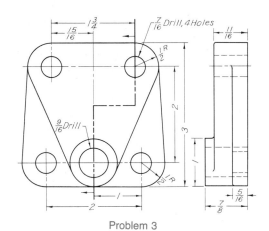

Problem 3

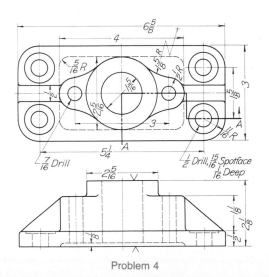

Problem 4

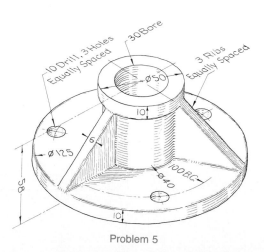

Problem 5

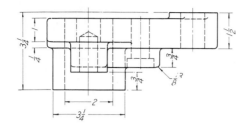

6. Draw views as follows: With the object in the position shown, draw the front view as shown, draw the left-side view as section *B-B,* and draw the new top view as an aligned view.

7. Draw these three parts assembled and sectioned.

8. Draw the left-hand half view as shown and the front view as a full section.

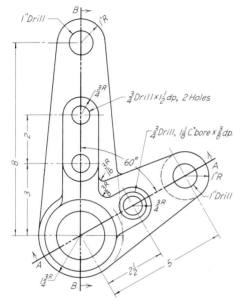

Problem 6

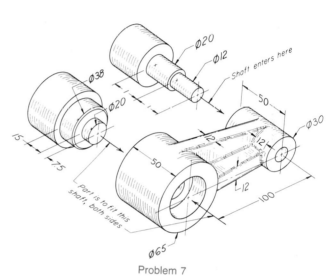

Problem 7

Problem 8

C H A P T E R 9

DIMENSIONING: CONCEPTS AND TECHNIQUES

1. INTRODUCTION

The proper placement of dimensions on a part is vital to getting the part made. A person must know the size and position of each feature of a part in order to successfully construct the part. The part may be a dish, a bolt, or an assembly of many parts, such as an electric motor. When the dimensions are accurate and appropriate, the production of the part can proceed smoothly. Inaccurate or inappropriate dimensioning can lead to confusion and perhaps even rejected pieces which fail to meet required specifications.

In this chapter we discuss as clearly as possible first the why and then the how of dimensioning. Suitable illustrations will highlight the reading. You should find these topics valuable, whether you are planning to manually draft a design or to use a CAD system.

2. CONCEPTS OF DIMENSIONING

It is extremely helpful to understand the basic concepts of dimensioning. Proper understanding and use of concepts enable you to properly dimension a part regardless of the drafting mode, manual or computer-aided. The many little rules and conventions of dimensioning fall neatly into place within the context of a few overall concepts. We look at three major concepts and give examples of each. Then we discuss specific ''rules'' or techniques which implement the concepts.

CONCEPT 1: THE CONTOUR PRINCIPLE

This concept is very important and takes first priority in dimensioning:

DIMENSION EACH FEATURE ONCE WHERE SHAPE SHOWS, except for outside diameters, which are dimensioned in the noncircular view.

Called the *contour principle,* this concept serves as an umbrella covering all other concepts and techniques. Look at the example in Fig. 1. The object is basically a flat baseplate with a raised cylindrical protrusion or "boss." There are two holes, one in the boss and one at the right front corner. A 90° radius is also at the right front corner. A notch has been angled off at the left rear corner. A top view and a front view are given. Note that the words in parentheses are for discussion purposes only and would not appear in an actual drawing.

Note also that the letter *S* stands for a *size* dimension such as height, width, or depth. The letter *P* means a *position* dimension, such as the location of the center of a hole. The letter *D* is for the *diameter* of a cylinder or hole and is used for a 360° arc. However, *R* is for *radius* and is proper for any arc less than 360°. These letters are used in Fig. 1 for discussion only. Actual drawings use actual numbers, as we shall see.

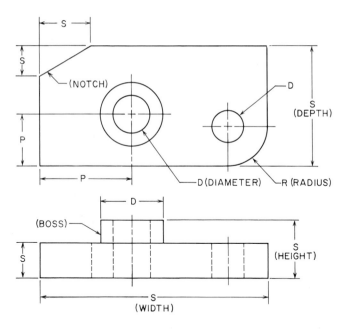

Figure 1
Illustration of the contour principle

A *feature* is defined within the concept as a portion of the object having a distinct geometric shape, such as a hole, a notch, or a thickness like that of the baseplate of Fig. 1. Geometric shapes are familiar to us. They commonly include cylinders, cones, prisms, and pyramids. Negative shapes are actually holes or missing material. The holes of Fig. 1 are negative cylinders, for example. The baseplate is a modified rectangular prism.

Let us return to concept 1. Each feature is to be dimensioned *once* where *shape shows.* Dimensioning a feature *once* is important because repeating a dimensioning only causes excess dimensioning and thus confusion. Dimensioning where *shape shows* is important because the reader of the drawing can best spot the contour of a feature where its shape is seen. For example, at the left rear corner of Fig. 1 the shape of the notch is shown clearly in the top view. It is hidden in the front view and cannot be well seen. It is therefore dimensioned in the top view.

Also in Fig. 1 radius R in the top view displays its shape there, not in the front view, and is properly dimensioned in the top view. The two holes reveal their shapes in the top view and are dimensioned there. The position P of the central hole and the boss are also seen in the top view and so are dimensioned in the top view. The overall depth S is shown in the top view.

The overall width S is seen in both the top view and front view. It could be properly dimensioned in either view. The front view was chosen arbitrarily. The overall height S in the front view is that of the baseplate.

The part has been fully dimensioned except for two strange discrepancies. In the top view there is no position P for the small hole at the right front. Also the outside diameter of the boss is seen in the front view, but its shape actually is revealed more clearly in the top view as a circle. What is going on?

For the small hole, no position dimension is needed for its center because it shares the same center as radius R. The numerical value of the position of the hole's centerline is identical to that of radius R. Since R is known, so is the implied position P of the centerline.

The outside diameter of the boss is shown in the noncircular view, the front view. Why? Note the qualifying phrase in concept 1: Dimension each feature once where shape shows *except for outside diameters, which are dimensioned in the noncircular view*. There is a valid reason for this limitation. See Fig. 2. This object has four circles, seen in the top view. Two represent inside diameters (holes), and two represent outside diameters. If the part were dimensioned as in case A, the diameters would indeed be dimensioned where shape shows. However, the viewer would have to determine which circles represented holes and which outside diameters. This is certainly possible by referring to the front view, but such a process is tedious and unnecessary. By specifically dimensioning the outside diameters in the noncircular view (case B), the viewer can instantly tell which diameters are inside diameters and which outside diameters. Therefore concept 1 contains this qualifying phrase for the sake of clarity. We can now quickly tell holes (negative cylinders) from outside diameters (positive cylinders).

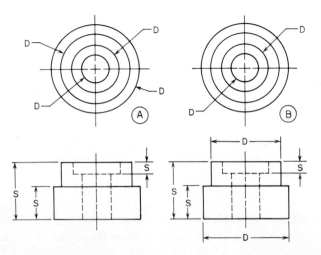

Figure 2
Placing of outside diameters in the noncircular view.

CONCEPT 2: INFLUENCE OF PRODUCTION METHODS ON DIMENSIONING

There is more than one way to dimension a part. Figure 3, for example, shows two somewhat random ways to dimension a particular piece. Only the top view is shown, to simplify the illustration. A front view would be required prior to production. Which of the two ways to dimension Fig. 3 is better? There is no correct answer to this question in that both ways do give the size and position of each feature. Only if we knew how the part was to be manufactured could we express a preference for case A, case B, or some other way.

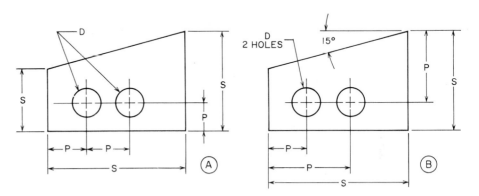

Figure 3
Variations in dimensioning.

The manufacturing method for a part plays a crucial role in how a part should be dimensioned. This book does not emphasize manufacturing methods, but we explore a few of the consequences of methods on proper dimensioning. We will note when coordinate versus angular dimensioning might be used. We discuss datum line versus incremental dimensioning also, including the use of finish marks. Finally, we treat the effect of machining precision on dimensioning.

a. Coordinate versus Angular Dimensioning

Some machine tools travel in linear paths described by (x, y) coordinates. Case A of Fig. 4 would be well dimensioned for such a machine tool. Moving the tool 4 in along the x coordinate and 3 in along the y coordinate locates the center for the 1-in-diameter hole. Other machine tools may travel more readily in circular arcs. Case B of Fig. 4 shows a proper dimension for such tools. With an (x, y) coordinate of $(0, 0)$ as the origin and a radius of 5 in, the tool is rotated 36.9° to locate the center of the hole.

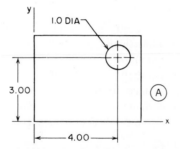 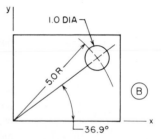

Figure 4
Coordinate vs. angular dimensioning.

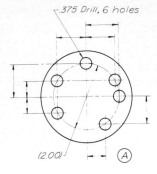

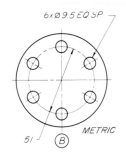

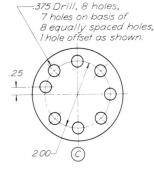

Figure 5
Additional example of coordinate vs.
angular dimensioning.

Another example is seen in Fig. 5. The part in case A is dimensioned in the coordinate system. All holes are positioned and sized. The outside diameter and thickness are missing in this example because the example concentrates on the holes. The dimension (2.00) is actually a *reference dimension,* meaning that it is not actually needed but is a useful reference. Note that the holes have been located from the two centerlines 90° to each other. This is a common practice. The centerlines serve as datum lines.

In case B an angular method is used because the note ''6 × φ 9.5 EQ SP'' is used. The note means that six holes of 9.5-mm diameter are equally (EQ) spaced (SP). The Greek letter phi (φ) represents *diameter* in the metric system of units. The six holes sit on a hole with a 51-mm diameter. Since six holes are equally spaced, there is 60° between any two holes. Another example of the angular method of dimensioning is shown in Fig. 6. The specific angles have not been filled in, but the intent is clear. The vertical centerline has been arbitrarily selected as a datum line.

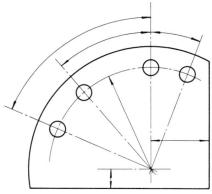

Figure 6
Holes positioned by angle from datum
line.

b. Datum Line versus Incremental Dimensioning

A major choice in dimensioning is whether to use datum line or incremental dimensioning. Again, this choice can depend on the method of production. If a machine tool is set up to use particular lines as datums, the *datum line method* is preferred. Datum line dimensioning is sometimes called *baseline* or *absolute dimensioning.* Figure 7 shows use of the datum line method. This technique was also seen in Fig. 5, case A. The designer of the part would pick this method (and machine tool) if the location of the holes from the datum lines were vital to the design.

A more complete example of datum line dimensioning is seen in Fig. 8. This part is set up for numerically controlled (NC) machining in which the tooling path is controlled by a computer program. Within the notes, ''φ 30 CBORE'' means a 30-mm-diameter counterbore, and ''M12 × 1.75'' means a 12-mm-diameter thread with 1.75-mm distance from thread to thread. The note ''φ 20 × 82° CSK'' indicates a 20-mm-diameter countersink having an 82° included angle. Notice that there is a machine zero position (a constant) as well as a setup zero for the particular part.

Notice in Fig. 8 the small V marks on the edges of some surfaces. These marks are called *finish marks,* and they denote surfaces which have been machined. These surfaces are smoother than those without the V marks. In some cases, finished surfaces are used as datums. The use of finish marks is discussed further under concept 3.

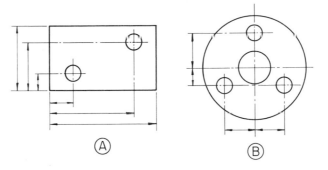

Figure 7
Dimensions from datum.

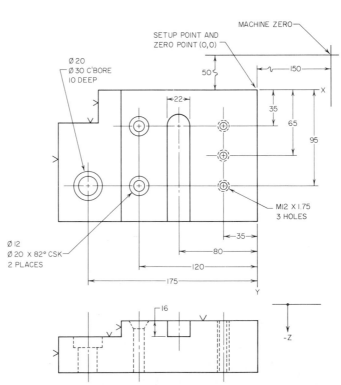

Figure 8
METRIC> Part dimensioned for
NC-controlled turret drill operation.

A designer should heed several suggestions when dimensioning for NC machining:

1. Use decimals for all dimensions including angles (for example, 12.75 in, 22.5°).

2. Bilateral tolerancing should be used, for example, 10 mm ± .05 mm, where ±.05 mm defines the range of permitted deviation, or tolerance,

about the nominal size of 10 mm. Therefore the size is allowed to vary from 9.95 to 10.05 mm. (Also see Chap. 10.)

3. Align the principal surfaces of the part so they are parallel to the x, y, and z axes.

4. Define specific geometric shapes, such as circles, parabolas, etc., by mathematical expressions.

In *incremental dimensioning,* however, each feature is located from the previous one. Figure 9 shows the difference between incremental and datum (absolute) dimensioning. For incremental dimensioning, the designer is more concerned with the distance between any two consecutive hole centers than with the distance between the hole centers and the edge of the part. The incremental method is less accurate than the datum line method in that any error between hole centers in the incremental method will accumulate from one center to the next. This problem is avoided in the datum line method because the position of each hole center is referenced to the same datum position.

It is also possible to mix the datum line and incremental methods as a designer sees fit. In Fig. 10 an arbitrary example is given. In the y direction, all holes are located from the x axis as the datum. However, in the x direction holes 1 and 4 are located from the y axis, while hole 2 is located in reference to hole 1 and hole 3 is located from hole 2 in an incremental mode.

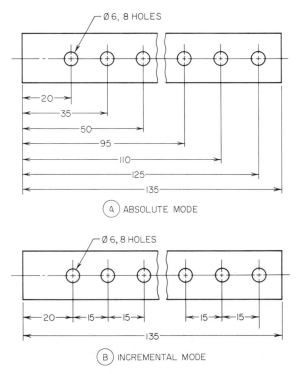

Figure 9
Absolute (datum) vs. incremental
dimensioning.

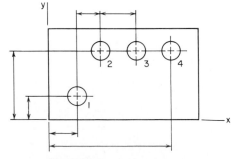

Figure 10
A mix of datum and incremental
dimensioning.

Operation	Tolerance
Casting	
Sand	
Small	±0.030
Medium	±0.060
Large	±0.015+
Die	
Small	±0.002
Medium	±0.008
Large	±0.010
Forging, size	
½–2 lb	±0.030
2–10 lb	±0.060
10–60 lb	±0.120
Drilling, diameter	
No. 60–No. 30	0.002
No. 29–No. 1	0.004
¼–½	0.006
½–¾	0.008
¾–1	0.010
1–2	0.015
Reaming, diameter	
0.2–0.5	0.0005
0.5–1.0	0.0010
1.0+	0.0015
Lath work	
Rough, diameter	
¼–½	0.005
½–1	0.007
1–2	0.010
2+	0.015
Finish, diameter	
¼–½	0.002
½–1	0.003
1–2	0.005
2+	0.007
Broaching, diameter	
½–1	0.001
1–2	0.002
2–4	0.003
Grinding	0.0005
Milling	0.002–0.005
Planing	0.005–0.010

Figure 12
Typical tolerances available with specific machining operations. (Values in inches. Multiply by 25.4 for millimeters.)

c. Effect of Machining Precision on Dimensioning

This brief discussion is, in a sense, a preview of Chap. 10, but it is very appropriate because it is an aspect which affects dimensioning. By *machining precision* is meant the degree of closeness or "fineness" that a particular tool can create. How accurate can or should a dimension be? Note that in Fig. 11 some arbitrary dimensions are given. The two position dimensions for the hole's center are theoretically proper, but they are very different. The number ¾ is not in the same format as .87535. One is a fraction, and the other is a five-place decimal. The size of the hole is a four-place decimal, .5001. What do these differences in format mean? Are the numbers realistic?

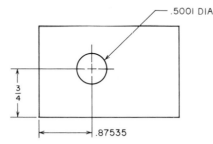

Figure 11
A variety of implied tolerances.

Recall in the discussion of NC machining reference to the term *tolerance*. Tolerance then and now is the range of permitted deviation on a part. A value of

$$1.75 \quad \begin{array}{l} + \ .00 \\ - \ .02 \end{array}$$

in ranges from 1.73 to 1.75. The tolerance is .02 in. A decimal tolerance is constrained by the number of significant figures given in the decimal dimension. A value of 1.75 in has .01 in as the minimum tolerance. A value of 2.137 in has .001 in as minimum tolerance. For 3.7 mm, .1 mm is the minimum tolerance.

A value such as ¾ in is fractional. The tolerance will be fractional, such as ± ¹⁄₃₂ in. Fractions do not have significant figures, as decimals do. Therefore the tolerance cannot be controlled in fractional dimensions by significant figures. But it is controlled by the part's performance specifications. In fractional formats, the tolerance is seldom less than ± ¹⁄₆₄ in. We could convert to a decimal base for smaller tolerances.

In Fig. 11, we could conclude that the dimensions are very unusual. The tolerances are not given, but the minima would range from .00001 for the .87535 value to perhaps ± ¹⁄₆₄ for the ¾ value. Why a designer would desire such a variety of tolerances is a mystery. Normally we keep tolerances as large as feasible to minimize production machining costs.

Machining precision is affected by the machine tool used to create a feature. If we wished, for example, a hole to have a tolerance of .001 in, what tool would we specify? Few drills can work that close, but a reamer could. It is helpful to have some idea of the accuracy of various tools because dimensions are controlled by tool accuracy. Figure 12 gives some approximate tolerances for common machining processes. We can see that if a ⅝-in-diameter hole is to be drilled, for example, the minimum tolerance expected is around .008 in. To give the dimension as .625 ± .010 is acceptable, but .625 ± .002 is unrealistic for a drill.

d. Effect of Surface Quality on Dimensioning

Surface quality refers to the degree of roughness or waviness on a surface of a part. No surface can be absolutely smooth, nor should it be. Under a microscope all surfaces show some variation from an absolutely smooth condition.

The condition of a surface varies according to the machine tool which generated it. The simple fact that a surface has been machined can be indicated by a finish mark. Figure 8 showed several finish marks, but Fig. 13 shows them more clearly.

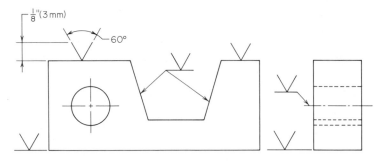

Figure 13
Finish marks.

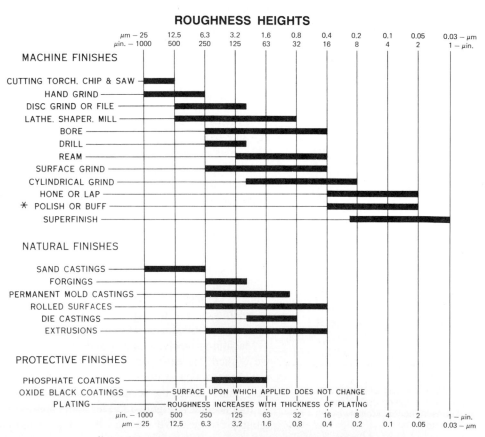

Figure 14
Roughness heights as related to machine finishes.

A finish mark may be placed on the edge of any surface which requires machining. Note the size of the V of the finish mark in Fig. 13. Processes that automatically generate a machined surface do not require finish marks. Therefore, a drilled hole does not have a finish mark because a drill always creates a machined surface.

Different tools create different degrees of surface roughness. Figure 14 indicates surface roughness heights for various machining operations. The range of roughness heights is given in both micrometers (μm) and microinches (μin), where 1 μin = 10^{-6} in. Therefore, 250 μin is .00025 in.

The meaning of surface roughness is seen in Fig. 15. The various modes of roughness in this figure are discussed thoroughly in ANSI Standard B46.1. Note that the dimensions in this surface-texture symbol can convey a wealth of information about a particular surface. The physical proportions of the symbol are shown in Fig. 16 as part of ANSI Standard Y14.36. You should use surface-texture symbols only when needed. The dimensions in the symbol have to reflect realistic values for the machine tools to be used. Generally, the smoother the surface, the higher the cost. Therefore, a designer wants a surface as rough as feasible in order to minimize machining costs.

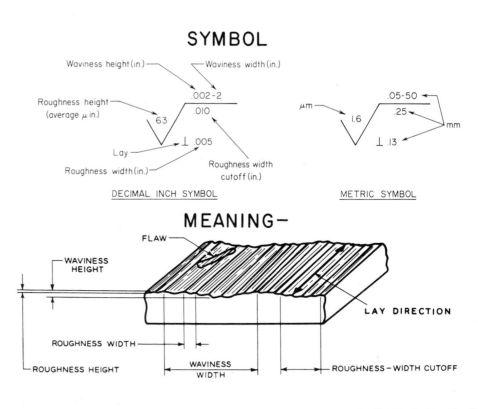

Figure 15
Interpretation of surface texture symbols.

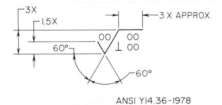

Figure 16
Size of surface texture symbol.

CONCEPT 3: AVOIDANCE OF REDUNDANCY

The user of a drawing, whether created manually or by computer, requires clear, unambiguous dimensions. Concept 1 attempts to emphasize the need for clear dimensions when it states, "Dimension each feature once where shape shows. . . ." Redundancies of all types simply clutter and confuse the drawing dimensions. We will look at redundancies to be avoided, including repetitive dimensioning and unnecessary dimensioning.

Look at Fig. 17A. There are both repetitive and unnecessary dimensions in this figure. Dimension A is clearly a repeated dimension. The overall height given by A in the front view is seen in the side view as S_1. Each feature is to be dimensioned *once*, so either A or S_1 must be deleted.

Also in Fig. 17A we see unnecessary dimensions. Both dimensions B and C are extraneous. The corner notch is described by S_2 and S_3. The presence of S_1 and S_4 ensures that B and C are known. Therefore dimensions B and C should be dropped. If we insist on keeping B and C, then we drop S_2 and S_3. It is normal, incidentally, to retain overall height, width, and depth dimensions (here S_1, S_4, and S_5, respectively). Figure 17B then becomes an example of correct dimensioning.

The process just described is universally accepted for machine parts and small parts of all kinds. There is one exception in architectural drawings. There it is usual for house plans and so forth to keep extra dimensions. All the dimensions of Fig. 17A are acceptable for large structures.

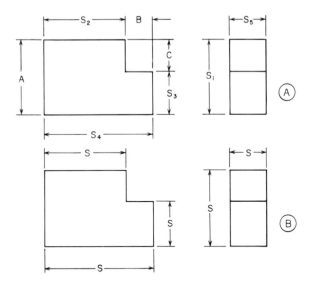

Figure 17
Redundant and unnecessary
dimensions.

Another example of the avoidance of redundancy is shown in Fig. 18. This object is correctly dimensioned. But where are the positions of the centers of radii R_1 and R_2 given? We should realize that these radii are *tangent radii*. *The centers of tangent radii are self-locating.* The positions of such centers are known without dimensioning because the (x, y) coordinates of any center of a tangent radius must be the value of the radius itself. If R_1 equals .75 in, for example, the position of its center must be .75 in from the left-hand edge and .75 in up from the bottom edge. If a radius is *not* tangent, as in Fig. 19, then the position of its center must be given. Returning to Fig. 18, notice that the overall height seems to be missing.

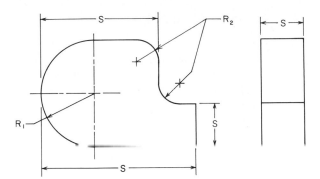

Figure 18
Avoidance of redundancy.

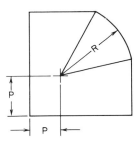

Figure 19
Dimensioning a nontangent radius.

However, the height *is* known because R_1 sweeps through 180° to create the semi-circular end. The height is therefore $2R_1$.

Figure 20 shows common excesses of unknowing drafters. All dimensions noted with an X are excessive or redundant. The D in the top view is a duplicate, since it is properly shown in the front view. Each of the two R's in the top view are redundant because the diameters to which they belong are shown in the front view. The P dimension in the front view is redundant because the difference of the two diameters divided by 2 is indeed this value.

You may ask, "Is there no way at all to show extra dimensions?" Perhaps an extra dimension is desired to emphasize or reinforce a particular feature's size or position. Yes, we *can* add an extra dimension by enclosing it in parentheses, as in Fig. 21. The value 1.750, given twice, certainly defines the sum, 3.500. If the drafter wishes to provide the value 3.500, the parentheses around it tell the reader that 3.500 is a *reference* dimension, an extra given for interest or courtesy. The value (2.00) back in Fig. 5A is also a reference dimension.

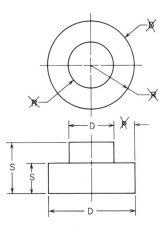

Figure 20
Excess dimensions.

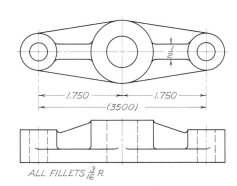

Figure 21
Use of a reference dimension.

■ 3. TECHNIQUES OF DIMENSIONING

A number of techniques are used in dimensioning to implement the concepts already discussed. These techniques are designed to make dimensioning information as clear and concise as possible for the user of the drawing. The discussion to follow is based largely on the standards given in ANSI Y14.5M-1982. The techniques apply to any mode of creating a drawing.

a. Units for Measurement

Typically drawings are in either the metric base or the English inch base. Metric units may be millimeters (mm), centimeters (cm), or meters (m), depending on the size of the part. The millimeter is commonly used for manufactured parts. The decimal inch (in) is more common in the English inch base, as opposed to a fractional system (for example, 2.75 versus 2¾ in). The way to express decimals is shown in Table 1, where metric and English decimals are compared.

TABLE 1   COMPARISON OF ENGLISH DECIMAL AND METRIC SYSTEMS

English Decimal	Metric	Comment
3,214,759	3 214 759 0.754 76 2476 *or* 2 476	Decimal system separates groups of three by commas; the metric system, by space.
.75 *or* 0.75	0.75	Metric system always uses a zero before decimal point, a feature that is optional in the English decimal system.
0.4010 *or* 0.40100	0.401	Common practice in the English decimal system is to keep a consistent number of figures to the right of the decimal point, including zeros; the metric system drops useless zeros.

Diameters and radii traditionally have been written as ''5 DIA'' and ''2R,'' for example. However, desired current practice is to denote the diameter by ϕ, as in ϕ5. Radius should be given as R2. In all cases, a drawing should contain a note to state units, such as ''Unless otherwise specified, all dimensions are in millimeters.'' The word *centimeters* or *meters* could be used instead of *millimeters,* of course. If an inch base were used, the word *inches* would replace *millimeters*.

The *scale* of the drawing must be given in a note, such as ''Scale: 1 in = 5 in.'' In every case the numerical values given as dimensions must be the *actual-size* numbers. If a feature is actually 7 in long, the number 7 must be used as the dimension, regardless of the scale used.

b. Elements of Dimensioning

To express a dimension, certain lines and arrowheads are employed. Many of these elements are shown in Figs. 22 and 23. In Fig. 22 we see the extension and dimension lines as well as the radius line. Note that the extension line does not quite touch the object. In Fig. 23 we see the use of a leader and a note for a 12-mm drilled diameter ϕ. Notes are simply one or more words used to convey information.

A *specific note* refers to a particular feature, as in Fig. 23. *General notes* are also possible, and they refer to conditions applicable to the entire drawing, for example, "All surfaces to be chrome-plated." Notes usually use *abbreviations,* such as OD for *outside diameter.* Consult ANSI Y1.1-1972(R1984) for a complete listing of abbreviations.

Arrowheads come in several styles (see Fig. 24). The open, closed hollow, and solid styles (Fig. 24A, B, and C, respectively) are common. The ratio of length to thickness is typically 3 : 1, as in Fig. 24C. Keep arrowheads reasonably small, on the order of .12 in (3 mm) long. On large drawings the size may be increased in keeping with the magnitude of the part.

Arrowheads should be placed so as to avoid crowding. Figure 25 illustrates four ways to place arrowheads, depending on the available space. Note that the arrowheads do not change size from one case to the next. However, arrowheads always point in opposite directions.

Leaders should also be placed to avoid crowding. Figure 26 shows several techniques as applied to radii. In all cases, the leader points to or originates at the center of the radius. Case B shows the technique when the actual center is not available. Radius R50 is along the centerline given but is farther away than the "dummy" center arbitrarily selected.

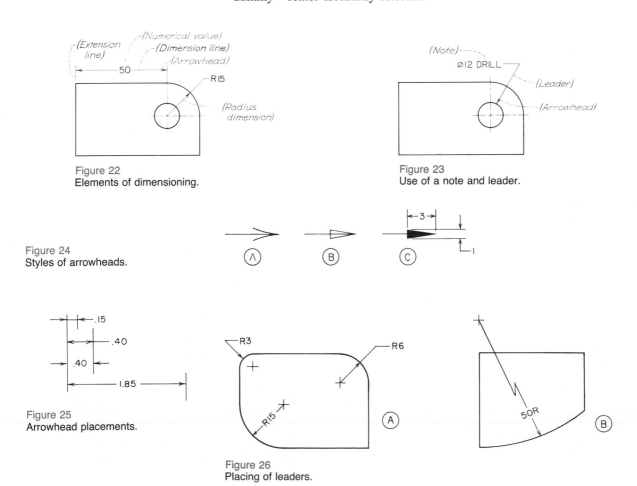

Figure 22
Elements of dimensioning.

Figure 23
Use of a note and leader.

Figure 24
Styles of arrowheads.

Figure 25
Arrowhead placements.

Figure 26
Placing of leaders.

Extension lines may cross one another, as in Fig. 27. Note also the use of the dimensional placement for an angle. *Dimension lines,* however, do *not* cross one another. See Fig. 28. Case A is an example of poor practice, except for certain occasions in architectural drawings. Case B is preferred for manufactured parts. Figure 29 is also a useful illustration of the placement of extension and dimension lines. Note in case A that longer dimension lines are placed outside the shorter dimension lines. Dimension lines are typically ⅜ in. from the object, with subsequent dimension lines at least ¼ in. from the previous dimension line.

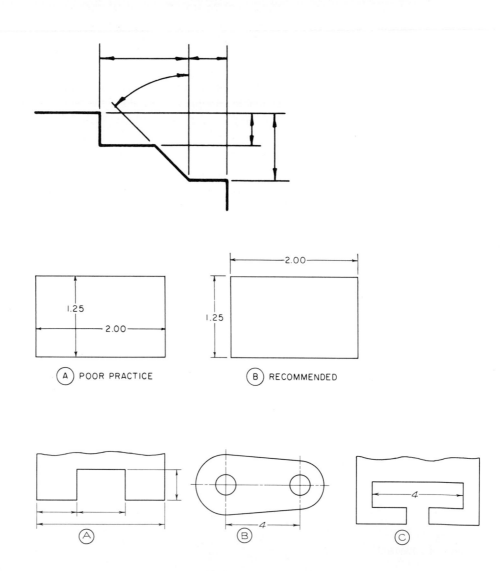

Figure 27
Crossing of extension lines.

Figure 28
Treatment of dimension lines.

Figure 29
Dimension placement.

Crowded placement of extension and dimension lines can be avoided by careful preplanning or by using an enlarged view. Figure 30 is an example of an enlarged view. In all cases, avoid jamming dimensions up against the part. You can place some dimensions on the part, as in Fig. 30, if no feature is obstructed and if the dimensions can be plainly seen.

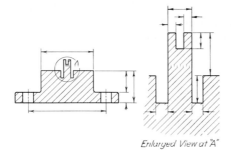

Figure 30
Use of enlarged view to clarify dimensions.

Enlarged View at "A"

c. Lettering for Dimensioning

Several guidelines can be offered concerning lettering techniques for dimensioning. Properly done lettering makes dimensions easier to read and less prone to misunderstanding.

Lettering style involves size, uppercase versus lowercase, font, and slant versus vertical lettering. Numerals and letters should be at least ⅛ in (3 mm) in height, as in Fig. 31. Lettering may be slightly larger on large drawings. Uppercase (capital) letters are generally preferred because they are easier to read.

The font works best when it is simple. The single-stroke style, derived from Gothic lettering, is preferred for both drafters and CAD application. Complex forms, such as italics or old German, are too time-consuming. And single-stroke styles are as readable as any. It is true that CAD software offers a wide choice of fonts, but the operator interested in efficiency will probably pick one of the simpler forms.

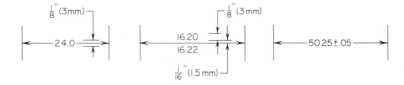

Figure 31
Size of decimals.

Slant versus vertical style is largely a question of personal preference or company policy. Vertical lettering seems to be the more common.

Feet, inches, and fractions can pose problems of clarity. CAD software enables the user to separate the foot portion of a value from the inch portion. For example, 3′–5″ is preferred to 3′5″. It is also common practice to indicate a zero for inches when there are no inches, as in 8′–0″. Fractions are most easily read when they are twice the height of the whole number, as in Fig. 32.

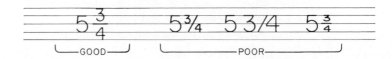

Figure 32
Treatment of fractions.

Position with reference to the dimension line is a matter of personal or company preference. Figure 31 showed the dimension *within* the dimension line. An alternative is to place the dimension *above* the dimension line. Particular software packages may dictate your choice in CAD applications.

The *reading direction* may be in *aligned* or *unidirectional* format. The aligned format is shown in Fig. 33, and the unidirectional format in Fig. 34. Both are acceptable and widely used. Again the choice is dependent on personal, company, and/or software options.

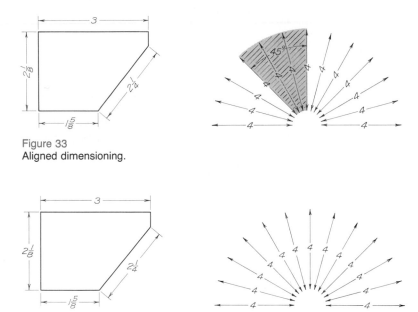

Figure 33
Aligned dimensioning.

Figure 34
Unidirectional dimensioning.

d. Dimensions for Specific Shapes

The contour principle (Sec. 2) for dimensioning is a strong authority to guide the drafter. You will seldom go wrong by using this principle. Several illustrations are offered for consideration. The treatment of round-end shapes is seen in Fig. 35. A careful study of this figure will be helpful. Specific machining operations are shown in Figs. 36 through 40. Figure 36 illustrates counterbored (CBORE) holes in cases A and B. Spot-faced (SF) holes are shown in cases C and D. Cases B, C, and D incorporate ANSI symbols for diameter, counterbore (or spot face), and depth. A more complete list of ANSI symbols can be found in Fig. 37 along with examples of each. ANSI symbols are used often on current drawings.

Countersunk holes are shown in various formats in Fig. 38. Styles of dimensioning the chamfers are shown in Figs. 39 and 40. Figure 39 gives external chamfers, and Fig. 40 shows internal chamfers. Note the difference in effect between using upper- and lowercase lettering in Figs. 36 through 40. Most drafters and users prefer the uppercase style.

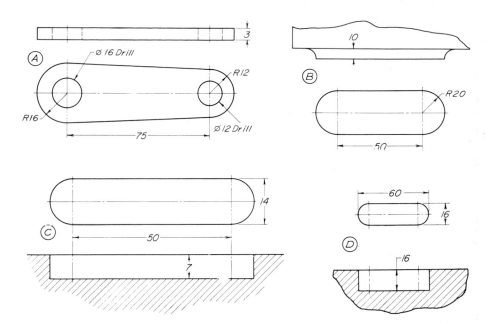

Figure 35
Dimensioning of round-end shapes.

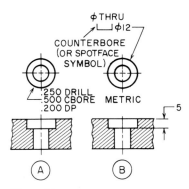

Figure 36
Dimensioning of counterbored and
spot-faced holes.

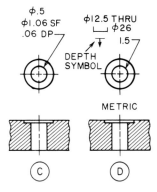

Figure 37
ANSI Standard Drawing Symbols
(Y14.5M).

SYMBOL FOR	ANS 1	EXAMPLE
Diameter	ϕ	$\phi6$
Spherical diameter	$S\phi$	$S\phi10$
Radius	R	R4
Spherical radius	SR	SR 8
Reference dimension	( )	(15)
Arc length	⌒	$\overparen{25}$
Square (shape)	▭	▭ 12
Dimension origin	⊕▸	⊕▸ 30
Conical taper	▷	▷ 0.3:1
Slope	◺	◺ 0.2:1
Counterbore/spotface	⌴	⌴ $\phi20$
Countersink	∨	∨ $\phi12 \times 90°$
Depth/deep	↧	↧ 16
Dimension not to scale	—	15
Number of times/places	X	10X

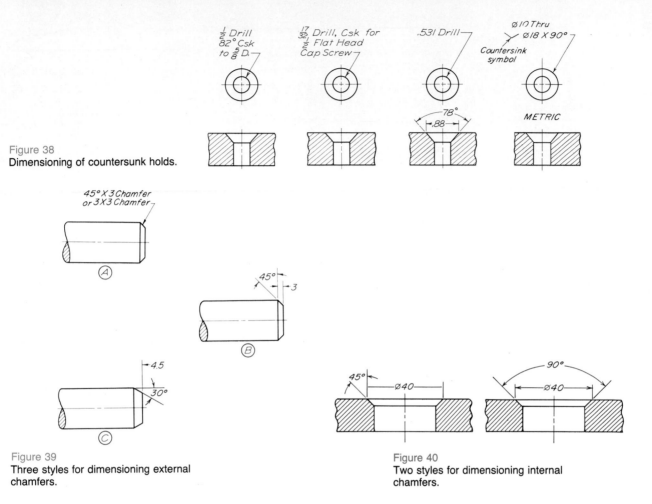

Figure 38
Dimensioning of countersunk holds.

Figure 39
Three styles for dimensioning external chamfers.

Figure 40
Two styles for dimensioning internal chamfers.

An interesting situation is shown in Fig. 41. Case A shows a circular object having a *half-view* top view. Half views are used to save space. In a half view the centerline is used as one boundary of the view. Since case A represents an object having a full diameter, diameters are used in dimensioning. Case B gives a semi-circular object, as revealed by a solid object-line boundary. Therefore case B is dimensioned by radii.

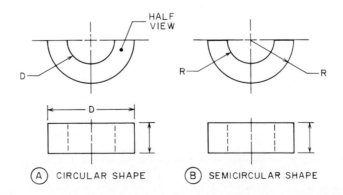

Figure 41
Use of a half view.

■ 4. SIMPLIFICATION IN DIMENSIONING

Dimensioning done in the simplest, most efficient way is helpful to drafter and drawing user alike. There are a number of effective ways to abbreviate or simplify dimensioning. We have seen some already. Others may be new to the reader.

a. Repetitive Features

Features which repeat themselves are easily handled with notes. For example, the multiple holes in Fig. 9 were dimensioned with one note: "φ6, 8 holes." The note indicates that there are eight 6-mm-diameter holes. Also Fig. 21 states, "All fillets ³⁄₁₆ R." This tells the user that all fillets (where the various portions of the casting blend together) have a ³⁄₁₆-in radius.

A note was also used in Fig. 5 to dimension the six holes. The expression "6 × φ9.5 EQ SP" concisely describes the holes as to number (6) and diameter (9.5 mm).

b. Use of Symmetry

Utilizing existing symmetry on a part can facilitate dimensioning. The note "6 × φ9.5 EQ SP" takes advantage of the angular six-part symmetry through the use of the abbreviation EQ SP (equally spaced).

Figure 42 shows another case in which dimensioning is simplified through symmetry. There is symmetry about the vertical centerline ℄. Therefore, only one-half of the object needs to be dimensioned, even though the dimensions actually used may be given on both halves. This technique can be a great time saver for a complicated part containing many dimensions.

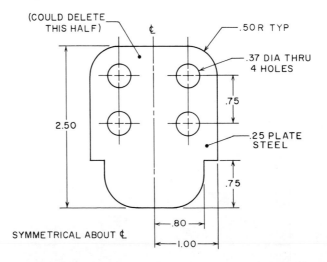

Figure 42
Use of simplified dimensioning.

Note also the note ".37 dia thru, 4 holes." Again use of a note is a concise means to efficient dimensioning. Another note on this part is ".50R typ," meaning .50-in radius typical. The use of *typ* (typical) means that any radius at the corners is indeed .50R. The term *typ* covers four places on this part. Alternatively, the note could read ".50R, 4 corners" or ".50R, 4 places."

The message "Could delete this half" in Fig. 42, placed there by the author, simply means that the drafter could have gotten by with just a half view. Thus much space and time can be saved on complex parts. We saw a simple half view in Fig. 41. In some situations *no* view is given for a particular part, only a note to describe it. Figure 43 shows a case where only a note is used to describe a screw and nut needed for assembly. Placement of other dimensions has been indicated but not filled in.

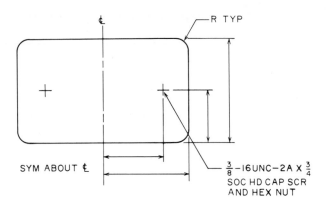

Figure 43
Parts described by a note only.

c. Use of Tabulated Dimensions

For features having coordinate positions, a table can greatly simplify the dimensioning. Note in Fig. 44 that 12 holes are all located from the *x* and *y* axes. Hole sizes and depths are also given. A tabular form such as this is very efficient and effective. A tabular form could be used in a polar (angular) system as well as the coordinate form illustrated here.

HOLE	DESCRIPTION	QTY
A	$\emptyset$ 7	1
B	$\emptyset$ 4.8	4
C	$\emptyset$ 3.6	6
D	$\emptyset$ 3.1	1

HOLE	FROM	X	Y	Z
A1	X,Y	64	38	18
B1	X,Y	5	38	THRU
B2	X,Y	72	38	THRU
B3	X,Y	64	11	THRU
B4	X,Y	79	11	THRU
C1	X,Y	19	38	THRU
C2	X,Y	48	38	THRU
C3	X,Y	5	21	THRU
C4	X,Y	30	21	THRU
C5	X,Y	72	21	THRU
C6	X,Y	19	11	THRU
D1	X,Y	48	6	12

ANSI Y14.5 M

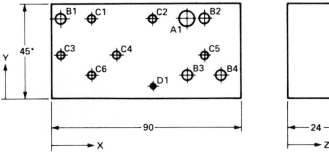

Figure 44
Dimensions in tabular form.

d. Use of Mathematical Formulas

Dimensioning for a geometric contour can be handled by providing the defining equation. This technique is especially useful in CAD applications where the part is to be produced by computer-driven tooling. In the technique known as computer-aided manufacturing (CAM), the tooling is programmed to create a desired contour—a parabola, circle, ellipse, or other form—that can be defined by a mathematical equation. If a contour does not fit a standard equation, it is possible to program a series of desired coordinate points and instruct the computer to interpolate a smooth curve from point to point.

5. DIMENSIONING PICTORIALS

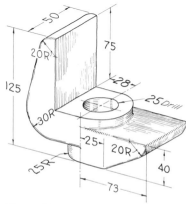

Figure 45
Dimensioning a pictorial within the planes of the features.

A drawing to be used in production is seldom in a 3-D pictorial format. Many parts are simply too complex to produce from a pictorial alone. Nevertheless, on some occasions we may want to dimension a pictorial. A colleague or client may wish to see the overall shape in one pictorial view along with dimensions.

Dimensions in pictorials are usually placed in the same plane as the feature being dimensioned. In Fig. 45, for example, the values 50 and 28 are in the same horizontal planes as the features themselves. Many of the other dimensions are heights, such as 125, 30R, and 40. These dimensions are therefore placed in a vertical plane. As a general rule of thumb, dimensions are placed along the x, y, and z axes to correspond to the x, y, and z directions of the particular features being dimensioned.

Sometimes a drafter will tend to keep the dimensions all in one direction. The person who dimensioned the part in Fig. 46 favored vertical dimensions. All are vertical except for the depth dimension of 30. The result created by this unidirectional dimensioning is clear and attractive. However, if the part were complex, clarity would soon suffer.

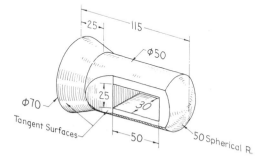

Figure 46
Extensive use of dimensions within a vertical plane.

6. DIMENSIONING ASSISTANCE IN CAD SYSTEMS

Many options for dimensioning placement and style are available in software programs that support CAD systems. Our brief discussion will touch on only a few of the possibilities. For complete information, a reference manual for specific software, such as CADKEY or AUTOCAD, should be consulted by the user of a

Figure 47
Rotation of notes.

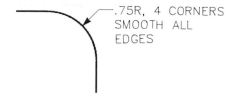

Figure 48
A left-justified note.

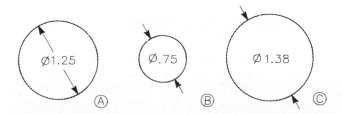

Figure 49
Arrowhead placements for circles.

particular system. Company manuals can be a superior source of detailed information. Nevertheless, the examples cited below give a feel for what any typical CAD software package can do.

a. Text Considerations

The options available for styles and placement of numbers, letters, and notes are much the same as for regular lettering. In Chap. 3, we saw that CAD enables users to control font style, letter heights, and aspect ratios. (A review of this material may be helpful.) Rotation of notes is also possible, as seen in Fig. 47. Also the notes can be aligned as to left justification, centered, or right-justified, much like the title blocks in Chap. 3. Figure 48 shows a typical left-justified note. Styles and placements in dimensioning are therefore very flexible when CAD software is employed.

b. Units

A user has a wide choice of units for dimensioning in CAD. Typically there is a menu of scaling units such as inches, feet, yards, millimeters, centimeters, or meters. User-created units can be designated, too. If the user does not choose a unit format, a default value is automatically used, which is often the inch.

Decimal point accuracy is another aspect of user choice. You can often select up to six-place accuracy. That is, you may request up to six digits to the right of the decimal point, as in 3.562475.

You may also control leading and trailing zeros. For the case of leading zeros, you can choose to use or not use them, as in 0.65 versus .65. Also you may select or decline trailing zeros, as in 7.00 versus 7.

c. Arrowhead Placement

You may choose to have arrowheads inside or outside the features being dimensioned. Figure 49 shows an example of each. Case A is for inside and case B for outside, but case C is not recommended because there is too much space between the arrowheads and the number. CAD users need to be discrete in selecting formats.

A CAD system will do only what it is told, regardless of whether the result is attractive.

Figure 50 shows typical treatments for radii, and Fig. 51 illustrates arrowheads in relationship to extension lines. Angles can be treated as in Fig. 52. In these and other examples, good software simply allows the user to do what can also be done manually by hand. Likewise, whatever can be done manually should be available in good software.

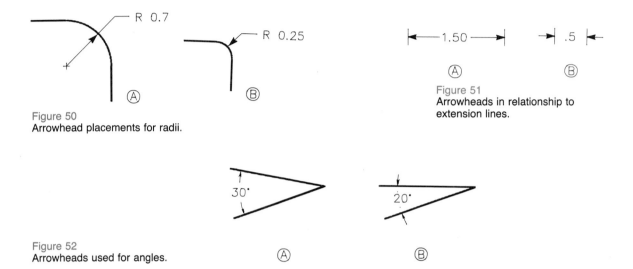

Figure 50
Arrowhead placements for radii.

Figure 51
Arrowheads in relationship to
extension lines.

Figure 52
Arrowheads used for angles.

d. Numeral Alignment with Dimension Lines

A final illustration shows how to control the placement of dimensioning numbers relative to dimensioning lines. In Fig. 53 there are four possibilities. The styles in cases A and D are called *unidirectional*. Case B is known as *aligned*. In case C the numeral has been rotated to remain perpendicular to the dimension line. Again, the software is merely making available what is done manually. CAD, however, can do dimensioning in a manner which is more consistent than the human hand. With practice, a CAD operator can do it faster in certain applications.

Whether it is done via CAD or by hand, proper dimensioning is essential in describing the size and location of features. Clearly executed dimensioning expresses the designer's wishes with a minimum of clutter and a maximum of information. The guidelines given in this chapter should help you to dimension with confidence, thus producing drawings that are of maximum value to the user. In the next chapter we look at how to express the desired variation, or tolerance, on feature size and location.

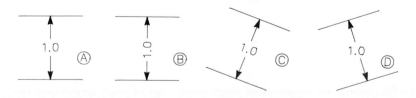

Figure 53
Dimension numbers relative to
dimension lines.

P R O B L E M S

For all problems, enlarge the size 5 times by using dividers. Place problems on 8½ × 11 in white paper. Fully dimension each problem.

1. Use the fractional inch or decimal inch basis and a scale set by your instructor.

Problem Set 1

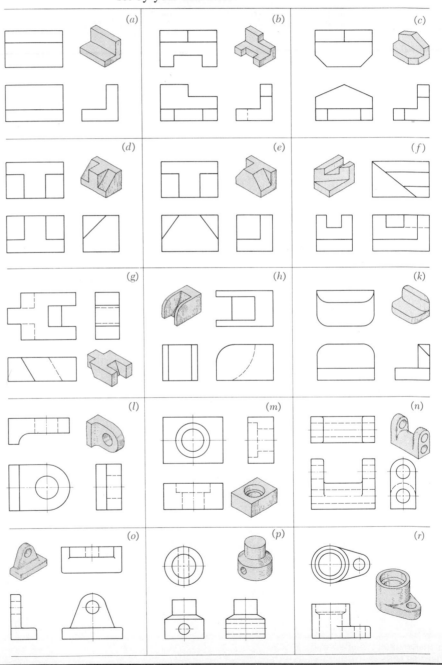

2. Use a metric scale set by your instructor.

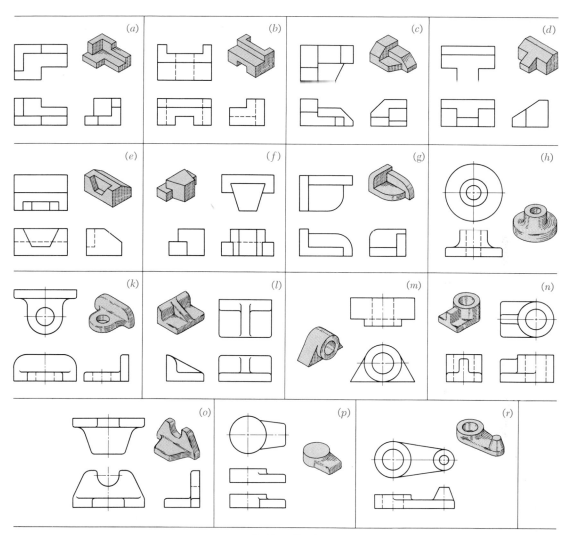

Problem Set 2

C H A P T E R 10

TOLERANCING:
SYSTEMS TO
CONTROL
PRECISION

■ 1. NEED FOR TOLERANCING

Products we see every day are designed to operate at certain performance levels. To operate at these levels, products are made with certain degrees of precision. Take as examples two very different products having a feature that performs a similar function: a wheel on an axle. Let one be a child's wagon and one be the wheel and axle assembly on an airplane. In both cases the purpose is to allow the vehicle to roll. Obviously the performance levels are quite different for the two cases, and the degree of precision needed for each assembly differs greatly. The need for precision and careful machining is far greater for the airplane than for the wagon.

Tolerancing of parts allows the designer to control dimensions and to imply a certain precision. Tolerancing controls the maximum and minimum sizes of parts. The part in Fig. 1 has a toleranced hole. The hole may vary from .500- to .508-in diameter. The range of allowed variation is the *tolerance* and is .008 in. (Tolerancing was briefly introduced in Chap. 9 under concept 2, the influence of production methods on dimensioning.)

The desired tolerance of a feature can affect the tooling selected to produce it. Numerically higher tolerances can use less precise tooling than lower ones. The hole of Fig. 1 might be made with a sharp drill, but if the tolerance is .0005, a process such as reaming might be needed. Refer to Fig. 12 of Chap. 9 once again.

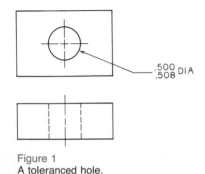

.500
.508 DIA

Figure 1
A toleranced hole.

We see, then, that the designer has a means of controlling the sizes of features. This control can influence part performance and the tooling needed. A designer normally selects the maximum numerical value of tolerance that can allow a part to perform as desired. Parts with high numerical values are generally cheaper to produce than ones with low values. The child's wagon no doubt has higher tolerance values on the wheel and axle assembly than the airplane does (after the factor of small versus large axles has been taken into consideration). The tooling cost is far lower on the wagon.

2. TYPES OF GENERAL FIT

We are now ready to look at the general kinds of interaction between holes and shafts. The interaction between a hole and a shaft is called a *fit*. Fits of shafts with holes are very common in products. Wheels on shafts, pistons in cylinders, and spigot stems in water faucets are just three examples. There are three types of general fits: clearance, interference, and transition. We offer examples of each now, using arbitrary sizes for the shafts and holes.

a. Clearance Fits

In a *clearance fit,* the shaft is always smaller than the hole. The shaft "clears" the hole, leaving an air gap. The amount of clearance or gap varies with the tolerance value on particular holes and shafts. Figure 2 shows an example. The shaft can vary from .493- to .497-in diameter; the hole from .500- to .508-in diameter. The tolerance is .004 in in the shaft and is .008 in on the hole.

The *maximum clearance* is found logically by subtracting the smallest shaft from the largest hole, that is, .508 − .493 = .015 in. The *minimum clearance* is found by reversing the process. Subtract the largest shaft from the smallest hole, that is, .500 − .497 = .003 in.

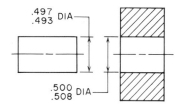

Figure 2
A clearance fit.

b. Interference Fits

There is an *interference fit* when the shaft is always larger in diameter than the hole prior to assembly. Interference fits are also known as *force fits* since the shaft is forced into the hole. A simple tap of a shaft into a hole may be sufficient to assemble a light force fit, but a heavy force fit may require that the shaft be cooled and/or the hole be heated to facilitate assembly.

Once assembled, an interference fits allows for a permanent assembly held together by friction. Disassembly can occur only if the shaft is forced out of the hole. In severe cases, the housing containing the hole may have to be cut off. Interference fits are an excellent way to assemble parts, such as holding a bearing on an axle.

Figure 3 shows an interference fit. The shaft is always larger than the hole. The tolerance happens to be .003 in on the shaft and .008 in on the hole.

The maximum clearance is found as above for the clearance fit. The smallest shaft is subtracted from the largest hole, or .508 − .509 = −.001 in. Note the minus sign, which makes this a *negative clearance*. For the maximum clearance

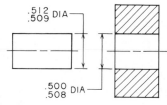

Figure 3
An interference fit.

the largest shaft is subtracted from the smallest hole, giving .500 − .512 = − .012 in, again a negative clearance.

For interference fits, the terms *minimum interference* and *maximum interference* are often used. How do these terms relate to the minimum and maximum clearance? They are related as follows:

$$
\begin{array}{l}
\text{Maximum clearance} = \text{minimum interference} \\
\text{Minimum clearance} = \text{maximum interference}
\end{array}
$$

In our example the maximum clearance was − .001 in, which is the least (minimum) interference. The minimum clearance of − .012 in was the most (maximum) interference.

c. Transition Fits

A *transition fit* exists when the maximum clearance is positive and the minimum clearance is negative. Therefore the shaft may clear the hole with an air gap or may have to be forced into the hole. Transition fits are used only for locating a shaft relative to a hole, where accuracy is important but either a clearance or an interference is permitted.

We see an example of a transition fit in Fig. 4. The shaft tolerance is .011 in, and the hole tolerance is .008 in. The maximum clearance is still found by subtracting the smallest shaft from the largest hole, or .508 − .498 = .010 in, a positive clearance. The minimum clearance is .500 − .509 = − .009 in, a negative clearance.

d. Comparison of Fits

It is helpful to summarize general fits of clearance, interference, and transition by using Fig. 5. Here we see the value of the clearance of the three fits just discussed. In clearance fits, the maximum and minimum clearances must both be

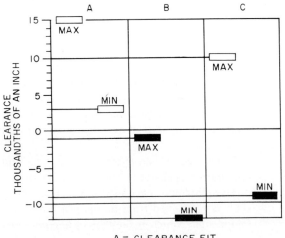

Figure 4
A transition fit.

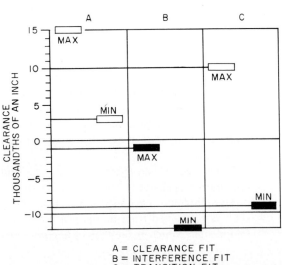

Figure 5
Comparison of fits for Figs. 2 to 4.

positive. Interference fits have both the maximum clearance (minimum interference) and the minimum clearance (maximum interference) negative. The transition fit has a positive maximum clearance and a negative minimum clearance.

The actual cases shown in Fig. 5 were arbitrary as to the precise positive or negative values. We have been discussing general fits. Specific fits which conform to established standards are discussed shortly.

■ 3. DEFINITIONS

It is appropriate to list here the important definitions related to tolerancing. An example is given for each definition. You may use this list for reference during subsequent discussion. We have reviewed some of these definitions already, but they are included for the sake of completeness.

1. *Nominal size:* The size used for general description. Example: ¾-in shaft.

2. *Basic size:* The size used when the nominal size is converted to a pure decimal and from which deviations are made to produce limit dimensions. Example: .7500-in shaft, which is the basic size for a ¾-in nominal size shaft.

3. *Limit dimensions:* The upper and lower permitted sizes for a single feature. Example: .7500 in − .7506 in, where .7500 in is the lower-limit dimension and .7506 in is the upper-limit one.

4. *Tolerance:* The total permitted variation in size for a feature. Tolerance equals the difference between the upper- and lower-limit dimensions for a feature. Example: For item 3 above, the tolerance is .7506 − .7500 = .0006 in.

5. *Bilateral tolerance:* A way to express tolerance by using both plus and minus variations from a given size. Example: 1.250 ± .003 in. The limit dimensions are 1.247 and 1.253 in. The total tolerance is .006 in.

6. *Unilateral tolerance:* A way to express tolerance by using only a plus or minus variation from a given size. Example:

$$2.125 \begin{array}{l} + .000 \\ - .005 \end{array} \text{in} \quad \text{or} \quad 1.375 \begin{array}{l} + .003 \\ - .000 \end{array} \text{in}$$

The first case uses a minus variation (− .005), and the second case uses a plus variation (.003).

7. *Fit:* The general term to describe the range of tightness designed into parts which assemble one into another, leading to the specific types of fits given in items 8, 9, and 10.

8. *Clearance fit:* A fit in which one part fits easily into another with a resulting clearance gap. Example: See Fig. 2.

9. *Interference fit:* A fit in which one part must be forcibly fitted into another. Example: See Fig. 3.

10. *Transition fit:* A fit in which the loosest case provides a clearance fit and the tightest case gives an interference fit. Example: See Fig. 4.

11. *Allowance:* An alternative term for tightest possible fit, that is, minimum clearance or maximum interference. Example: In Fig. 2 the allowance is .003 in.

12. *Basic-hole system:* A system in which the basic size appears as one of the limit dimensions of the hole, but not of the shaft. Example: For a basic size of 2.000, the limit dimensions of the hole might be 2.000 and 2.007 in. For the corresponding shaft, the limit dimensions could be 1.994 and 1.989 in, as an example.

13. *Basic-shaft system:* A system in which the basic size is included as one of the limit dimensions of the shaft, but not of the hole. Example: For a basic size of 2.000, the limit dimensions on the shaft could be 2.000 and 2.005 in. The corresponding hole could be 2.011 and 2.018 in. This example gives the same tolerance, minimum clearance, and maximum clearance as for the basic-hole system.

14. *Maximum-material condition:* The condition in which a hole is at its smallest limit dimension and a shaft is at its largest limit dimension. This condition exists at minimum clearance (or maximum interference). Example: In Fig. 4 the maximum-material condition is .500 in for the hole and .509 in for the shaft.

15. *Minimum-material condition:* The condition in which a hole is at its largest limit dimension and a shaft is at its smallest limit dimension. Example: This condition exists at maximum clearance (or minimum interference), which in Fig. 4 is at .508 in for the hole and .498 in for the shaft.

4. STANDARDIZED TOLERANCES

So far we have discussed general fits and given examples having arbitrary sizes. One may be arbitrary if only oneself is involved. A one-of-a-kind design built at home in the basement need satisfy only that person. There would be no worry about the interchangeability of parts in replications of the design. However, in mass production it is crucial to have standardized tolerances so that people can access tables of possible fits. A specific fit, such as ANSI RC3, will mean the same thing to any designer in the world. Ambiguity is thus avoided and accuracy enhanced.

Standardized tolerances are applied to holes and shafts for both the decimal inch system and the metric system. The widely accepted ANSI standards are used. For cylindrical fits, the decimal inch system uses ANSI Standard B4.1, and the metric uses ANSI Standard B4.2.

5. DECIMAL INCH SYSTEM FOR CYLINDRICAL FITS

There are five ANSI fits in the decimal inch system for cylindrical fits:

RC: running or sliding fit
LC: locational clearance fit
LT: locational transition fit
LN: locational interference fit
FN: force or shrink fit

A description of each fit is given next. Each is described much as in ANSI B4.1.

a. Running and Sliding Fits

There are nine such fits. The lower RC numbers are the tighter fits; the higher numbers are the looser fits.

RC1   Close sliding fits are for the accurate location of parts which must be assembled without noticeable play.

RC2   Sliding fits are for accurate location but with greater maximum clearance than class RC1. Parts made to this fit move and turn easily but are not intended to run freely, and in the larger sizes they may seize under small temperature changes.

RC3   Precision running fits are about the closest fits that can be expected to run freely. They are intended for precision work at slow speeds and light bearing pressures, but are not suitable where appreciable temperature differences are likely.

RC4   Close running fits are mostly for running fits on accurate machinery with moderate surface speeds and bearing pressures, where accurate location and minimum play are desired.

RC5 and RC6   Medium running fits are intended for higher running speeds or high bearing pressures or both.

RC7   Free-running fits are used where accuracy is not essential or large temperature variations are likely or both.

RC8 and RC9   Loose running fits are intended for use where wide commercial tolerances may be required on the shaft.

b. Locational Fits

These fits are divided into three groups: clearance, transition, and interference fits. Locational fits are for location of mating parts only, not for running machinery.

LC   Locational clearance fits are for parts which are normally stationary but which can be freely assembled or disassembled. They run from snug fits for parts requiring accuracy of location through the medium-clearance fits to the looser fastener fits where freedom of assembly is important.

LT   Locational transition fits lie between clearance and interference fits, where accuracy of location is important but a small amount of clearance or interference is permitted.

LN   Locational interference fits are used where accuracy of location is of prime importance and for parts requiring rigidity and alignment with no special requirements for bore pressure. Such fits are not for parts designed to transmit frictional loads from one part to another by virtue of the tightness of fit. These conditions are covered by force fits.

c. Force Fits

Force fits are a type of interference fit which seeks to maintain constant bore pressures for all sizes. The interference varies almost directly with the diameter.

The difference between the minimum and maximum interference is kept low to ensure that resulting pressures are reasonable.

FN1 Light drive fits are those requiring light assembly pressures, and they produce more or less permanent assemblies. They are suitable for thin sections or long fits or in cast-iron external members.

FN2 Medium drive fits are for ordinary steel parts or for shrink fits on light sections. They are about the tightest fits that can be used with high-grade cast-iron external members.

FN3 Heavy drive fits are suitable for heavier steel parts or for shrink fits in medium sections.

FN4 and FN5 Force fits are for parts which can be highly stressed or for shrink fits where the heavy pressing forces required are impractical.

d. Examples of ANSI Fits

We give an example of an ANSI fit to help you use App. 6, where all ANSI cylindrical fits are provided. Let us select an RC7 basic-hole fit for a 1½-in hole and shaft. We are to provide the limit dimensions for the hole and shaft as well as the maximum and minimum clearances. In App. 6A for Running and Sliding Fits we see that 1.5-in lines are in the range of 1.19 to 1.97. The information in the RC7 column is as follows:

Limits of Clearance	Hole	Shaft
3.0	+2.5	−3.0
7.1	0	−4.6

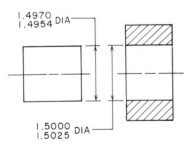

1.4970 / 1.4954 DIA

1.5000 / 1.5025 DIA

Figure 6
Example of an RC7 fit.

This formation gives the deviation in *thousandths* of an inch from the basic size of 1.5000 in. Therefore for the limit dimensions of the hole, add first .0025 in and then 0 in to 1.5000. See Fig. 6. For the shaft subtract from 1.5000 first .003 in and then .0046 in, to get the limit dimensions seen in Fig. 6. Note that limits are often given in the direction of minimum-material condition, that is, from large to small shaft and from small to large hole.

For our example the maximum clearance is 1.5025 − 1.4954 = .0071 in. The minimum clearance is 1.5000 − 1.4970 = .003 in. The values .0071 and .003 are given in the RC7 column as the limits of clearance. The arithmetic in our calculation verifies these values.

A second example is for a force fit. Let us choose a basic-hole FN3 fit on a 2-in hole and shaft. Turn to App. 6E for Force and Shrink Fits, where we see that 2.0 in lies within the range of 1.97 to 2.56. The information under the FN3 column is as follows:

Limits of Interference	Hole	Shaft
1.3	+1.2	+3.2
3.2	−0	+2.5

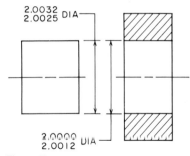

Figure 7
Example of an FN3 fit.

Apply this information to the hole and shaft, and the result is seen in Fig. 7. The maximum clearance is always the smallest shaft subtracted from the largest hole, or 2.0012 − 2.0025 = − .0013 in. The minimum clearance is 2.0000 − 2.0032 = − .0032 in. These clearances are *negative*, as expected for a force fit. They can be checked by the limits of interference in the FN3 column (1.3 and 3.2).

e. Basic-Shaft Fits

Both examples above are for the basic-hole system, because the basic size appears as the smaller of the limit dimensions on the hole. In a basic-*shaft* system, the larger limit dimension of the shaft equals the basic size. Such a system is sometimes employed if a shaft of fixed diameter is to be used with a group of holes.

Here is how we convert from the basic-hole system to the basic-shaft system:

1. *Clearance fits*. The limit dimensions of the hole and shaft are *increased* by the amount needed to make the maximum shaft equal the basic size.

2. *Transition and interference fits*. The limit dimensions of the hole and shaft are *decreased* by the amount needed to make the maximum shaft equal the basic size.

Refer to Fig. 8. A basic-shaft system is verified by the letter S attached to the fit notation. Therefore RC6 becomes RC6S; FN4 becomes FN4S. Note that maximum and minimum clearances do *not* change during these conversions.

	BASIC-HOLE SYSTEM			BASIC-SHAFT SYSTEM	
	Hole	Shaft		Hole	Shaft
RC 6	1.000 1.002	0.9984 0.9972	RC 6S*	1.0016 1.0036	1.000 0.9988
FN 4	2.000 2.0012	2.0042 2.0035	FN 4S	1.9958 1.9970	2.0000 1.9993

Figure 8
Comparing basic-hole and basic-shaft systems.

*RC 6S limits were obtained by bringing the maximum limit on the shaft, 0.9984, up to 1.000, and adding this factor of 0.0016 to all other limits.
FN 4S limits were obtained by bringing the maximum limit on the shaft, 2.0042, down to 2.000, and subtracting this factor of 0.0042 from all other limits.

■ 6. METRIC SYSTEM FOR CYLINDRICAL FITS

The metric system of dimensioning and tolerancing is widely used throughout the world. Indeed, many countries use metric units exclusively. The United States, however, seems stuck in the position of only partially using metric units, even though industries doing extensive exportation of their products use a metric base. The aerospace and heavy off-road equipment businesses are only two of many. ANSI Standard B4.2 offers metric cylindrical fits to drafters and designers.

a. Definitions

A number of definitions exist beyond those common to the decimal inch system. The definitions given below are in addition to those in Sec. 3, which also apply to the metric system. Refer to Fig. 9 as you review the definitions.

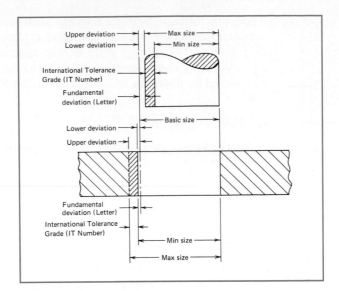

Figure 9
Illustration of definitions. (ANSI B14.2—1978.)

1. *Deviation:* The difference between any given size and the basic size.

2. *Upper deviation:* The difference between the maximum allowable size and the basic size.

3. *Lower deviation:* The difference between the minimum allowable size and the basic size.

4. *Fundamental deviation:* The upper or lower deviation, whichever is closer to the basic size.

5. *Tolerance zone:* The zone representing the tolerance and its position relative to the basic size.

6. *International tolerance (IT) grade:* A group of tolerances which give the same general level of accuracy within a given grade.

Note that fundamental deviation provides the position of the tolerance zone relative to the basic size. Fundamental deviations are given by *tolerance position letters,* seen in Fig. 10 and discussed shortly. Capital (uppercase) letters denote holes; lowercase letters denote shafts.

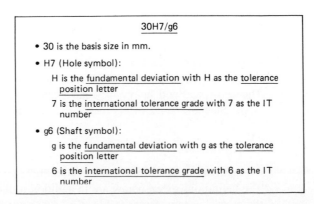

Figure 10
Analysis of a complete tolerance symbol.

Also IT grade gives the amount of the tolerance zone permitted for holes and shafts. Tolerances are given by *grade numbers* which relate to the IT grades, denoted by the prefix *IT*. There are 18 IT grade numbers; the smaller the number, the smaller the tolerance zone.

b. Tolerance Symbols

A tolerance symbol consists of the combination of the IT grade number and the tolerance position letter. A particular symbol specifies the upper- and lower-limit dimensions for a part. A symbol preceded by the basic size of a part completely defines the dimensional limits. Refer to Fig. 10.

The symbol ''30H7/g6'' in Fig. 10 defines the *fit* for this particular hole and shaft combination. A fit always consists of the basic size (30 mm) followed by the hole symbol (H7) and the shaft symbol (g6).

c. Preferred Fits

Many fits are available. The total number can be confusing unless you study ANSI B4.2 carefully. However, a series of preferred fits has been developed to simplify the selection of workable fits. See Fig. 11. Note the existence of clearance

Figure 11
Description of preferred fits. (ANSI B4.2.)

| | ISO symbol | | |
	Hole basis	Shaft* basis	Description
Clearance fits	H11/c11	C11/h11	*Loose running* fit for wide commercial tolerances or allowances on external members
	H9/d9	D9/h9	*Free running* fit not for use where accuracy is essential, but good for large temperature variations, high running speeds, or heavy journal pressures
	H8/f7	F8/h7	*Close running* fit for running on accurate machines and for accurate location at moderate speeds and journal pressures
	H7/g6	G7/h6	*Sliding fit* not intended to run freely, but to move and turn freely and locate accurately
	H7/h6	H7/h6	*Locational clearance* fit provides snug fit for locating stationary parts; but can be freely assembled and disassembled
Transition fits	H7/k6	K7/h6	*Locational transition* fit for accurate location, a compromise between clearance and interference
	H7/n6	N7/h6	*Locational transition* fit for more accurate location where greater interference is permissible
Interference fits	H7/p6	P7/h6	*Locational interference* fit for parts requiring rigidity and alignment with prime accuracy of location but without special bore pressure requirements
	H7/s6	S7/h6	*Medium drive* fit for ordinary steel parts or shrink fits on light sections, the tightest fit usable with cast iron
	H7/u6	U7/h6	*Force* fit suitable for parts which can be highly stressed or for shrink fits where the heavy pressing forces required are impractical

More clearance ... More interference (shown alongside table, right side)

*The transition and interference shaft basis fits shown do not convert to exactly the same hole basis fit conditions for basic sizes in range from 0 through 3 mm. Interference fit P7/h6 converts to a transition fit H7/p6 in the above size range.

fits, transition fits, and interference fits, just as in the decimal inch system. Various combinations of hole and shaft symbols are listed in Fig. 11 for both hole- and shaft-basis conditions. A description of each fit is provided.

The fits of Fig. 11 were used to construct App. 7. Here limit dimensions are given for a range of *preferred* basic sizes. Appendix 7 is based on *first-choice* preferred sizes compiled by ANSI, as listed in Fig. 12. If a size is needed but not listed, ANSI B4.2 gives a method for calculating the limit dimensions.

A helpful graphical comparison of the preferred fits can be seen in Figs. 13 and 14. The fits of Fig. 11 have been graphed to illustrate all fits. Figure 13 shows the relationship of holes and shafts for the *hole-basis* fits. The interaction of the shaft with the hole is distinctly seen from the clearance fits at the left side of the figure to the interference fits at the right. Note that the smallest hole is always equal to the basic size. Also the position letter is always H for the hole.

A similar illustration is seen in Fig. 14 for the *shaft-basis* fits. However, here the upper limit on the shafts is always the basic size. Note that the position letter is always h for the shaft.

As an example of actual limit dimensions, let us find the limit dimensions for a 60-mm-diameter hole and shaft. We arbitrarily select a close running fit, hole basis. From Fig. 11, fit H8/f7 is needed. Appendix 7A gives the information seen in Fig. 15. The appendices for metric fits are easy to use in that the actual upper- and lower-limit dimensions are given. The minimum clearance is .030 mm, and the maximum clearance is 0.106 mm.

7. GEOMETRIC TOLERANCING: AN OVERVIEW

We have seen how to control the fit for holes and shafts by using specific limit dimensions. However, the precision of fits for holes and shafts alone cannot begin to cover the necessary controls on other features of parts. A designer, for example, may have concerns about the control of parallelism between two surfaces or the position of one hole relative to another. We need a way to control both the form and the position of features.

A system of *geometric tolerancing* has been developed to document the control of form and position. This system is detailed in ANSI Standard Y14.5M. Highlights of this standard give a basic understanding of geometric tolerancing.

a. Symbols

A number of symbols need to be listed, along with certain abbreviations and drafting sizes for these symbols. Figure 16 gives all symbols relating to control of form and position. Figure 17 provides appropriate abbreviations, some seen previously in Chap. 9. Figure 18 gives ANSI-approved sizes for the symbols. References will be made to these three figures.

Figure 12
Preferred sizes.

BASIC SIZE, mm		BASIC SIZE, mm		BASIC SIZE, mm	
First choice	Second choice	First choice	Second choice	First choice	Second choice
1		10		100	
	1.1		11		110
1.2		12		120	
	1.4		14		140
1.6		16		160	
	1.8		18		180
2		20		200	
	2.2		22		220
2.5		25		250	
	2.8		28		280
3		30		300	
	3.5		35		350
4		40		400	
	4.5		45		450
5		50		500	
	5.5		55		550
6		60		600	
	7		70		700
8		80		800	
	9		90		900
				1000	

(ANSI B4.2—1978.)

Figure 13
Preferred shaft basis fits. (ANSI B4.2.)

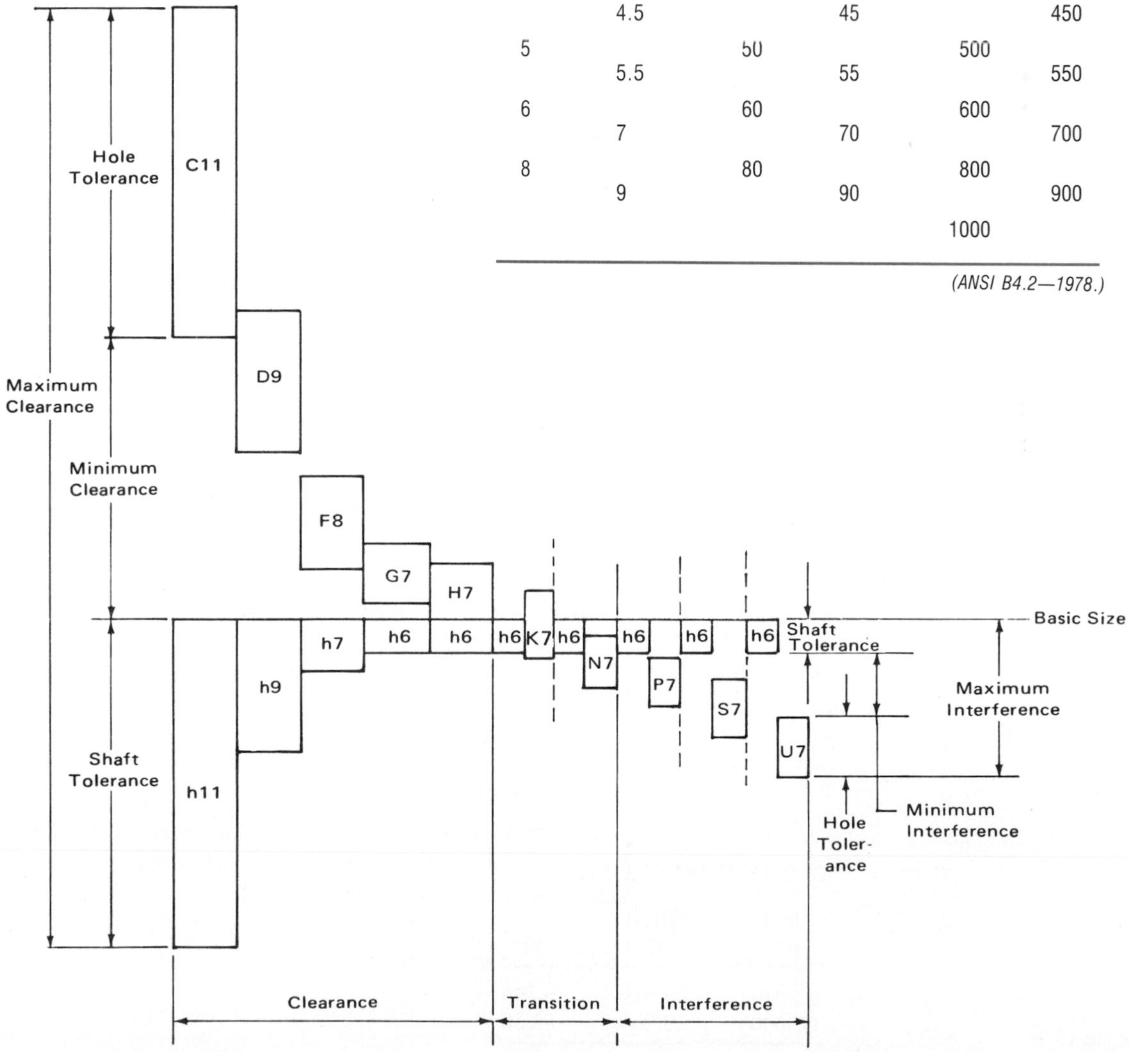

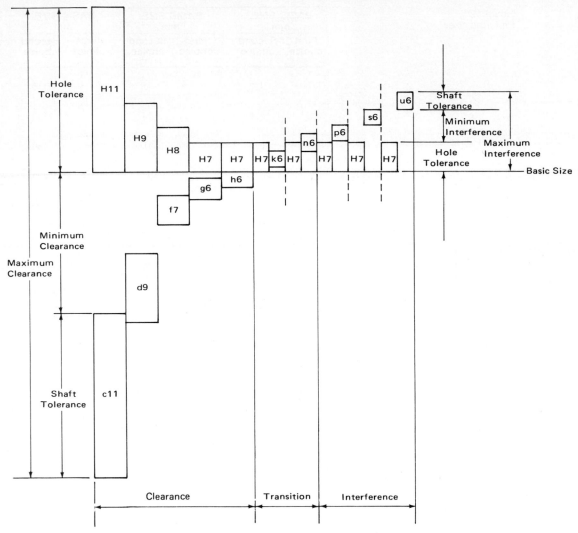

Figure 14
Preferred hole basis fits. (ANSI B4.2.)

CLOSE RUNNING FIT

Hole H8	Shaft f7	Fit
60.046	59.970	0.106
60.000	59.940	0.030

Figure 15
Example of H8/17 fit.

	TYPE OF TOLERANCE	CHARACTERISTIC	SYMBOL
FOR INDIVIDUAL FEATURES	FORM	STRAIGHTNESS	—
		FLATNESS	▱
		CIRCULARITY (ROUNDNESS)	○
		CYLINDRICITY	⌀
FOR INDIVIDUAL OR RELATED FEATURES	PROFILE	PROFILE OF A LINE	⌒
		PROFILE OF A SURFACE	⌓
FOR RELATED FEATURES	ORIENTATION	ANGULARITY	∠
		PERPENDICULARITY	⊥
		PARALLELISM	//
	LOCATION	POSITION	⊕
		CONCENTRICITY	◎
	RUNOUT	CIRCULAR RUNOUT	↗ *
		TOTAL RUNOUT	↗↗ *

*Arrowhead(s) may be filled in.

Figure 16
Symbols for geometric tolerancing.
(ANSI Y14.5M.)

TERM	SYMBOL
AT MAXIMUM MATERIAL CONDITION	Ⓜ
REGARDLESS OF FEATURE SIZE	Ⓢ
AT LEAST MATERIAL CONDITION	Ⓛ
PROJECTED TOLERANCE ZONE	Ⓟ
DIAMETER	⌀
SPHERICAL DIAMETER	S⌀
RADIUS	R
SPHERICAL RADIUS	SR
REFERENCE	( )
ARC LENGTH	⌒

Figure 17
Abbreviations for modifying symbols.
(ANSI Y14.5M.)

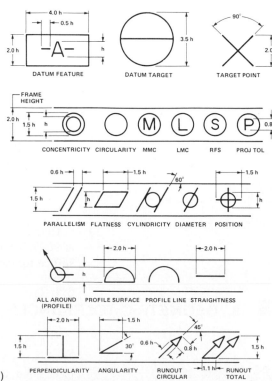

Figure 18
Relative sizes for geometric
tolerancing symbols. (ANSI Y14.5M.)

b. Datums

To properly express controls on forms and positions, we need to understand the meaning of datums and how they interact with each other. A datum is a reference feature on a part that serves to locate another feature of the part relative to the datum. A simple example is given in Fig. 19. The surface of the part along the X axis serves as a datum for dimension A, which positions the center of the hole. Similarly, the surface along axis Y is a datum for dimension B. The center of the hole is "referenced" from the X and Y axes.

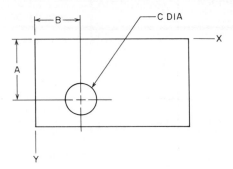

Figure 19
X and Y axes as datums.

Datums are not limited to a 2-D format. A part occupies a 3-D space containing the X, Y, and Z axes. In Fig. 20 datum planes are shown along each of the three axes. Datum A has been chosen as the primary datum. Datum B is the secondary datum, and datum C is the tertiary (third) datum. Alternative positions for datums A, B, and C could have been selected.

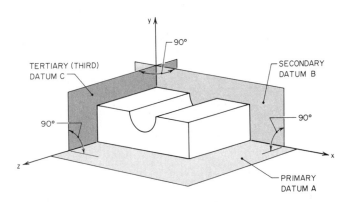

Figure 20
Datum planes in space.

Datum A is defined by three points of contact with the part. Since datum B is at 90° to datum A, two points of contact are sufficient. One point of contact will suffice for datum C since it is also at 90° to both A and B.

8. GEOMETRIC TOLERANCES OF FORM

Tolerance of form refers to the control of certain conditions of lines and surfaces of a part. We discuss the tolerances of Fig. 16 in the categories of form, profile, orientation, and runout. Tolerances of location are discussed last. Form types deal with individual features only, such as flatness. Profile types can relate to individual *or* related features. Additional tolerances, orientation and runout, are for related features only, such as parallelism of one surface related to another surface.

a. Straightness

Figure 21 illustrates the control of straightness for a cylinder. The symbol for straightness (—) from Fig. 16 is combined with a numerical value (here .15 mm) within a *feature control frame*. A feature control frame is merely a rectangular box enclosing the symbol and numerical value.

Straightness control dictates the degree of straightness of any line element along the length of the cylinder. The meaning of the control can be seen in the lower part of Fig. 21. Straightness tolerance must always be less than the size control, here φ20.0 to φ20.4.

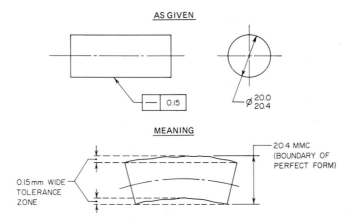

Figure 21
METRIC. Straightness symbol controlling surface elements.

In Fig. 22 the size control is above the feature control frame. The frame implies control of axis straightness. Straightness control is independent of outside diameter and is thus applied in a condition known as *regardless of feature size* (RFS). Whenever you see RFS on a drawing, you know that a particular control is independent of the feature size.

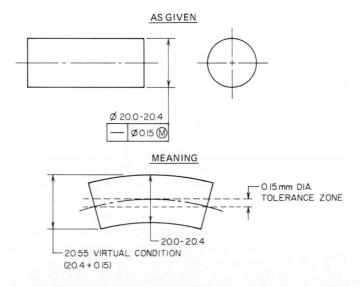

Figure 22
METRIC. Straightness symbol controlling axis.

Notice in Fig. 22 the term *virtual condition*. Virtual condition is simply the most severe case that can occur. It is found by adding the form tolerance and the size at the maximum-material condition (MMC), here .15 mm plus the maximum diameter of 20.4 mm, or 20.55 mm.

b. Flatness

Flatness control deals with a *plane,* not a line as in straightness. In Fig. 23, all portions of a surface must lie between two parallel planes a specified distance apart (.005 in). Again the symbol for this type of tolerance control is taken from Fig. 16. Flatness exists at RFS.

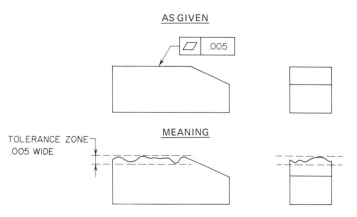

Figure 23
Flatness symbol.

c. Roundness

Roundness is an easy tolerance control to understand. In Fig. 24 control is provided to points on the surface which are in any plane perpendicular to the axis. The tolerance zone consists of two concentric circles, as seen. Taper is not controlled by roundness tolerance. Roundness tolerance must not exceed size tolerance.

d. Cylindricity

Cylindricity establishes a tolerance zone consisting of two concentric cylinders, as in Fig. 25. This type of tolerance control is used only for cylinders. It controls straightness, roundness, and taper, making cylindricity tolerance a powerful tool. Cylindricity tolerance must be less than size tolerance.

e. Profile of a Line

Profile tolerance controls the profile or contour of a part. The desired perfect profile in Fig. 26 is given in the front view by the values R25, R20, and 38, each of which is boxed in without tolerance. The tolerance zone is given in the feature control frame and exists from position *X* to position *Y*. Surface *A* is the primary datum, and surface *B* is the secondary datum.

The tolerance zone covers every vertical cross section that could be placed in the left-side view. The contour of each cross section needs to be within the .15-mm-wide tolerance zone. Also in the front view between positions *X* and *Y*, each line element of the surface along any cross section must be within the .15-mm tolerance zone.

AS GIVEN

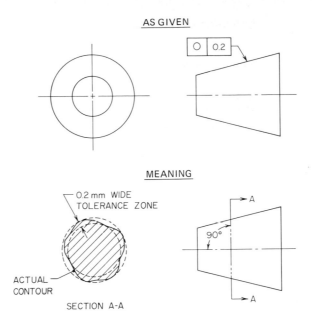

MEANING

0.2 mm WIDE
TOLERANCE ZONE

ACTUAL
CONTOUR

SECTION A-A

90°

Figure 24
METRIC. Roundness symbol.

AS GIVEN

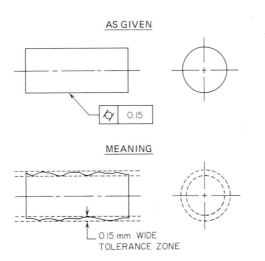

MEANING

0.15 mm WIDE
TOLERANCE ZONE

Figure 25
Cylindricity symbol.

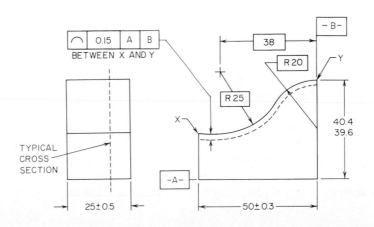

| ⌒ | 0.15 | A | B |

BETWEEN X AND Y

TYPICAL
CROSS
SECTION

25±0.5

-B-

38

R 20

Y

R 25

X

40.4
39.6

-A-

50±0.3

Figure 26
METRIC. Line profile symbol.

f. Profile of a Plane

This type of tolerance is easier to express than the profile of a line. Figure 27 presents the symbols and their meanings. The fact that the dashed control line is on the *inside* of the surface means that unilateral tolerance goes inward from the profile. For outside unilateral tolerance, the dashed line is outside the surface. For bilateral tolerance, no dashed line is used. The symbol in Fig. 27 for *all around* means that the tolerance zone is to go entirely around the part. This is an option.

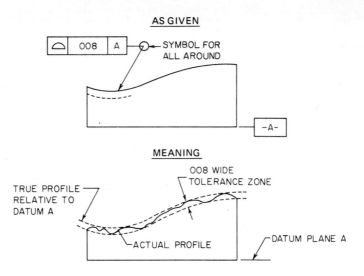

Figure 27
Surface profile symbol.

g. Angularity

Figure 28 shows angularity tolerance. This useful tolerance controls the angle (other than 90°) of an axis or surface to some datum. In Fig. 28 the tolerance zone is between two parallel planes separated by .1 mm. The desired "perfect" angle of the zone is the boxed-in (basic) 60° shown. The surface within the zone may be of any contour and still be acceptable. Here we see that angularity tolerance control also regulates the flatness of the surface.

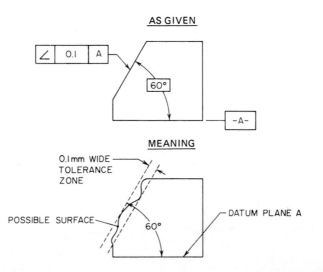

Figure 28
METRIC. Angularity symbol.

AS GIVEN

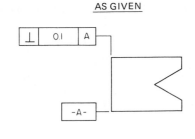

MEANING

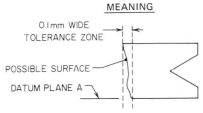

Figure 29
METRIC. Perpendicularity symbol applied to two planes.

h. Perpendicularity

Control of the perpendicularity is important in a variety of applications, which all can be found in ANSI Y14.5M. Perpendicularity control can be applied to an axis with an axis, to an axis with a plane, and to a plane with a plane.

Figure 29 shows control of a plane with a plane. The vertical left-hand edge of the part is to be perpendicular to datum base *A* within a .1-mm-wide tolerance zone. This control also serves as a flatness control for the vertical edge.

i. Parallelism

Another useful tolerance control governs parallelism. It can be applied to axes or planes. Control of a plane to a plane is seen in Fig. 30. The left-hand surface is to be parallel to datum surface *A* within .1 mm. The flatness of the left-hand surface is also controlled.

Control of parallelism between two axes is seen in Fig. 31. The axis of the larger hole is designated to stay within a .25-mm-diameter tolerance zone. The cylinder described by this zone must itself be parallel to the axis of datum cylinder *A*. As given, the parallelism of the two axes is RFS (regardless of feature size). Refer to ANSI Y14.5M for the application of parallelism under other conditions, such as at maximum-material condition.

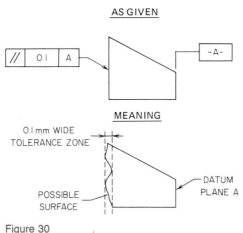

Figure 30
METRIC. Parallelism symbol applied to two planes.

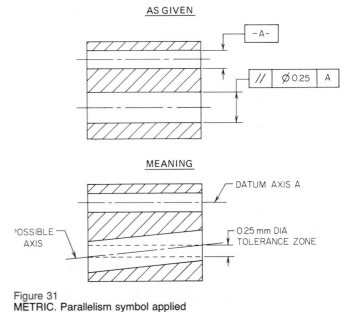

Figure 31
METRIC. Parallelism symbol applied to two axes.

j. Runout

Runout expresses deviation from an ideal shape as a part is rotated 360°. Runout is measured by the net change on a dial indicator while the part is rotated one full turn. The net change on the dial is called the *full indicator reading* (FIR) or *total indicator reading* (TIR).

Both *circular runout* and *total runout* can be expressed. Figures 32 and 33 show the difference between the two. Circular runout is seen in Fig. 32. Here the dial indicator is kept perpendicular to the surface and is not allowed to move parallel to axis *A*. The .03 FIM value is the maximum variation permitted around a *single* circular element of the part.

Total runout, as seen in Fig. 33, controls an entire surface, not just a circular element. For the example in Fig. 33, the dial indicator is moved parallel to datum axis *A*. A maximum deviation of .04 mm is allowed. Both profile and circular elements are controlled, making total runout a broad-based control for form tolerance.

Notice that a single arrow in the feature control frame of Fig. 32 indicates circular runout. A double arrow in Fig. 33 specifies the total runout. Both types of runout exist on an RFS basis.

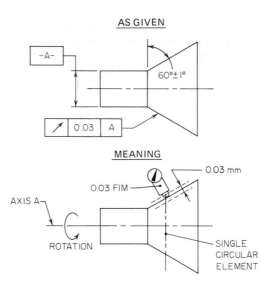

Figure 32
METRIC. Circular runout.

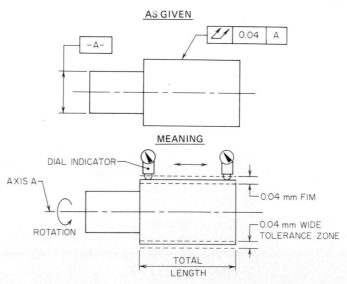

Figure 33
METRIC. Using dial indicators to read total runout.

■ 9. GEOMETRIC TOLERANCES OF LOCATION

Notice that Fig. 16 shows two types of location tolerance: position and concentricity. Tolerances of location do just that; they control the *location* of features, not shapes as in those tolerances previously discussed. Positional tolerancing, also known as *true-position tolerancing,* is used more often than concentricity tolerancing, and so we discuss it first.

a. Positional Tolerancing

The need for this type of tolerancing is seen in Fig. 34. The center of the hole is located (positioned) by ordinary coordinate dimensions of 35 ± .2 mm in the *x* direction and 25 ± .2 mm in the *y* direction. You might think that the center of the hole is being held to a ± .2-mm tolerance, or .4 mm.

But this is not true. What is really being described with the .4-mm tolerance is a *square* tolerance zone. The distance across the diagonal of the zone is .57 mm, 41 percent *more* than .4 mm. If a *circular* rather than a square tolerance zone were specified, the actual tolerance control would be improved. This is precisely what positional tolerancing does (see Fig. 35).

In Fig. 35 the coordinate system of position control has been converted to positional tolerancing. The boxed-in dimensions of 25 and 35 mm are the basic, or perfect, positional dimensions. Since no dimensions can be perfect (that is, without tolerance), the feature control frame provides the tolerance. The center of the hole

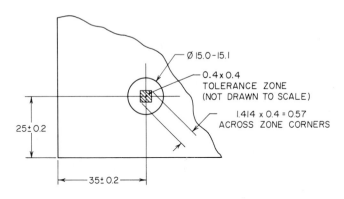

Figure 34
METRIC. Effect of coordinate dimensioning.

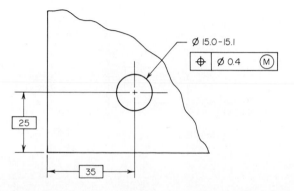

Figure 35
METRIC. Positional tolerancing for Fig. 34.

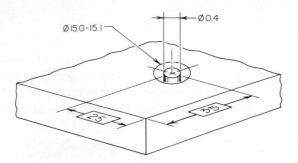

METRIC. Interpretation of positional tolerancing.

is allowed to move within a .4-mm-diameter cylinder at MMC, as seen in Fig. 36. As long as the centerline axis of the hole stays within the .4-mm-diameter cylinder, the position of the hole is acceptable. We must realize that the control of the *position* of the hole is completely independent of the control of the *size* of the hole, here having a .1-mm tolerance. Study ANSI Standard Y14.5M for additional applications of positional tolerancing.

b. Concentricity Tolerancing

The extent to which axes of cylinders may be offset from one another can be controlled via concentricity tolerancing. In Fig. 37 the centerline of the smaller cylinder is to lie within a .1-mm diameter relative to datum diameter *A* of the larger cylinder.

Normally a designer would select a runout tolerance over a concentricity runout to control the axial position of one diameter relative to another. Actual centerline axes are harder to locate than the offset measurement of diameters. Still concentricity tolerancing is an available technique to control location.

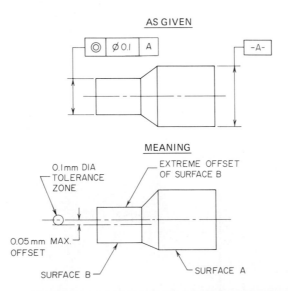

METRIC. Concentricity control.

■ 10. SUMMARY

The designer and drafter have at hand a number of ways to express tolerances on parts. Tolerances may be placed on linear dimensions, on holes and shafts, and on forms and locations. Considerable care and experience are needed to properly set the degree of precision for a particular part. Close tolerancing is expensive and might be unnecessary. However, when it is necessary, close control of dimensions can be accomplished by using well established procedures.

The tolerancing techniques may involve hand drawing or computer-aided drafting. If CAD is used, consult the documentation for the software. Then you can efficiently use or create the various symbols needed in tolerancing, such as those in Fig. 16.

A final illustration is Fig. 38. This very fully toleranced part involves much geometric tolerancing. The part would be expensive to produce compared to one with fewer tolerance controls, but the example does indicate available procedures for clearly indicating tolerances.

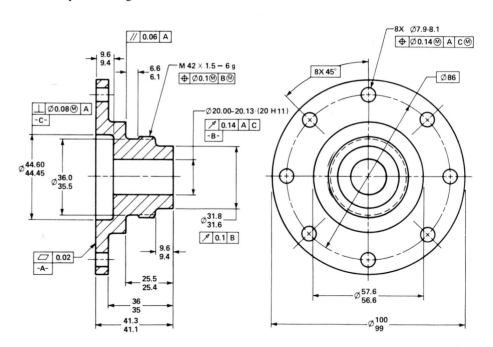

Figure 38
Use of geometric tolerancing. (ANSI Y24.5M.)

P R O B L E M S

Fully dimension the following problems, using the
tolerancing specifications indicated.

1. Given: A stud shaft shown half size, machined from
steel-bar stock. Give the proper dimensions for diameter
A to conform to an H8/f7 fit. The thread is coarse metric,
M 20 × 2.5.

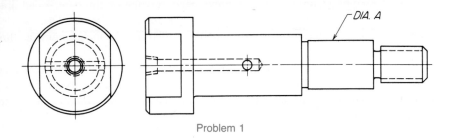

Problem 1

2. Given: A shaft bracket shown half size, made from
malleable iron. The slot is to be given a surface-texture
symbol, with roughness appropriate to a milling operation.
Diameter *A* is to have an H7/h6 locational clearance fit.
The diameter of the H7/h6 hole is to be perpendicular to
surface *A* within a .1-mm diameter.

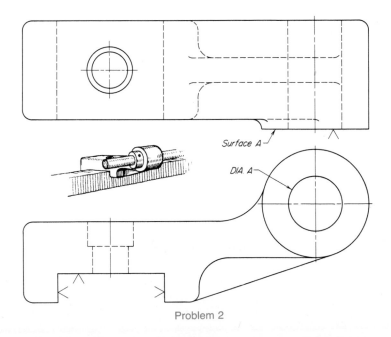

Problem 2

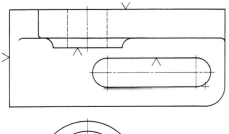

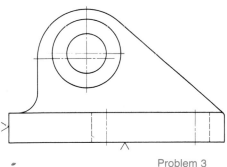

3. Given: An idler bracket shown one-third size, made of cast iron. The hole is bored and reamed; the slot is milled. Dimension the hole to an RC6 fit. Give a feature control frame so that the base is flat within .008 in. Give a surface-texture symbol for all indicated finished surfaces consistent with roughness common to milling operations. Dimension with decimals.

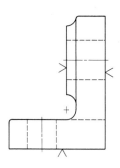

Problem 3

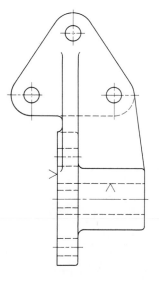

4. Given: A filter flange shown half size, made of cast aluminum. The small holes are drilled. Dimension the large diameter to an LC4 fit. The small holes are to be given a feature control frame so that the holes are positionally located for angularity within a .006-in diameter at MMC. Dimension with decimals.

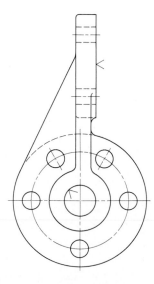

Problem 4

5. Given: A connecting link made of cast iron. Using decimals, dimension the piece. The centerlines of the two holes are to be concentric within a .010-in-diameter tolerance zone. Use a feature control frame. The holes are to be an FN1 fit.

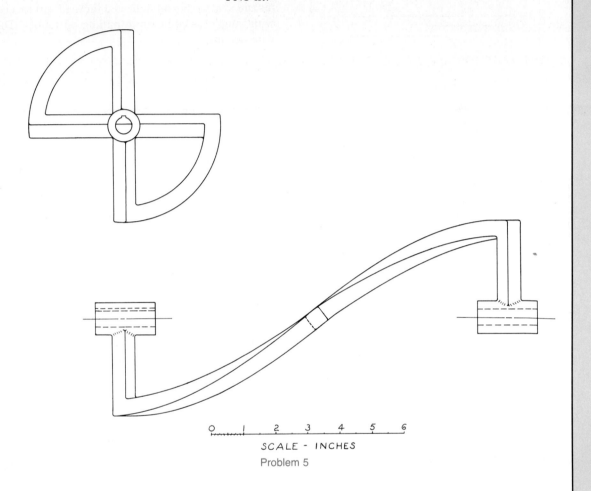

SCALE - INCHES

Problem 5

PART D

SPATIAL ANALYSIS

C H A P T E R 11

SPATIAL ANALYSIS: LINES AND PLANES

![bar]

■ 1. INTRODUCTION

The discussion to this point has dealt with shapes and parts that are volumes. That is, the parts have height, width, and depth. Most parts we can touch in this world occupy a volume. We have studied pictorials of such parts and their 2-D top, front, and side views. Much has been learned about describing shapes.

We have not studied, however, much about analyzing parts that are not volumes. We have not learned about useful relationships between lines and lines, lines and planes, and many other combinations. As an example, note Fig. 1. Here is a vertical pole supported by three guy wires *A, B,* and *C*. Top and front views are given along with a scale. If you gave a drawing of these wires and pole to a person to install them, two likely questions would arise: What are the true lengths of the wires, and what angles do the wires make with the ground? How can we find the answers? Certainly what has been learned so far is not enough.

Figure 1 illustrates a problem in the general area of *spatial geometry,* also known as *descriptive geometry*. Spatial geometry involves working with lines and planes, as in Fig. 1, where wires *A, B,* and *C* and the pole are represented as lines and the ground is a plane, seen as an edge view (EV) in the front view. Analysis of volumes is also carried out in spatial analysis.

Much information can be extracted from spatial analysis which is very valuable to designers of parts. Sometimes the data can be obtained from the usual top view, front view, or side-view multiview. Figure 2 shows such a case. The angle of ramp *A* with the ground is available in the front view. However, in Fig. 1, the true lengths of the wires and their angles with ground are not given.

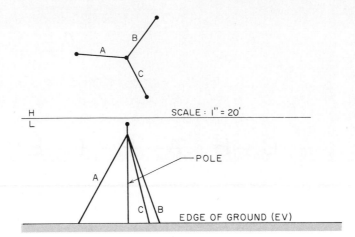

Figure 1
Problem involving lines and a plane.

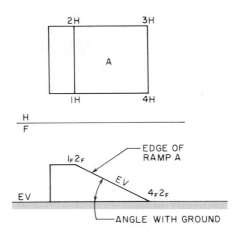

Figure 2
Problem having information available
in front view.

We now begin a useful study of spatial analysis. We will learn to obtain information not always found in top, front, and side views. A number of common types
of problems are reviewed, although the study is by no means exhaustive. A standard
book devoted to descriptive geometry can supply additional problem types.

The concepts drawn on to understand the problems are equally valuable for
solutions done manually or via CAD. An edge view of a plane, for example, has
the same meaning and looks the same whether it is done by hand or by CAD.
Learning concepts of spatial analysis will make you much more knowledgeable
when using CAD software.

2. BASIC STRATEGIES

To obtain information about lines, planes, and volumes in space, we have to
know what is desired. Do we wish to know the true length of a line? Is the true
surface area of a plane needed? How about the shortest distance from a point to a
plane?

First, know *what* is desired. Second, develop a logical strategy to *show* what is
desired. Each application of spatial analysis follows the strategy of illustrating what

is desired, followed by a direct procedure to obtain the needed information. Alternative procedures for the same solution are offered for some cases.

The primary analyses to be considered are as follows:

1. *Line:* true length, bearing, slope, point view
2. *Plane:* edge view, true surface, angle between planes
3. *Line-plane combinations:* parallelism, perpendicularity, angle between line and plane (Chap. 12)
4. *Shortest distances:* from a point to a line, a line to a line, and a point to a plane (Chap. 12)
5. *Intersections:* between a line and a line, a line and a plane, a line and a solid, a plane and a plane, a plane and a solid, and a solid and a solid

■ 3. TYPES OF LINES

Clearly the line is one of the most basic elements of any design. The line can stand by itself in a design, as in the analysis of centerlines of a piping system. Or a line can interact with other elements such as a plane (see Fig. 1). We need to learn as much as possible about lines.

We must understand the types of lines before attempting analysis of lines. There are two types of lines: *principal* and *oblique lines*.

a. Principal Lines

Principal lines are parallel to at least one *principal plane*. A principal plane can be the horizontal (*H*), the frontal (*F*), or the profile (*P*) plane of projection. Figure 3 shows the *H, F,* and *P* planes, also seen in Chap. 6.

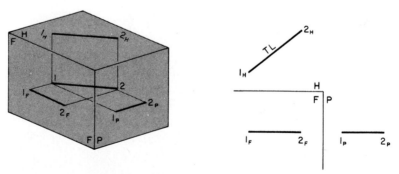

Figure 3
A horizontal line.

A line parallel to a principal plane is *true length* (TL) in that plane. In Fig. 3, line 1-2 is parallel to the *H* plane and is TL in that plane. Because line 1-2 is TL in the *H* plane, line 1-2 is called a *horizontal line* (HL). Figure 4 shows a *frontal line* (FL), and Fig. 5 shows a *profile line* (PL). *A line is always named for the plane in which it is true length.*

A line may be true length in one or two views. Figures 3, 4, and 5 show lines that are TL in one view only. Line 7-8 in Fig. 6 shows the line TL in both the *H* and *P* views. Therefore line 7-8 is called a *horizontal-profile line* (HPL). Similarly, we could have a *horizontal-frontal line* (HFL) and a *frontal-profile line* (FPL), actually a vertical line.

In summary, principal lines fall into these types:

- ◼ Horizontal line
- ◼ Frontal line
- ◼ Profile line
- ◼ Horizontal-profile line
- ◼ Horizontal-frontal line
- ◼ Frontal-profile line

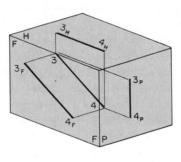
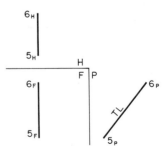

Figure 4
A frontal line.

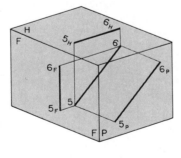

Figure 5
A profile line.

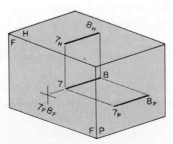
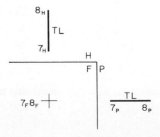

Figure 6
A horizontal-profile line.

b. Oblique Lines

An *oblique line* (OL) is *not* parallel to any principal plane (*H, F,* or *P*). An oblique line therefore is not true length (TL) in any principal plane. Figure 7 shows an oblique line.

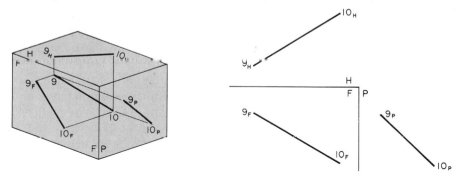

Figure 7
An oblique line.

4. TRUE LENGTH OF A LINE

Being able to find the true length of a line is basic to any manufactured product, whether it be a wheel axle or a porch railing. How do we know if a line is TL? Refer to Fig. 3. Line 1-2 is TL in the horizontal (*H*) view because it is parallel to the *H* view, as seen from the front (*F*) view.

Alternatively, we may say that line 1-2 is TL in the *H* view because the line of sight is *perpendicular* to line 1-2 when the *H* view is made. Note in the *F* view that the arrow represents the line of sight needed to produce the *H* view. The line of sight is at 90° to line 1-2. Therefore, *any line viewed perpendicularly becomes true length*.

Some people call the view in which a line appears TL the *normal view*. The phrase *normal to* means *perpendicular to*. Therefore a normal view is found by looking perpendicularly to a line.

Now comes the big question. How do we find the TL of a line if it is not given TL? Fortunately we are not at a loss. There are three methods to find TL that we will review: true-length diagram, revolution, and auxiliary view.

5. TRUE LENGTH BY TRUE-LENGTH DIAGRAM

This simple but clever method is shown in Fig. 8. Note first that Fig. 8 is a repetition of oblique line 9-10 in Fig. 7. We had decided that line 9-10 was not TL in the *H, F,* or *P* view because it is not parallel to any principal plane of projection.

The true-length diagram method is based on the fact that if two sides of a right triangle are known, the third side is also known. Therefore a 9-10-11 right triangle is made as shown. Side 9-11 is vertical, side 10-11 is horizontal, and the original line 9-10 is the hypotenuse. If we can find lines 9-11 and 10-11 TL, then line 9-10 must also be TL.

Triangle 9-10-11 is to be built from TL sides in a convenient space, such as to the right of the front view. Vertical line 9-11 is TL in the front view, since it is parallel to the front (as seen in the *H* view). Line 9-11 is therefore placed into the TL diagram.

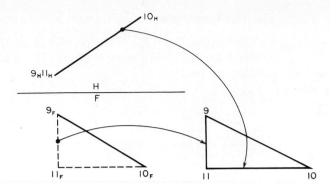

Figure 8
True length by TL diagram.

Line 10-11 is parallel to the *H* view (as seen in the *F* view) and is therefore TL in the *H* view. This TL of line 10-11 is then placed into the TL diagram. With the TL of lines 9-10 and 10-11 in place, the hypotenuse line 9-10 must be TL. By using some known scale, line 9-10 can be measured. The solution is complete.

■ 6. TRUE LENGTH BY REVOLUTION

The method of revolution for the TL of a line is unique and powerful. Revolution as a general method can be used with points, planes, and solids. Revolution applied to an oblique line is seen in Fig. 9. Let us explore what happens.

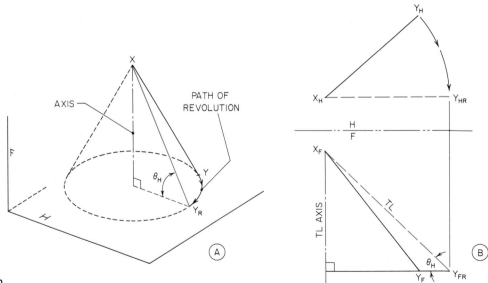

Figure 9
True length of a line by revolution.

1. Revolution involves an axis and a circular path of revolution which is perpendicular to the axis, as in Fig. 9A.

2. Line *XY* is revolved about a vertical axis until *XY* becomes parallel to the frontal plane *F*. Line *XY* is then TL in the *F* view, as seen in Fig. 9B.

3. The angle that line *XY* makes with the horizontal plane stays constant when the axis is vertical. This angle is known as the *slope angle* θ_H, which we

discuss more thoroughly later. Interestingly, for the wires in Fig. 1 the true lengths and angles with the ground (slope angles) could be found by using revolution.

7. TRUE LENGTH BY AUXILIARY VIEW

For the first time in this book, we use an *auxiliary projection plane,* which is simply a projection plane that is not a horizontal, frontal, or profile plane. We move our line of sight to give a view which is not an *F, H,* or *P* view. However, the system of orthographic projection is still used; that is, the line of sight continues to be perpendicular to the projection plane.

Study Fig. 10. Line *AB* is an oblique line like those just discussed. It is not true length (TL) in the *F* or *H* view, nor would it be TL in the *P* view, if given. We could use the true-length diagram method or the method of revolution. Instead, we employ the auxiliary-view method. This method is of great value in solving other problems later on, as we shall see.

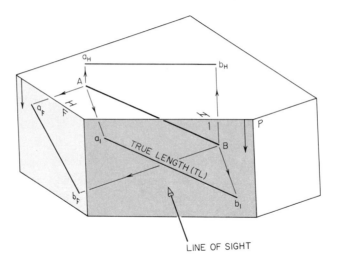

Figure 10
Pictorial showing TL by auxiliary view.

LINE OF SIGHT

In Fig. 10 the line of sight is made *perpendicular* to the actual line inside the projection box. The auxiliary view therefore is parallel to the line. The resulting projection of the line onto the auxiliary view must be TL. Constructing the TL is now necessary. The process is identical to making *any* view in orthographic projection, a process done many times in previous chapters.

Now, however, more care will be taken with the *fold lines* between views. In Fig. 10 the fold line (or reference line) between the *H* and *F* views is labeled *H/F*. Between the *H* and auxiliary views, the fold line is labeled *H/1*, since the auxiliary view has been arbitrarily called view 1. The same notation is used in Fig. 11 when the TL is constructed in 2-D format. In every case two attached planes, such as *H/F* and *H/1*, are always 90° apart in space. In Figs. 10 and 11 view *F* and view 1 are each at 90° to the *H* view.

The method of constructing the true length is as follows. (Remember that this process is used to make *any* view in orthographic projection, including the usual *H, F,* and *P* views.)

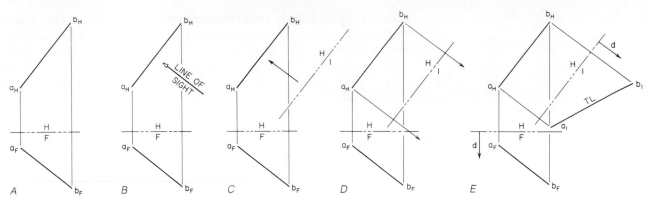

Figure 11
Steps for finding TL by auxiliary view.

a. Set Line of Sight

In Fig. 11 line *AB* is given as an oblique line in step A. In step B of Fig. 11 the line of sight is set at 90° to *AB*. This action will force a TL view to be seen.

b. Place a Projection Plane Perpendicular to the Line of Sight

Step C shows that plane 1 has been placed perpendicular to the line of sight (and parallel to line *AB*). Labeling the fold line *H*/1 tells the user that plane 1 is at 90° to plane *H*. The actual distance of the *H*/1 line from line *AB* does not matter because the parallel projectors of orthographic projection (step D of Fig. 11) ensure the constant size of any object.

c. Project Points into the View

Step D shows the line's endpoints *A* and *B* being projected into view 1. Any points must project *perpendicularly* across fold line *H*/1 because orthographic projection is used. Notice that the projectors also go perpendicularly across the *H*/*F* fold line, separating the *H* and *F* views.

d. Transfer Points into the View

Step E of Fig. 11 can complete the process of obtaining the TL of line *AB*. Points *A* and *B* must be transferred into view 1 along the projectors for *A* and *B*. How do we locate *A* and *B* along the projectors? One major concept will help: *All distances taken perpendicularly away from the same plane have the same direction in space.*

In our case, perpendicular away from the *H* plane into the *F* plane is in the same direction as perpendicular away from the *H* plane into auxiliary plane 1. This direction happens to be *height,* and it is shown as an arrow in Figs. 10 and 11. Therefore the direction *d* perpendicular to plane *H* in Fig. 11E is transferred from the front view to auxiliary view 1. Use dividers to transfer these distances.

The solution above used an auxiliary view adjacent to (attached to) the horizontal *H* plane. This is not the only route to a TL of line *AB*. We could, for example, place an auxiliary view adjacent to the front view *F*. This is shown in 3-D format in Fig. 12. Plane 1 is placed parallel to line *AB* in the front view. The 2-D solution is shown in Fig. 13 and follows exactly the procedure used to find the TL of *AB* just completed in Fig. 11. Now in Fig. 13 the transfer distances for points *A* and *B* are taken perpendicular to plane *F* as shown, instead of perpendicular to plane *H* as in Fig. 11. The distances transferred are depths, rather than heights as in Fig. 11. As a general comment, you may look perpendicularly at a line in *any* view to find the true length. It is your choice.

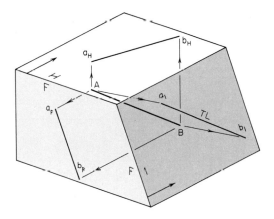

Figure 12
TL in auxiliary view adjacent to front view.

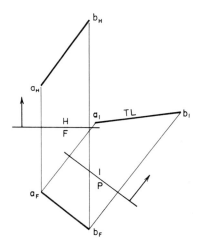

Figure 13
Solution for line given in Fig. 12.

■ 8. BEARING AND AZIMUTH OF A LINE

A useful piece of information is the bearing of a line. *Bearing* relates to map work and is the deviation of a line from the north or south compass direction. Maps of terrain are actually horizontal views. Therefore, we must use the *horizontal* view of a line, and only the horizontal view, to find the bearing.

Note in Fig. 14A that a north-south line has been placed through point *A*, the beginning of lines *AB*, *AC*, and *AD*. The smaller acute angle (less than 90°) is always selected. A line going east, however, would be said to be *due east*, not N90°E or S90°E. Similarly, lines can go due west, due north, and due south.

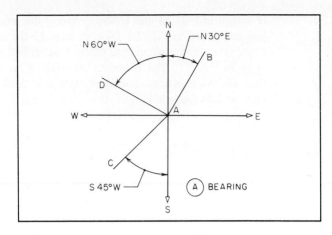

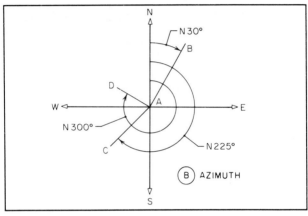

Figure 14
Bearing and aximuth of a line.

The horizontal direction of a line can also be given by the azimuth. It is read clockwise from north only, as seen in Fig. 14B. The bearing values of Fig. 14A are seen as azimuths.

9. SLOPE, SLOPE ANGLE, AND GRADE OF A LINE

A line can yield still more information. The slope, slope angle, and grade of a line are expressions of the same theme: the relationship of a line to the ground. Refer to Fig. 15 to help you understand these three terms.

Slope is

$$\frac{\text{Rise}}{\text{Run}} = \frac{Y}{X} = \tan \theta_H$$

where θ_H is the *slope angle*. And *grade* is given as

$$\text{Grade} = (\tan \theta_H)(100\%)$$

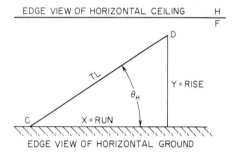

Figure 15
Relationship of a line to the ground.

To obtain any of these three values, we must have a view containing the TL of the line *and* the edge view of the ground. These conditions are met in Fig. 15. However, if the line is not TL, the TL must be found in a view adjacent to the *H* view where the edge view of the ground would exist. This is the case in Fig. 16, the same line that we worked with in Fig. 11.

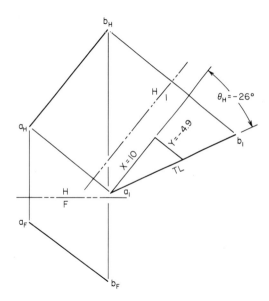

Figure 16
Slope, slope angle, and grade for an oblique line.

The slope, slope angle, and grade are considered positive if the line rises during travel from beginning to end. In Fig. 15 line *CD* rises from the beginning at *C* to the end at *D*. (The first letter or number defines the beginning of a line.) In Fig. 16 line *AB* drops from point *A* to *B*. Therefore, the slope, slope angle, and grade are all negative.

One neat way to determine the value of the slope or grade is to let the *X* component be set to 10 in the ratio *Y/X*. This can be done with any convenient scale. Then simply read the *Y* component. For Fig. 16 we get

$$\text{Slope} = \frac{Y}{X} = \frac{-4.9}{10} = -.49$$

The grade is therefore -49 percent.

10. POINT VIEW OF A LINE

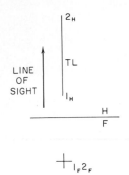

Figure 17
Point view of a line within given views.

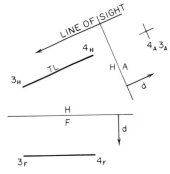

Figure 18
Point view of a line using one auxiliary view.

To be able to find a line in point view can help solve many problems in spatial analysis. A *point view* of a line means that the line appears to be a single point because the two ends of the line coincide. We must know what condition causes a line to be seen in point view and then cause that condition to happen. In Fig. 17 a principal line is seen in point view. Horizontal line 1-2 is a point view in the front view. Why? The line of sight to make the front view happens to be *parallel* to a *true-length* view of the line, as in the *H* view. Therefore, *a line is made a point view by looking parallel to a true-length view of the line.*

In Fig. 18, horizontal line 3-4 is made a point view by constructing an auxiliary view with the line of sight parallel to the TL view. As always, the fold line between the *H* view and auxiliary view *A* is made perpendicular to the line of sight. The transfer distance *d* is taken perpendicularly away from the *H* view in the front view and is placed perpendicularly away from the *H* view in auxiliary view 1. The process of making a new view is exactly the same as that in Sec. 7.

When a line is not given TL in a principal view but is instead an oblique line, two methods may be used to find the point view: revolution and auxiliary view. Figure 19 shows the revolution method in use. First, line *AB* is swung into a TL position, by applying ideas discussed in Fig. 9. It was arbitrarily decided to make the line TL in the *H* view, rather than the *F* view. Therefore a TL axis was placed in the *H* view so as to be perpendicular to the *F* view, making the axis a point view in the *F* view. The line is revolved until it is parallel to the *H* view, forcing the line to be TL in the *H* view. Remember that the path of revolution is perpendicular to the axis in the *H* view. Once TL in the *H* view, line *AB* is made a point view in view 1 exactly as in Fig. 18.

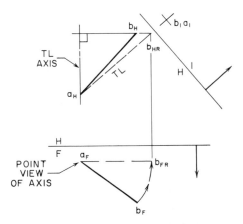

Figure 19
Point view of an oblique line using revolution.

Let us solve the same problem by the auxiliary-view method. Refer to Fig. 20. First the line is made TL, just as in Fig. 11. Making line *AB* TL uses one auxiliary view. Now a *second* auxiliary view is needed, a view looking parallel to the TL view of *AB*. The process of constructing the view is as follows:

a. Set the Line of Sight

This is to be parallel to the TL of line *AB*, as shown.

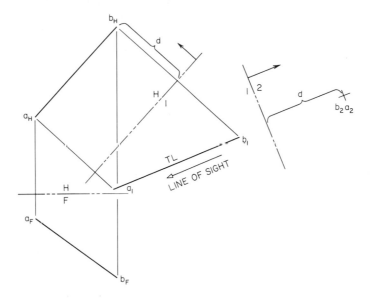

Figure 20
Point view of an oblique line using auxiliary views.

b. Place a Projection Plane Perpendicular to the Line of Sight

This is shown and is labeled 1/2 since we are leaving view 1 and are entering view 2. View 2 is at 90° to view 1, as are any attached views.

c. Project Points into the View

Points *A* and *B* share the same projector, as seen. This projector must be perpendicular to fold line 1/2.

d. Transfer Points into the View

The arrows show that perpendicular from view 1 into view 2 is the same direction as perpendicular away from view 1 into view *H*. Remember the statement in Sec. 7: All distances taken perpendicularly away from the *same* plane have the same direction in space. Therefore distance *d* is taken from view *H* and transferred into view 2. Since distance *d* is identical for points *A* and *B*, a point view of line *AB* exists.

■ 11. EDGE VIEW OF A PLANE

It is important to be able to find the edge view (EV) of a plane. In an EV, all lines of a plane appear together in a straight line. When available, an EV can enable us to find items such as the slope angle of a plane, to see lines perpendicular to planes, and to see the angle between planes. Finding an EV of a plane is essential to many problems in spatial analysis.

Let us observe an existing edge view. Figure 2 is repeated as Fig. 21. An EV exists, but why? Note that line 1-2 is seen as a point view in the front view. Thus *when any line of a plane is seen in point view, the plane itself is an edge view*. If

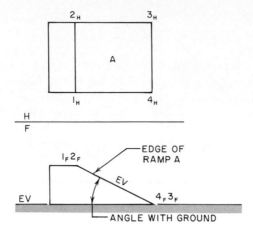

H
F

Figure 21
Figure 2 repeated, showing edge view of a plane.

a plane needs to be made EV, we need only make some line of the plane into a point view.

Let an edge view be made of plane *ABC* in Fig. 22. To make an EV, some line of the plane must be made a point view. A point view requires that a TL of the line be available, as we have learned (see Fig. 18). Line *AB* in plane *ABC* is *given* TL in the *H* view. Therefore make *AB* into a point view. This is done in auxiliary view 1. Transfer distances are taken from the *F* view. Points *A* and *B* fall along the same projector. Point *C* has its own projector. The slope angle θ_H happens to be available in auxiliary view 1 with no extra work. The *slope angle* for a plane is the angle between the EV and the horizontal plane (or ground, if shown).

If no true length is given in the plane, how can we make an edge view? The answer is direct: *Add* a TL line to the plane. Note in Fig. 23 that line 2-4 has been added as a TL line. Line 2-4 is TL in the *H* view because it was first placed in the *F* view *parallel* to the *H* view, forcing line 2-4 to be TL in the *H* view. Any line parallel to the *H* view could have been added to the plane in the *F* view. Line

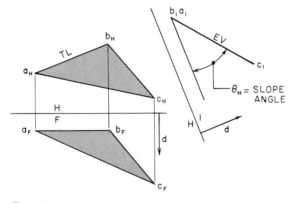

Figure 22
Edge view with TL line given.

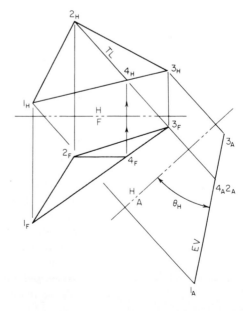

Figure 23
Edge view with TL line added.

2-4 happened to be convenient because it could use existing point 2. With line 2-4 TL in the *H* view, the edge view is found in exactly the same way as done in Fig. 22.

Revolution may also be employed to generate an edge view of a plane. This is done in Fig. 24. An added line *AA'* is TL in the *H* view. Line *AA'* is revolved in the *H* view until *AA'* is perpendicular to the *F* plane. Now line *AA'* must occur in a point view in the *F* view, and plane *ABC* becomes EV. Notice that during the revolution of points in the *H* view, all points revolve through the *same angle*. The process of creating an EV by revolution is not necessarily better or faster than the auxiliary-view method. It is simply one choice. Some CAD software programs, however, make revolutions fairly easy, and so the use of revolution could be an advantage in such cases.

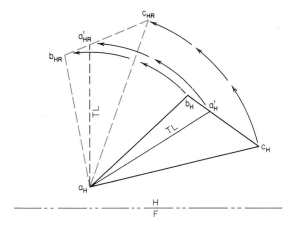

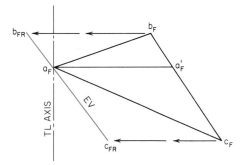

Figure 24
Edge view by revolution.

12. TRUE SURFACE OF A PLANE

If we can find the true surface of a plane, much information about the plane can be revealed. We can, for example, calculate the area of the plane, measure the angle between lines of the plane, and find the shortest distance from a point to a line in the plane. These examples all see practical use in everyday design and construction.

How can we recognize a *true surface* (TS) of a plane? In Fig. 25 the plane is TS in the *H* view because the line of sight for the *H* view is *perpendicular* to the *edge view* seen in the *F* view. Therefore, *a plane is seen as true surface when an edge view of the plane is viewed perpendicularly*.

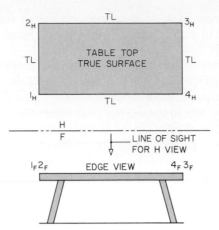

Figure 25
True surface seen in given views.

Note that our discussion of true lengths, edge views, and true surfaces leads to a logical chain. This logical chain dictates the progression from one solution to the next:

> TL leads to EV leads to TS

That is, a true length enables us to obtain an edge view which allows us to obtain a true surface. This logical chain is one of the most powerful in spatial analysis. Many problems can be solved via this chain.

In Fig. 25 the plane was given as TS. What if TS is not given? First, an EV must exist before a TS can be found. Look at Figs. 26 and 27, which give the 3-D and 2-D formats of the same object. Here we see plane 1-2-3-4 given as an EV in the *H* view of Fig. 27. To create a TS, simply look perpendicularly at the EV. This is done in Fig. 27, and the resulting TS is shown for plane 1-2-3-4. Note

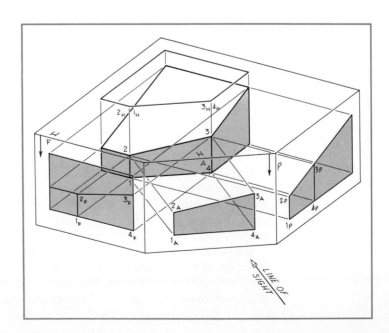

Figure 26
Pictorial showing line of sight for a true surface.

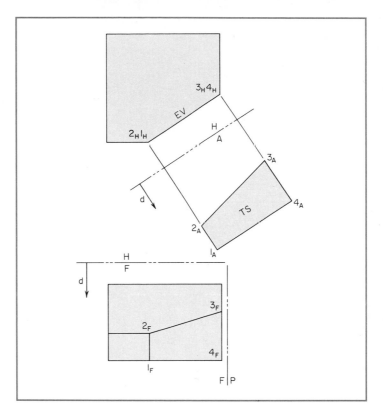

Figure 27
Orthographic solution for Fig. 26;
EV given.

that auxiliary view *A* gives a *partial* auxiliary view. Only plane 1-2-3-4 was projected into view *A*. The other planes of the object are not needed if the goal is to find the TS of plane 1-2-3-4 and nothing more.

So far we gave one example for finding the TS with the TS given (Fig. 25) and one with only the EV given (Fig. 27). Now comes the most general case for finding TS: No TS is given, and no EV is given. How can a TS be found if no EV is given? The process is direct: First find an EV. Recall the logical chain above: TL leads to EV leads to TS.

See Fig. 28. This is Fig. 23 but taken one step farther. The EV of plane 1-2-3 has been viewed perpendicularly to obtain a TS. Second auxiliary view *B* is attached 90° in space to first auxiliary view *A*. The transfer distances needed in view *B* are found in view *H*, since the arrows in views *B* and *H* both point perpendicularly away from the same plane, plane *A*. Notice that the slope angle θ_H is available in view *A*. Also in the TS we can measure angles between any lines of plane *ABC*. Therefore, *to measure the angle between any two lines, obtain a TS of the plane described by the two lines.*

True surface may be found by using revolution as well. Let us find the TS of plane *ABC* in Fig. 24. Recall that in Fig. 24 an EV had been found by revolution. We *could* revolve the EV in the *F* view until it was parallel to the *H* view. The plane in the *H* view will then be TS. However, the total drawing will become cluttered with the many lines on top of one another.

Instead, let us use revolution, as in Fig. 29. An EV is made after the addition of TL line *CC'* in the *F* view. The EV is swung parallel to the *F* view, forcing the plane to become TS in the *F* view. Note that point *A*, being on the axis, does not move, but points *B* and *C* move perpendicularly to the axis.

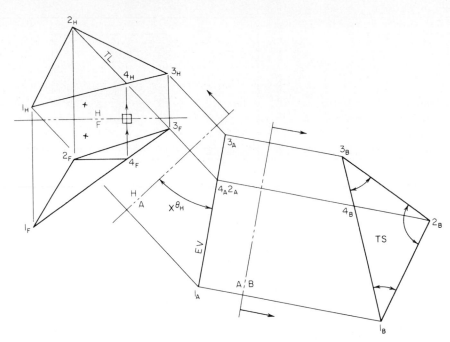

Figure 28
Finding true surface; EV not given.

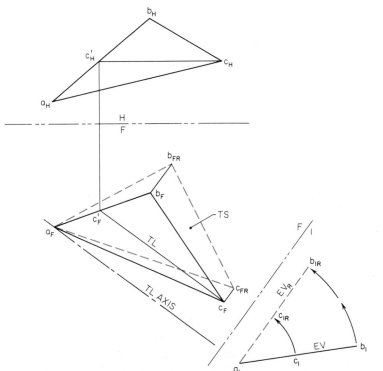

Figure 29
True surface by revolution.

You may notice that the method of revolution has the feature of saving *one* view compared to the method of auxiliary views. Plane *ABC* of Fig. 29 would require two auxiliary views if it were done by the auxiliary-view method, as in Fig. 28. Only one auxiliary view was needed by using revolution. In solving spatial problems we must decide which method is preferred. With auxiliary views we must move the line of sight to new positions to obtain the desired solution. In revolution, we move the object, not the line of sight. Since CAD software is often good at rotating objects, consider seriously the use of revolution when you are using CAD.

The concepts discussed have been applied to simple planes such as triangles, but can be used as well for shapes on actual parts. A basic example is seen in Fig. 30. For a vertical tab, the true shape is seen in an auxiliary view adjacent to the horizontal view. This is only one example of many.

In this chapter we discussed a number of basic conditions for lines and planes. In each case the strategy has been to see what condition would allow us to see the solution desired. Then a process to find the solution was developed. In Chap. 12 we continue to examine basic interactions among lines, planes, and solids.

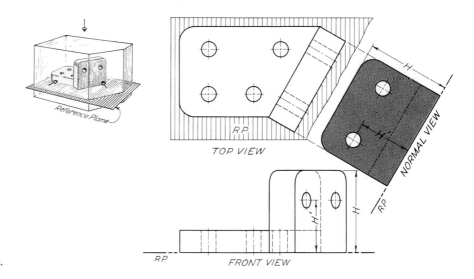

Figure 30
True surface found for an actual part.

PROBLEMS

1 to 3. Draw given views and add normal views to the inclined surface.

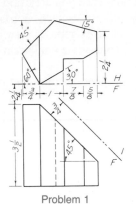

Problem 1

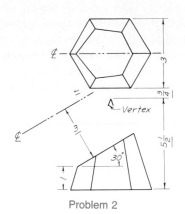

Problem 2

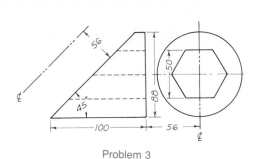

Problem 3

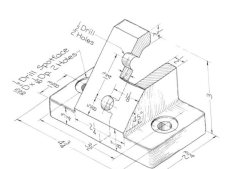

Problem 4

4. Draw the front view, partial top view, and normal view of the inclined surface.

5. Draw the views and partial views that best describe the part.

6. Draw top and front views and a normal view of the inclined face. Will the normal view of the inclined face show the true cross section of the square hole?

Problem 5

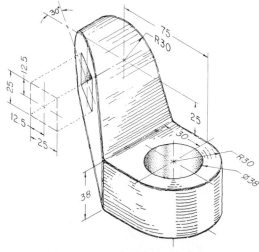

Problem 6

7. Draw the views given, using edge and normal views to obtain the shape of the lugs.

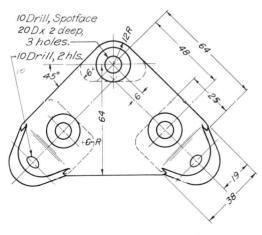

10 Drill, Spotface
20 Dx 2 deep,
3 holes.

10 Drill, 2 hls.

45°

12 R

64

48

25

6

64

6 R

19

38

Problem 7

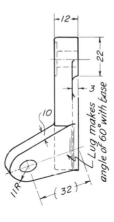

12

22

3

10

1 R

Lug makes
angle of 60° with base

(32)

8. By use of an auxiliary view projected from the top view, find the true length of *AB*. Scale: $1'' = 1'\text{-}0''$.

9. Line *CL* slopes upward from *C* with a 60 percent grade. Draw the front view of *CL*. Find the distance from *C* to *L*. Scale: $1'' = 50'$.

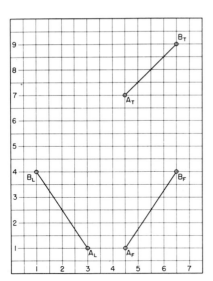

B_T

A_T

B_L

B_F

A_L A_F

Problem 8

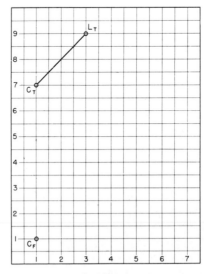

L_T

C_T

C_F

Problem 9

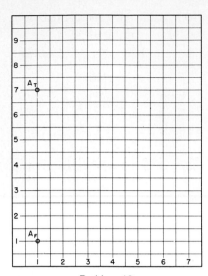

Problem 10

10. Line *AB* is to be established with a bearing of N60°E with a 60 percent positive grade from *A*. The distance from *A* to *B* is 336 ft. Draw the top and front views of *AB*. Scale: 1″ = 100′.

11. Using the layout of Prob. 8, show the end view of *AB* by projecting from a first auxiliary view projected from the top view. Identify all reference planes, and label all points.

12. Show the edge view of *RSP* by projecting parallel to a horizontal line of *RSP*.

13. Using the layout of Prob. 12, draw the normal view of *RSP* by projecting from an edge view of *RSP* projected from the top view. Label all points, and identify the reference planes used.

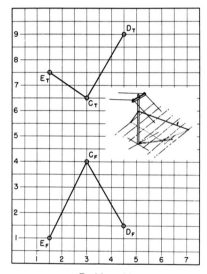

Problem 11

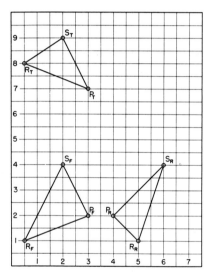

Problem 12

C H A P T E R 12

SPATIAL ANALYSIS: INTERACTION OF LINES, PLANES, AND SOLIDS

■ 1. INTRODUCTION

Chapter 11 dealt with information that can be learned about *individual* lines and planes. Now we study the *interaction* or combination of lines, planes, and solids. All applications are reasonably basic and practical to the needs of drafters and designers. The concepts shown apply equally well to CAD work and manually done solutions.

■ 2. LINES: TEST FOR PARALLELISM

It is helpful to be able to recognize when lines are parallel. We might say that if two lines are parallel in two adjacent views, they are truly parallel. This logic is correct if the two lines are oblique lines, as in Fig. 1. Lines *AB* and *CD* appear parallel in both the *H* view and the *F* view. Indeed, the lines are parallel. We can state that *parallel lines appear parallel in all views*.

However, principal lines, such as profile lines *AB* and *CD* in Fig. 2, *may* appear parallel in the *F* and *H* views but not really be parallel. A check in the *P* view shows that the lines are not actually parallel. Therefore, principal lines may need to be checked in all three principal views: *F, H,* and *P*.

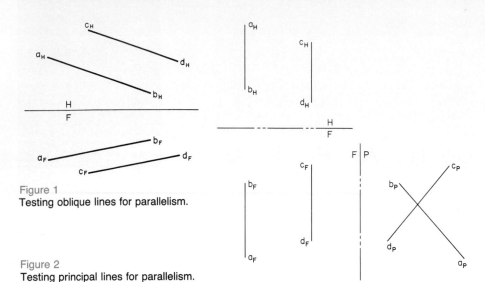

Figure 1
Testing oblique lines for parallelism.

Figure 2
Testing principal lines for parallelism.

■ 3. LINES: TEST FOR PERPENDICULARITY

Two lines are perpendicular if there is a 90° angle between them when at least one line is true length. Let us show this concept in an illustration, Fig. 3. In case A, *both* lines appear true length, *and* a 90° angle exists between them. The lines are definitely perpendicular. In case B, only line *GH* is TL, but a 90° angle still exists between them. The lines are still perpendicular. In case C, however, neither line is TL, and no 90° angle exists. Are the lines perpendicular? We do not know until we construct an auxiliary view that shows one of the lines TL. *If* a 90° angle exists between the lines in the auxiliary view, then the lines are perpendicular. If no 90° angle exists, the lines are not perpendicular. As a further comment, in a view of two lines in which no line is TL *and* a 90° angle exists in that view, the lines are *not* perpendicular.

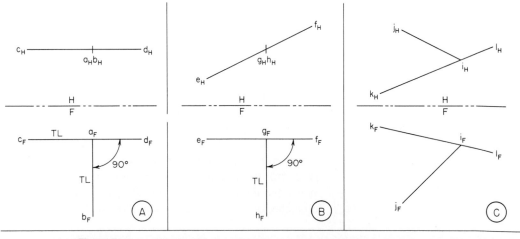

Figure 3
Testing lines for perpendicularity.

4. LINES: TEST FOR INTERSECTION

Often we want to know whether two lines actually intersect each other. The test is direct: *The point of intersection of two lines must stay aligned in all views.* Note the two cases in Fig. 4. In case A, the intersection point is aligned (has the same projector) from one view to the next. Lines *AB* and *CD* definitely intersect in case A. In case B, there is no alignment of the supposed intersection point between the views. The lines do not intersect.

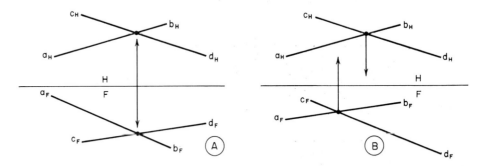

Figure 4
Testing lines for intersection.

5. A LINE IN A PLANE

It is not difficult to transfer a line in a plane to another view. In Fig. 5 the *H* view is given with line *AB* to be in plane 1-2-3-4. If line *AB* is to remain in the plane in the *F* view, the intersection of line *AB* in the *H* view with lines 1-2 and 3-4 must *align* with corresponding intersections in the *F* view. Therefore, the intersection points of line *AB* in plane 1-2-3-4 are projected into the *F* view, as seen. The direction of line *AB* is now set in the *F* view, and endpoints *A* and *B* are projected into the *F* view. This process works for any two adjacent views. In summary, *a line is in a plane if intersection points of the line with the plane are in alignment between any two views.*

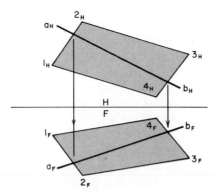

Figure 5
Line on plane.

6. A LINE PARALLEL TO A PLANE

We may wish to construct a line parallel to a plane. *A line is parallel to a plane if the line remains parallel to a corresponding line of the plane in all views.* This concept is illustrated in Fig. 6 where line 1-2 in the *H* view is to be parallel to plane *ABC*. First, a line *BD* parallel to line 1-2 is added to the plane in the *H* view. Line *BD* is projected into the plane in the *F* view. Second, line 1-2 is forced to be parallel to *BD* in the *F* view. Line 1-2 is now parallel to the plane.

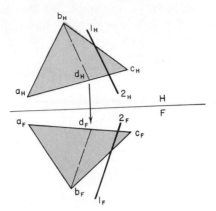

Figure 6
Line parallel to a plane.

7. A LINE PERPENDICULAR TO A PLANE

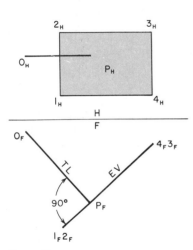

Figure 7
Conditions needed for a line to be perpendicular to a plane.

It is very useful to know how to make a line perpendicular to a plane. This basic construction has many uses in design, such as finding the shortest distance from a point to a plane. The proof that a line is perpendicular to a plane is given in Fig. 7. We see here that *a line is perpendicular to a plane when the line is true length at a 90° angle to an edge view of the plane*. The line beginning at point *O* intersects plane 1-2-3-4 at point *P*. We could measure the TL of line *OP* in the *F* view. We know that line *OP* is TL in the *F* view because *OP* is parallel to the *F* view, as seen in the *H* view. Line *OP* is a frontal line. The length of *OP* in the *F* view is actually the shortest distance from point *O* to the plane.

If we do not have an edge view of a plane, we construct an EV and then add a line perpendicular to the plane. This is the case in Fig. 8. The *F* and *H* views of plane 1-2-3-4 and point *O* are given. A line is to be constructed from *O* perpendicular to the plane. First, we create an EV of the plane in auxiliary view *A*, using the same process as in Chap. 11. Point *O* is transferred into view *A* in the same manner as points 1, 2, 3, and 4. We simply transfer the distances perpendicularly from plane *H* in the *F* view into view *A*. Note the directions of the arrows. With the EV of plane 1-2-3-4 and point *O* located in view *A*, a perpendicular can be extended from point *O* to the EV of the plane. Line *OP* is called TL in view *A* because it *must* be TL if line *OP* is to be perpendicular to the plane.

Point *P* is sent back into the *H* view along its projector. The position of point *P* on its projector in the *H* view is known to be on a line *parallel* to the H/A fold line. Why? Line *OP* was called TL in view *A*. Therefore, line *OP* must be made parallel to the H/A fold line in view *H*, or it could never be TL in view *A*. Point *P* is found in the *F* view by projecting it from the *H* view and transferring distance *d* from view *A* into the *F* view along its projector.

The solution is complete, except for one important detail. We need to know the *visibility* of line *OP* in the *F* and *H* views. That is, is line *OP* hidden or visible as it passes by the plane in each view? Visibility is of no concern in view *A*, but it

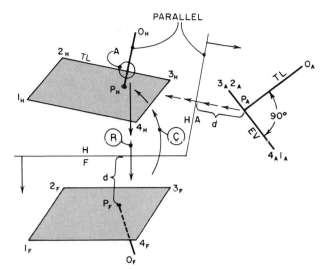

Figure 8
Constructing an edge view to permit perpendicular from point to plane.

certainly is in the *F* and *H* views. Visibility can be found for any problem by the same direct process:

1. Choose a position in one view where the line and a line of the plane cross. Let us begin in the *H* view at position *A* where *OP* crosses line 2-3.

2. Travel along projector *B* into an adjacent view to see which of the two lines is seen *first*. That line will be visible in the view in which we start. Here we see that line 2-3 is seen first; line *OP*, second. Line *OP* is therefore hidden in the *H* view.

A closed loop exists. We start at position *A*, travel along projector *B* for the check of visibility, and return *C* to the view in which we started. Consider an amusing analogy. A person up in a tree at position *A* drops an apple. The apple falls into the *F* view along path *B*. Someone in the front view cries out that the apple has landed on line 2-3. The message is relayed back (path *C*) to the person in the tree, who now knows that line 2-3 is above line *OP*, making *OP* hidden in the top view.

A similar process can give visibility in the *F* view. In the *F* view, shoot an arrow at the position where line *OP* seems to cross line 1-4 of the plane. A person in the *H* view could see the arrow hit line 1-4. Therefore, line *OP* is behind line 1-4 of the plane, making *OP* hidden in the front view. Note that the visibility of a line relative to a plane must be checked independently for each view. The visibility of a line in one view does *not* indicate visibility in another view.

8. ANGLES OF LINES WITH PLANES

It is useful to know the angle at which lines are attached to planes. This situation arises in all areas of design: a strut to an aircraft panel, support wires for an outdoor antenna, a fuel line through a bulkhead. In all cases, the same concept holds: *The true angle between a line and a plane shows in the view where the plane is an edge view and the line is true length.*

We saw a special case of this situation in Sec. 7 when a line made a 90° angle with a plane. The plane was EV, and the line was TL. What can we do to ensure EV and TL in the same view for *any* line and *any* plane? Quite simply, we need to make sure that both an EV of the plane and a TL of the line occur in the same view. We discuss the case for the angle of a line with the principal planes (*H, F, P*) and with an oblique plane.

a. Angle between a Line and the Principal Planes

A designer may need to know the angle that a line makes with one or more principal planes *H, F,* and *P*. We already know how to find the angle between a line and the horizontal plane, since this is the slope angle discussed earlier. The angle with the frontal and profile planes might also be needed. Figure 9 shows the method of finding the angle between a line and *any* principal plane. We see that the proper angle shows when *the line is true length in a view showing the edge view of the desired plane.*

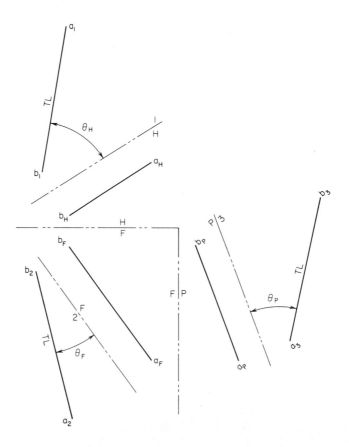

Figure 9
Angles between a line and the
principal planes using auxiliary views.

The angle between line *AB* and the *H* plane is seen in view 1 adjacent to the *H* view, because the *H* view is EV in view 1. Similarly, the angle between line *AB* and the *F* plane is adjacent to the *F* view in view 2. The angle between the line and the *P* view is seen in view 3 where the *P* plane is an EV.

We may also use the revolution technique to find the angles between a line and the principal planes. This method was used before to find the slope angle (see Fig. 9 of Chap. 11). The method is shown again in Fig. 10, which uses the same line *AB* as in Fig. 9. In all three cases of Fig. 10, the axis of revolution is *perpendicular* to the plane with which the angle is to be found. In case A the axis is perpendicular to the *H* plane. This ensures that the angle that the line makes with plane *H* will not change during revolution. Similarly, the axis is perpendicular to plane *F* in case B and is perpendicular to plane *P* in case C. Notice in case C that a profile view of the line had to be made first, so that the axis could be a point view, a condition needed to swing the line. Some people may like to use revolution because auxiliary views as used in Fig. 9 are not needed.

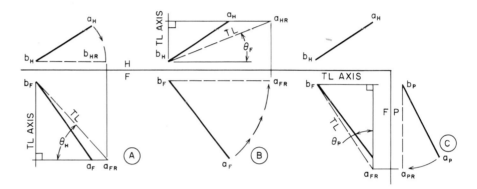

Figure 10
Angles between a line and the principal planes using revolution.

b. Angle between a Line and a Nonprincipal Plane

If a given plane is *not* a principal plane, how can we find the angle between that plane and a given line? The concept is the same as before: *The line must be true length in a view in which the plane is an edge view.*

Figure 11 shows an inclined plane 1-2-3-4 as an edge view in general view A. In case A, line *RS* is true length, so the true angle is available. In case B, the line is *not* TL, so the true angle is *not* available.

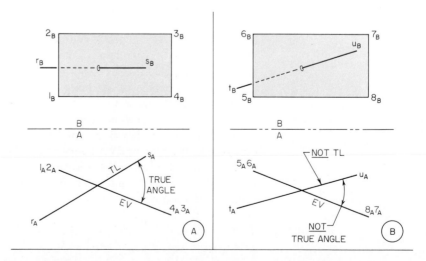

Figure 11
Conditions needed to find the angle between a line and a plane.

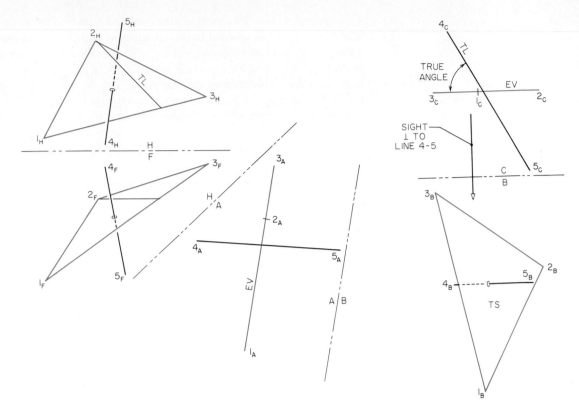

Figure 12
Angle between an oblique line and an oblique plane.

An oblique plane and an oblique line are shown in Fig. 12. This represents the most general case possible. However, the method of finding the angle between the line and the plane remains the same: The line must be seen TL in a view having the plane as an EV. How can *two* items (TL and EV) occur simultaneously? This can happen if *one* of the items occurs automatically.

We can get an automatic EV if a view is taken adjacent to a true surface (TS) of the plane. Or we can get an automatic TL if we take a view adjacent to a point view of the line. If one item is automatic, we can get the other item by using a proper line of sight.

Here is an example of obtaining an automatic EV, as seen in Fig. 12. Plane 1-2-3 is made TS, as in Chap. 11. A TL line was added to the plane in the *H* view, leading to an EV in view *A*. Then the EV was viewed perpendicularly, leading to the TS in view *B*. Line 4-5 is carried along into views *A* and *B*. In view *C* the plane becomes an EV automatically. The line of sight for view *C* is perpendicular to line 4-5, forcing 4-5 to be TL in view *C*. The true angle between the EV and TL can now be measured. Note the use of visibility between the line and plane in the various views.

■ 9. ANGLES BETWEEN PLANES

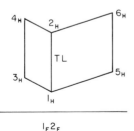

Figure 13
Angle between planes with edge views given.

To build a number of products, the angle between planes is needed. The angles between the planes of a roof and ducts of an air conditioning system are two examples. The concept of finding the angle between planes is shown in Fig. 13. Here we see that *the angle between two planes is seen when both planes appear as edge views in the same view.*

How can we force both planes to be edge views in the same view? We already know that when a line in a plane becomes a point view, that plane becomes an EV. Therefore, if the line common to two planes, the *line of intersection,* is made a point view, then both planes become EVs simultaneously. In Fig. 13 the line of intersection, line 1-2, is given as a point view in the *F* view. Therefore planes 1-2-3-4 and 1-2-5-6 are both EVs in the *F* view.

In Fig. 14 the line of intersection, line *AB,* is not given in point view in either the *F* or the *H* view. However, line *AB is* true length in the *F* view. Line *AB* is made a point view in auxiliary view 1, causing both planes to be EVs. The angle between them can now be measured.

Revolution could have been used in Fig. 14 also. We would revolve line *AB* in the *F* view until it was perpendicular to plane *H* (making *AB* vertical). Then line *AB* would be a point view in the *H* view, and the EVs of both planes would be seen in the *H* view.

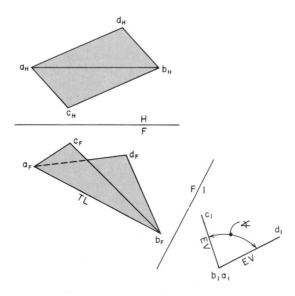

Figure 14
Angle between planes with line of intersection given true length.

If the line of intersection is *not* given TL in a given view, it must be made TL before the EVs of the planes can be found. This most general case is seen in Fig. 15. Neither the given *F* view nor the given *H* view shows the line of intersection *AB* as TL. Therefore, auxiliary view 1, attached to the *H* view, is constructed to force line *AB* to be TL. The line of sight has been made perpendicular to *AB,* to cause the TL to occur in view 1. In auxiliary view 2, line *AB* appears as a point view because the line of sight for view 2 was parallel to the TL of line *AB* in view 1. The angle between the planes can now be measured in view 2.

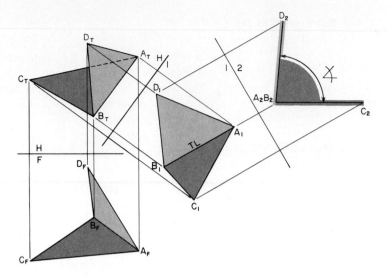

Figure 15
Angle between planes with line of intersection not given true length.

■ 10. SHORTEST DISTANCE FROM A POINT TO A LINE

This use of spatial analysis has practical applications. If, for example, we want to hook up a waterline from a point in a house to the water main, how can we find the shortest distance? The shortest distance saves material costs, all other things being equal.

Figure 16 illustrates the concept that *the shortest distance from a point to a line is a perpendicular from the point to the line.* The shortest distance shows *true length* when the original line is a *point view.* In case A of Fig. 16, the point view of line 1-2 is given in the *F* view, so the shortest distance *OP* is seen TL. Note that since *OP* is to be TL in the *F* view, line *OP* must be made *parallel* to the *F* view, as seen in the *H* view.

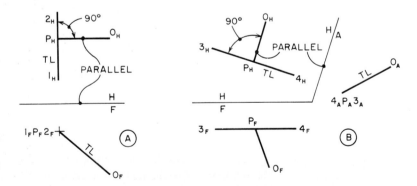

Figure 16
Concept of the shortest distance from a point to a line.

Also when line 1-2 is TL, a 90° angle exists between the line and the constructed shortest distance. This condition satisfies the test for perpendicularity. That is, if one or more lines are seen TL in a view having a 90° angle between the lines, the lines are perpendicular. In case A the 90° angle shows in the *H* view.

Case B of Fig. 16 also needs a point view of the given line 3-4 to see the TL of the shortest distance. Auxiliary view A provides this condition. In the H view, point P must lie along a line from O *parallel* to the H/A fold line if OP is to be TL in view A. Once point P has been found in the H view, it is simply dropped into the F view onto line 3-4. Note the 90° angle in the H view, because line 3-4 is TL. However, in the F view neither line 3-4 nor line OP is TL. Therefore, a 90° angle is *not* seen.

Let us assume that the given line is *not* TL in a principal view. How, then, can we find the shortest distance from a point to that line? Again, the shortest distance is seen as TL when the given line is made a point view. Therefore, the given line must first be made TL. Figure 17 shows the process for this general case. In view 1, line AB is made TL. In view 2, line AB is made a point view. Transfer distances into view 2 are taken from view H, shown by the arrows going perpendicularly away from plane 1. In view 2, the TL of the shortest connector OP is seen. Then line OP is returned to the other views. Again, line OP in view 1 is made parallel to the 1/2 fold line so that OP can be TL in view 2.

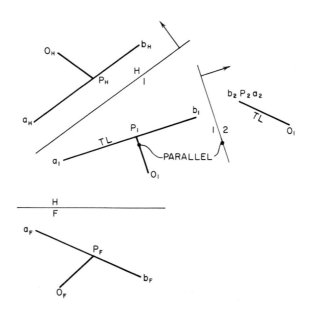

Figure 17
Shortest distance from a point to an oblique line.

■ 11. POINT REVOLVED ABOUT AN AXIS

There is a close relationship between Fig. 17 and Fig. 18. A point may be revolved around an axis when the axis is a point view. In Fig. 18 point O is revolved 90° clockwise about axis RS. The path of revolution for point O is as always perpendicular to the axis. Therefore when the axis is TL, as in view 1, the path of point O is at 90° to the axis.

If it is revolved 360°, the path of point O becomes a true-surface circle in view 2 and an edge view in view 1. In views H and F the path will be elliptical. Analyses

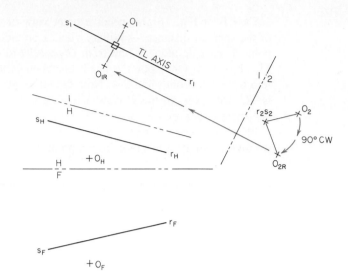

Figure 18
Revolution of a point about an axis.

such as seen in Fig. 18 are useful when you run into problems concerning appropriate clearances, such as the revolving motion of a valve handle in a piping installation.

12. SHORTEST DISTANCE FROM A POINT TO A PLANE

The shortest distance from a point to a plane is a *perpendicular connector*. This idea was discussed in Sec. 7 (see Figs. 7 and 8) and is repeated here for the sake of completeness concerning shortest distances. Reread Sec. 7 if you have a question about the procedure.

13. SHORTEST DISTANCE FROM A LINE TO A LINE

In design work we may need the shortest connector between two lines which are not parallel and do not intersect. Such lines are called *skew lines* (see Fig. 19). We note that *the shortest connector between two skew lines is the connector perpendicular to each line*. This connector shows TL when one of the original lines is seen as a point view. In Fig. 19, line 1-2 is already a point view in the *F* view. Therefore, the shortest connector *OP* is made TL in the *F* view and is connected perpendicularly to line 3-4. Line *OP* is found in the *H* view by projecting point *P* onto line 3-4 and then running it parallel to the *H/F* fold line until it intersects line 1-2 at *O*.

The concept is continued into Fig. 20, which shows the general case. A point view of either line *AB* or *CD* is needed. Line *AB* arbitrarily was made TL and then a point view. Line *CD* was carried along from view to view. In view 2 the shortest distance *OP* is added as a TL connector from line *AB* to line *CD* at a 90° angle to *CD*. Connector line *OP* is then projected back through the various views. Again line *OP* in view 1 is parallel to the 1/2 fold line to force the TL of *OP* in view 2. Line *OP* will also make a 90° angle with TL line *AB* in view 1.

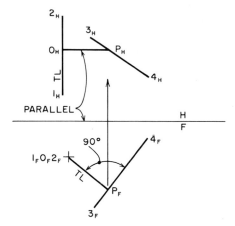

Figure 19
Concept of shortest distance between
skew lines.

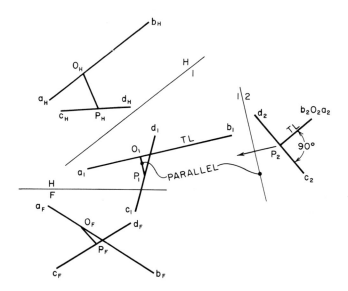

Figure 20
Shortest distance between oblique
skew lines.

14. INTERSECTIONS: AN OVERVIEW

An intersection is the coming together of two design elements. We are all familiar
with the term *intersection,* as in the intersection of two streets at a corner. In design
work, there are various forms of intersections. Some forms are common, such as
a line intersecting a plane or a wire attached to a wall. Some intersections are rare
and exotic, such as a cone wrapping around a pyramid, and do not merit attention
in our study. The particular basic intersections to be discussed are listed below.
Understanding how they are found will help anyone involved with design and
drafting.

- Line and line
- Line and plane

■ Line and solid

■ Plane and plane

■ Plane and solid

■ Solid and solid

■ 15. INTERSECTION: LINE AND LINE

Clearly lines do not necessarily intersect. Parallel lines, for example, never intersect. Skew lines, discussed in Sec. 13, never intersect because they are *defined* to be nonparallel and nonintersecting.

We did test for intersecting lines, however. Refer to Fig. 4. Recall that lines intersect only if the point of intersection remains in alignment between any two adjacent views, as in case A of Fig. 4. Nonintersection is seen in case B.

■ 16. INTERSECTION: LINE AND PLANE

There are two good methods for finding the intersection of a line and a plane: the edge-view method and the cutting-plane (CP) method.

a. Edge-View Method

This method is visibly obvious because when a plane is an EV, the point where a line contacts or passes through the plane is very apparent. Look at Fig. 21 in which an EV of plane 1-2-3 has been found in the usual manner. Line 4-5 is carried into view *A* and passes through the plane. The intersection point is readily seen, is projected back into the *H* view onto line 4-5, and is then dropped into the *F* view. Note that line 4-5 did *not* have to be true length in view *A*. Line 4-5 would need to be TL only if the angle between line and plane were desired (Fig. 12).

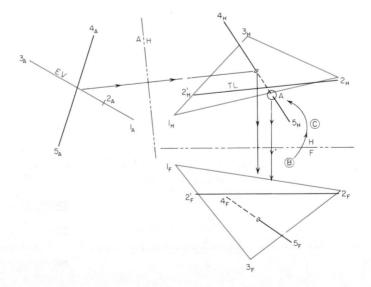

Figure 21
Intersection of line and plane: edge-view method.

Visibility is found as in Fig. 8. Visibility is checked at position *A* in the *H* view of Fig. 21. Which of lines 1-2 and 4-5 is seen first? Noting where lines 1-2 and 4-5 cross, travel along projector *B* into the *F* view. Line 1-2 is seen first and line 4-5 second. Therefore, return to the *H* view (step c) and make line 4-5 hidden. In the *F* view, check where lines 2-3 and 4-5 cross. In the *H* view, line 4-5 is first, making line 4-5 visible in the *F* view. Always use a closed loop: Start in a chosen view, check which of the two lines is seen first in an adjacent view, and return to the view in which you start to apply visibility.

b. Cutting-Plane Method

This method is powerful and efficient. No edge view is needed. We can use the existing views only. Look at Fig. 22, which is the same problem as in Fig. 21. There are three distinct steps for this method.

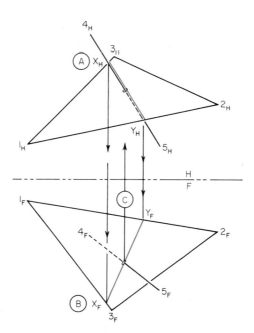

Figure 22
Intersection of line and plane: cutting-plane method.

Step 1. Pick a view in which to begin. Here view *H* is selected. View *F* could have been used just as well. We realize that if line 4-5 is to hit plane 1-2-3, the intersection must occur somewhere along a path across the plane starting at point *X* on line 1-3 and ending at point *Y* on line 1-2. Therefore, we add or "cut" line *XY* across the plane. Our logic is that when line 4-5 hits line *XY*, line 4-5 has intersected the plane.

Step 2. Line *XY* is projected into the *F* view, as shown by the arrows. Be sure to place point *X* on line 1-3 and point *Y* on line 1-2. Line *XY* now exists in the *F* view. We see that line 4-5 does indeed cross, or intersect, line *XY*. The intersection of line 4-5 with the plane has been found.

Step 3. The intersection point is returned to the *H* view and placed on line 4-5. The problem is finished. Only visibility remains to be found, and it is done exactly as for the EV method of Fig. 21.

17. INTERSECTION: LINE AND SOLID

Many examples could be offered in the category of an intersection of a line and a solid. Solids could be prisms, pyramids, cylinders, cones, or spheres. All solutions are variations on the same theme. We choose only one: the intersection of a line and a pyramid, as in Fig. 23.

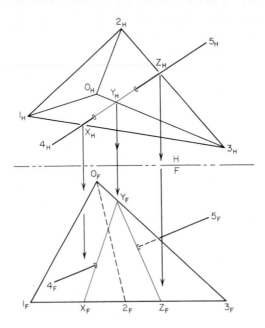

Figure 23
Intersection of line and plane: cutting-plane method.

We could use either the edge-view method or the cutting-plane method. The EV method, however, would be tedious. An auxiliary view would be needed to make an EV of each plane selected for a possible intersection with the line. No one wants all that work. Therefore, the cutting-plane method is much preferred. The process used in Fig. 22 is merely extended.

In Fig. 23 we realize that line 4-5 will intersect the pyramid in *two* places (although in theory line 4-5 could just graze an edge of the pyramid at one spot). We should be on the lookout for two intersection points. The line must intersect the pyramid somewhere along the path from *X* to *Y* to *Z*, as seen in the *H* view. We "cut" a path *XYZ* around the pyramid and project points *X*, *Y*, and *Z* into the *F* view (see arrows). We are careful to keep points *X*, *Y*, and *Z* on the *same* respective lines as in the *H* view. Line 4-5 does intersect triangular path *XYZ* as seen in the *F* view. The two points of intersection are returned to the *H* view. Visibility is determined, completing the problem.

18. INTERSECTION: PLANE AND PLANE

A plane intersects a plane along a *line*. In everyday life we see examples of the intersection of planes, such as two roof planes intersecting or the intersection of one plane of a heating duct with another. As in other cases discussed, two methods can be employed to find intersections: the edge-view method and the cutting-plane method.

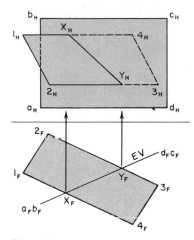

Figure 24
Intersection of two planes: one plane
given EV.

a. Edge-View Method

We want to find one of the two planes in edge view. Then the one plane can be seen to pass through the other plane. Figure 24 shows the case where one of the planes, *ABCD*, is *given* as an EV in the *F* view. Clearly in the *F* view the line of intersection is line *XY*. Line *XY* is then projected into the *H* view, and visibility is found.

A line of intersection between two planes is *always* visible, making line *XY* visible. Note also that the *F* view shows line 1-2 to be *above* plane *ABCD*, making line *AB* hidden underneath plane 1-2-3-4 in the *H* view. Also in the *F* view line 3-4 is *below* plane *ABCD*, making line 3-4 hidden in the *H* view.

The EV of a plane is *not* given in the *F* or *H* view of Fig. 25. Therefore an EV of one of the planes is made, and the other plane is carried into auxiliary view *A*. Either plane 1-2-3-4 or plane 5-6-7 could have been made an EV. Plane 1-2-3-4 was arbitrarily chosen to be made an EV. Line 4-4' was added so as to be TL in the *H* view, allowing the EV to occur in view *A*. In view *A* the line of intersection is available and is projected back into the *H* view, as the arrows show. The line of intersection is then projected down into the *F* view. Finding visibility completes the problem.

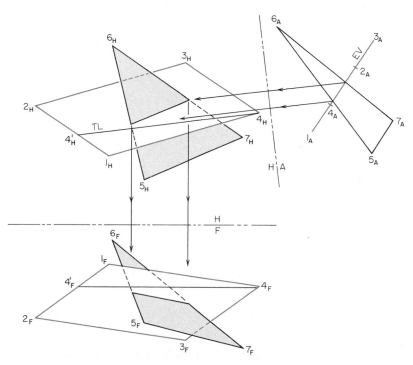

Figure 25
Intersection of two planes: EV method
with no EVs given.

b. Cutting-Plane Method

The problem just solved in Fig. 25 is reworked in Fig. 26 by using the cutting-plane method. A line of intersection has two endpoints. Therefore the intersection of two lines is needed, but which two lines? As we study Fig. 26, we see several lines that might intersect a plane: lines 1-4, 5-6, and 6-7. All other lines do *not* cross a plane in at least one view.

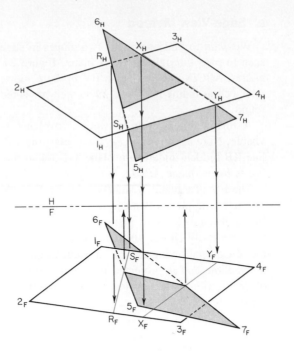

Figure 26
Intersection of two planes: cutting-plane method.

Two of lines 1-4, 5-6, and 6-7 actually intersect a plane. We do not know initially which two, but fear not. If the CP method yields no intersection for one line, we try another line. Success is found with lines 5-6 and 6-7. A cut *RS* is placed along line 5-6 in the *H* view. Also cut *XY* is placed along line 6-7 in the *H* view. Projection of cuts *RS* and *XY* into the *F* view, as shown by the arrows, gives the intersection of lines 5-6 and 6-7 with plane 1-2-3-4. Then we find visibility. The power of the CP method is evident, but we must use care in the projection of cutting lines.

19. INTERSECTION: PLANE AND SOLID

Things become more complex with the intersections of planes and solids. However, the two cases discussed are rather basic yet useful: the intersections of a plane with a prism and of a plane with a cone. Other more specialized cases are explored in texts about descriptive geometry.

a. Intersection of a Plane and a Prism

A typical example is seen in Fig. 27. A vertical prism with parallel edges intersects an oblique plane. We could solve the problem by the edge-view method, the cutting-plane method, *or* a combination of the two.

To use an auxiliary view to make an EV of plane 1-2-3-4 would be a waste of time. We would like to use the existing *F* and *H* views. Edge views are used where possible, then cutting planes are used.

A distinct procedure is recommended.

Step 1. Count the expected number of intersection points. In the *H* view lines 1-4 and 2-3 hit the edge views of the prism, giving a total of four intersection

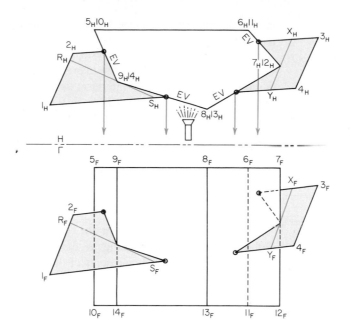

Figure 27
Intersection of a plane and a solid.

points. Also lines 9-14 and 7-12 must cross plane 1-2-3-4 somewhere since these two vertical lines lie within the boundary of plane 1-2-3-4. Lines 9-14 and 7-12 each have one intersection point, raising the total to six intersection points.

Step 2. Find all intersection points. We are fortunate to have vertical edge views of the prism. Lines 2-3 and 1-4 intersect, as shown by the small circles. We drop four points of intersection onto the respective lines in the *F* view, shown by the arrows. We are careful to project any intersection point onto the proper line. All points which can be located by the edge-view method have been found.

We must locate the remaining points, one on line 9-14 and one on line 7-12, by the cutting-plane method. Any cuts passing through the point views of lines 9-14 and 7-12 in the *H* view may be used. We choose cut *RS* for line 9-14 and cut *XY* for line 7-12. Projection of the cuts into the *F* view gives the needed intersection points.

Step 3. Join the intersection points. Planes intersect planes with lines. In Fig. 27 there is no continuous single path of intersection, but there are two paths. One is on the left-hand side of the prism; the other, on the right-hand side.

The left-hand path goes from the intersection point on *line 2-3* to the point on *line 9-14* to the point on *line 1-4*. These three points are joined in the *F* view. The right-hand path goes from the intersection point on *line 2-3* to the point on *line 7-12* to the point on *line 1-4*. The points are connected in the *F* view.

Step 4. Find the visibility. A helpful way to find the visibility of a plane intersecting a solid is to turn on a "flashlight." The view requiring visibility is the *F* view. Therefore the light is shown on the prism, as seen in the *H* view. Planes of the prism lighted by the flashlight are visible in the *F* view. Thus all lines of intersection on the left side of the prism are visible. However, plane 6-7-11-12 on the right side of the prism is in darkness, making the line of intersection from line 2-3 to line 7-12 hidden. The line of intersection from line 7-12 to line 3-4 is visible

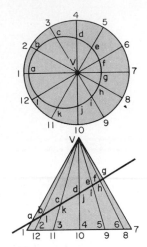

Figure 28
Intersection of a plane and a cone:
EV given.

in the *F* view because plane 8-7-12-13 is in light. The visibility of the lines of intersection is now known.

Yet remaining is the visibility of lines of the plane and prism. Our flashlight will help again. Line 1-4 of the plane is out front, lighted. It is therefore visible in the *F* view. Any lines of the prism *behind* line 1-4 will be hidden in the *F* view. From the *H* view we see that lines 5-10, 9-14, 7-12, and 6-11 are all behind line 1-4. Therefore in the *F* view all four lines are *hidden* as they cross line 1-4. This observation allows us to conclude visibility for the entire problem.

The four steps just described work well for all problems involving the intersection of planes and solids and even of solids and solids. The steps are logical and useful.

b. Intersection of a Plane and a Cone

We will look at two cases. In one case the edge view of the plane is given, and in the other case it is not. In Fig. 28 the EV of the plane shows in the lower (front) view. We need only draw elements of the cone from the apex to the base. Twelve elements (V-1, V-2, etc.) have been selected. As each element passes through the EV, a point of intersection is found. A smooth curve, actually an ellipse, is drawn through the located points.

If the plane is *not* given as an EV, we have the case in Fig. 29. The cutting-plane method is the better method to use, as opposed to the EV method. We choose various vertical cutting planes, each passing through the apex and therefore cutting straight-line elements down the side of the cone. The typical cutting plane shown cuts lines V-2 and V-8 on the cone and line *XZ* across the plane. The intersection of *XZ* with V-2 and V-8 in the lower (front) view gives points of intersection. Repetition of this process gives sufficient points to make a smooth curve of intersection.

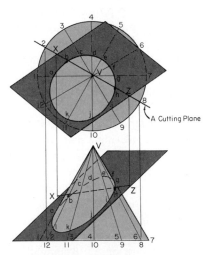

Figure 29
Intersection of a plane and a cone:
EV not given.

■ 20. INTERSECTION: SOLID AND SOLID

A large number of examples could be given for the intersection of solids. Some are practical, others are rarely used. All involve variation on the same general procedures for solution. We select several of the more common and useful types.

Rarer types of intersections can be found in texts on descriptive geometry. We discuss the following:

■ Intersection of prisms

■ Intersection of cylinders

■ Intersection of a cone and cylinder

a. Intersection of Prisms

We use Fig. 30 for this problem. The vertical four-sided prism has edges labeled *AA'*, *BB'*, *CC'*, and *DD'*. The inclined three-sided prism has edges *E*, *F*, and *G*. Actual points of intersection, when found, will be denoted by numbers (1, 2, 3, etc.). Cutting-plane cuts will be denoted by lowercase letters (*mn, op,* etc.).

The process of finding the intersection of two prisms is very similar to that for a plane and solid, described in Sec. 19. We use the same step-by-step procedure here.

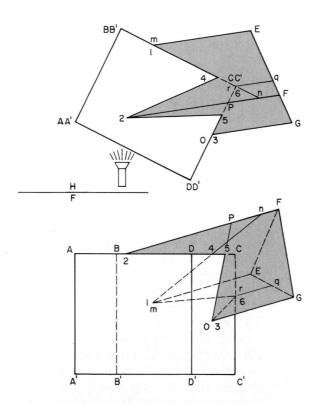

Figure 30
Intersection of two prisms.

Step 1. Count the expected number of intersection points. The three edges (*E, F, G*) of the triangular prism are all expected to hit the vertical prism. This will give three intersection points. Vertical edge *CC'* of the vertical prism should hit the triangular prism, giving one point. It is also likely that edges *BC* and *DC* of the vertical prism will hit the triangular prism, adding two more points. It seems, then, that a total of six points of intersection is expected.

Step 2. Find all intersection points. As before, we use a combination of the edge-view method and the cutting-plane method. Intersection points by the EV method are the easiest to find, so we locate them first. Line *E* of the triangular prism hits the vertical prism at point 1, as seen in the *H* view; line *F* hits at point 2, seen in the *F* view; line *G* hits at point 3, seen in the *H* view. Points 1, 2, and 3 are projected immediately into the adjacent views. Points 1, 2, 3 were rather easy to find, we are glad to say.

We must turn to the cutting-plane method to find the remaining points of intersection. Let us start off with line *BC*. Where does *BC* hit the triangular prism? Cut a line *mn* along the triangular prism in the *H* view from point *m* on line *E* to point *n* on line *F*. Project line *mn* into the *F* view. (Note that point *m* is shared with point 1.) Line *BC* does cross line *mn* at point 4. Point 4 is projected up into the *H* view.

Where does line *DC* hit the triangular prism? Cut line *OP* along the triangular prism in the *H* view from point *O* on line *G* to point *P* on line *F*. Project line *OP* into the *F* view. Line *DC* crosses line *OP* at point 5. Project point 5 into the *H* view.

Finally, where does line *CC′* hit the triangular prism? Since line *CC′* is a point view in the *H* view, the cut line running through it may go in any direction. Cut line *QR* has been selected, running parallel to edge lines *E, F,* and *G* in the *H* view. Cut line *QR* will remain parallel to lines *E, F,* and *G* in the *F* view. When so placed, line *QR* hits line *CC′* at point 6. All six intersection points have now been located.

Step 3. Join the intersection points. We realize that the intersection of any two solids is a closed *path*. We must be able to "walk around" the entire path, from one intersection point to the next. Where we start the walk does not matter. What does matter is that we can only connect two points in the *same* plane as we travel along from point to point.

Let us arbitrarily start the path at point 3 in the *F* view where line *G* hits the vertical prism. We are allowed to move upward to point 5 because points 3 and 5 are in the same plane (*CC′D′D*). At point 5, we travel on to point 2, seen clearly in the *H* view. Then we move to point 4 in the *H* view. Points 5, 2, and 4 are all in the same plane (*ABCD*).

From point 4 we travel down to point 1 and over to point 6. Points 4, 1, and 6 are all in plane *BB′C′C*. From point 6 we conclude the path of intersection by moving to point 3, the point of origin for the walk around the path.

Step 4. Find the visibility. The visibility must be found for the path of intersection and for the edges of the prisms. Let us do the path first. The visibility in the *F* view is found by turning on the flashlight seen in the *H* view. Any hidden plane will have the path of intersection hidden on its surface. Note that plane *BB′C′C* on the back side of the prism is in darkness and is therefore hidden. Point 1 on the plane is hidden. Any lines of intersection going to or from a hidden point of intersection are hidden. Therefore lines 1-4 and 1-6 are hidden in the *F* view.

Conversely, line 3-5 in the *F* view is visible because points 3 and 5 are visible. However, point 6 is hidden, because it is on line *CC′* hidden behind line *G*. Therefore line 3-6 is hidden. Visibility in the *F* view is achieved.

Visibility in the *H* view is fairly easy to find. Lines 2-4 and 2-5 are on visible plane *ABCD* and so are visible. Other lines of intersection (lines 4-1, 1-6, 6-3, and 3-5) are on edge views and cannot be seen.

The visibility of the edges of the prisms is done in the same manner as in prior sections. Line *F* is visible in the *H* view because it is the highest of all lines. Line *G* in the *F* view is visible because it is the most forward of all lines. This process allows us to complete the visibility.

b. Intersection of Two Cylinders

This case can be solved rather directly. The process is shown in Fig. 31. Curved solids intersect curved solids in a curved path of intersection. Any curve can be approximated if a sufficient number of points can be found.

Any point of intersection is on *both* cylinders, that is, is common to both. The pictorial in Fig. 31 illustrates the concept. Passing a cutting plane parallel to the axes of each cylinder cuts rectangles on each cylinder. The intersection of the rectangles defines two points for each cut. The cut shown is created by the cutting plane passing along position *B*, providing points 2 and 2' on the path of intersection. Note the arrow connecting the pictorial to the *H* view. Repeat the cutting process along other positions (*A, C, D*) until a sufficient number of points are found. Draw a smooth curve through the points in all views.

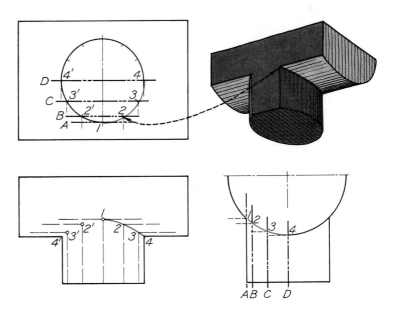

Figure 31
Intersection of two cylinders.

c. Intersection of a Cone and a Cylinder

Figure 32 shows two techniques to find the path of intersection. In case A the cutting plane is passed from the apex of the cone down across the cone to its base. For each cut a *triangle* is cut on the cone, and a *rectangle* is cut on the cylinder. The pictorial shows this effect. Each cut generates two points on the path of intersection. Join the located points with a smooth curve.

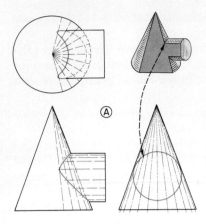

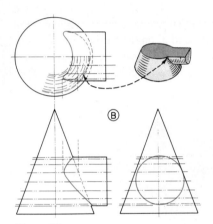

Figure 32

In case B the same problem is solved by cutting planes which are *horizontal*. Any horizontal cutting plane creates a *circle* on the cone and a *rectangle* on the cylinder. Each cut generates two points at the intersection of any particular circle and rectangle. Again, join the located points with a curve.

This concludes our study of intersections. These examples and others in the chapter should help you understand spatial analysis. You should now be able to handle most basic applications of spatial analysis as design problems arise. You can be more effective in both manual and CAD modes of problem solving. In all cases ask yourself, What do I need to find and by what process can I find it?

P R O B L E M S

1. Locate the top and front views of P, the point where line JK pierces plane EFG.

2. Line AB is the axis of a duct of irregular cross section. The duct is to be cut off in the direction determined by plane KLM. Show the top and front views of the cut. Determine the true shape of the cap that will fit this cut. (Neglect bend-overs, etc.)

3. Find the line of intersection between planes ABC and DEF. Show visibility.

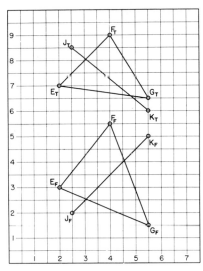

Problem 1

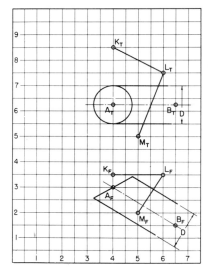

Problem 2

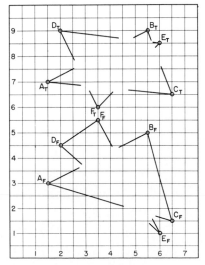

Problem 3

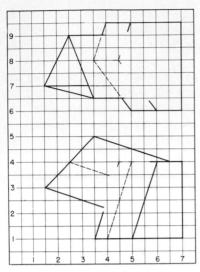

Problem 4

4. Find the line of intersection, and complete the views of the two hollow sheet-metal shapes shown. The top of the right-hand shape is enclosed.

5. Find the line of intersection, indicating visible and invisible parts and considering prisms as pipes opening into each other.

6 and 7. Find the line of intersection, indicating visible and invisible portions and considering cylinders as pipes opening into each other.

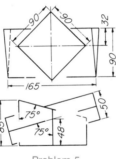

Problem 5

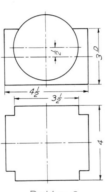

Problem 6

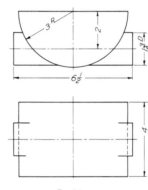

Problem 7

P A R T E

VISUAL TECHNIQUES
TO COMMUNICATE
AND ANALYZE DATA

despite their powerful ability to communicate and analyze data. Paradoxically, they are also old in the sense that most of the techniques currently used were developed in the eighteenth and nineteenth centuries.

Data may be graphically portrayed in many different ways, and this brings up two of the three most important principles of presentation graphics. First, do not distort the data. Note that data can be graphed in a misleading way inadvertently as well as intentionally. Second, select the mode of presentation which best represents the data. Third, properly identify everything on the graph, including the graph itself and the source of the data.

Style is very important in graphing, too. Two rules are suggested by Edward Tufte in his excellent book *The Visual Display of Quantitative Information*. First, integrate graphs with the main text by treating the graph as a paragraph. Try to avoid sending the reader to another page or an appendix. It is not always possible to do this. Sometimes the graph(s) will require a page or even an appendix of their own. Still, this should be an exception, and graphs should not be blown up so that a whole page is used for a small amount of data.

The second rule suggested by Tufte is that "chart junk" should be eliminated. In this category Tufte includes unnecessary decorative features such as pseudo three-dimensional effects, grid lines (in most cases), and area-filling techniques that use parallel lines which in turn produce shimmering moiré effects. A moiré effect is a watered or wavy pattern, and in this case reference is to the inability of the eye to maintain a steady image of a set of closely spaced parallel lines. Instead, the eye sees a set of lines that seem to be wavy, blurred, and in motion.

In general, Tufte argues that most of the ink should be used on a graph to represent the data and that "nondata" ink should be kept to a minimum. Of all types of chart junk, the pseudo 3-D effect is the most widely used. In some cases, it may enhance a graph somewhat. The best use is probably the pie chart where a 3-D effect may enhance viewer perception and give a more tangible sense of the proportions represented (Fig. 1).

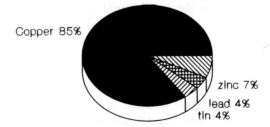

Figure 1
3-D pie chart for red brass.

2. A TYPOLOGY OF CHARTS

Many software packages for presentation graphics enable the user to do much more than just draw graphs. So even though we are primarily concerned with graphing, we do present a general typology of charts here as an overview.

The typology consists of four main types: text, free-form charts, graphs, and data maps. Each has many subsidiary forms, and each is available in most good software, although there is considerable variation in the subsidiary forms in different software packages. Only the graphs are covered in detail here; in fact, a number of software packages specialize in graphing to the exclusion of the other types.

■ 3. GRAPHING NONDATA

a. Text

A text chart (Fig. 2) is used for title pages and summary lists, particularly for making overheads or slides to be used in a presentation. These may be produced most quickly on a typewriter, but good software enables you to use any size font, to make centering automatic, to add bullets (checkmarks or other symbols sometimes placed at the beginning of a new statement for emphasis), and to add a wide variety of logos, maps, or sketches. You will also be able to get color output if you use a plotter or ink-jet peripheral, but this is true of all types of presentation graphics.

Energy and the Future

Energy Source	Present Usage	Next 30 Years
Oil	high	declining
Gas	medium	rising
Coal	high	rising
Nuclear fission	medium	steady
Nuclear fusion	none	none
solar	low	rising
hydroelectric	low	steady
geothermal	low	steady
wind	very low	rising
tide	very low	steady
agricultural	low	rising

No database, illustrative purposes only

Figure 2
Text chart for energy.

b. Free-Form Data

This catch-all category includes everything from an advertisement to an organization chart. The former may include a mixture of drawings, symbols, and text. The latter is a series of lines and boxes with accompanying text. Drawings can be executed by using functions for lines, boxes, circles, and other primitives, perhaps in conjunction with symbols and maps from a prepared library. See Fig. 3. Flowcharts for computer programs and classification charts are some options of interest to engineers. If you need to do a lot of artwork, you should get specialized art software or at least a paint or sketch package (these are very inexpensive).

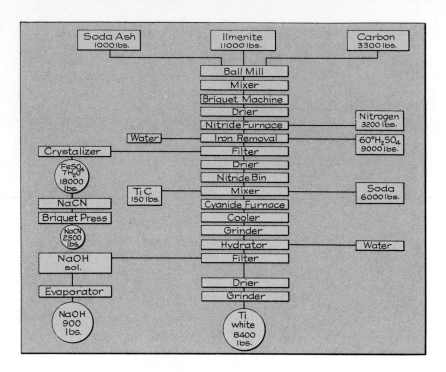

Figure 3
Flowchart for chemical process.

■ 4. GRAPHING DATA

a. Data Maps

Maps are 2-D graphs, but they may include additional dimensions when they are used to show the geographical distribution of quantities such as elevation, rainfall, atmospheric pressure, population, molybdenum deposits, or trade flows. Also spatial displays of local phenomena, such as isothermal lines showing the temperature distribution of the exhaust from a jet engine, may be thought of as data maps. With some software these data may even be displayed with three spatial dimensions. Presentation graphics software is weak in the area of data mapping, and so more specialized software designed for handling scientific data must be used. Data mapping is, however, a very useful tool in engineering. Figure 4 shows the deflection of a membrane under pressure. In this case, we are looking at a third variable which is, in fact, the third spatial variable, just highly magnified.

b. Graphs

Graphing begins with univariate data (one variable), and in this case any graph is a frequency distribution of the one variable for which data exist. This can take the form of a curve or a histogram (discussed shortly). If the distribution is normal (symmetric), there is probably no need for the graph. To communicate the data you need only the description of the sample (how many data, how obtained, of what), the mean (average value), and the standard deviation (a measure of the degree to which the values are concentrated or dispersed about the mean).

DEFLECTION OF A MEMBRANE DUE TO A UNIFORM FORCE

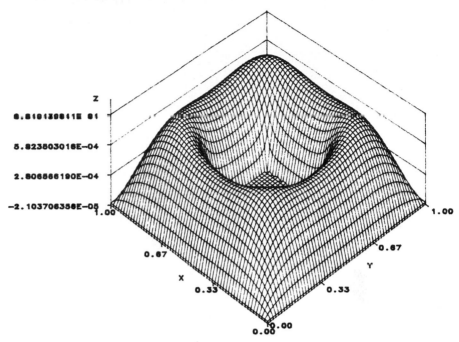

Figure 4
Data map for a membrane displacement. (Courtesy N. J. Salamon, Penn State, 1988.)

The data for a variable may vary in a nominal way, such as the federal budget which is divided into defense, social services, and debt service for a single year. In this case, to graph the data, we should use a pie chart. Once again, we question whether a graph is needed at all. In Fig. 5 the same data are provided in a table and as two pie charts. The tabular form in Fig. 5A is better. It stands out more clearly than the text, thus emphasizing it, and does not have the flashy hype and ink-wasting quality of the pie charts (Fig. 5B). The table is also the best way to present data for 2 or 3 years, particularly when the percentage changes from year to year are of interest. For more than 3 years, multiple line, or bar, graphs are best (time is a second variable, so we can go to an *XY* format).

PSU INCOME SOURCES
TOTAL OPERATING BUDGET

SOURCE	1977-78	1987-88	% CHANGE
State Appropriation	29.1%	22%	-24.4
Tuition and Fees	22.7	24.5	7.9
University Hospital	8.7	12.9	48.3
Restricted funds	15.8	16.5	4.4
Other	24.7	24.1	-2.4

Figure 5A
Tabular display of data.

PSU INCOME SOURCES
TOTAL OPERATING BUDGET

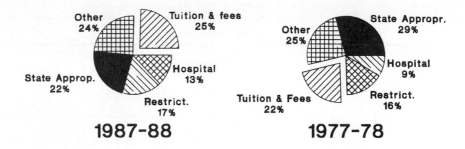

Figure 5B
Pie-chart display of data of Fig. 5A.

With engineering or science data which consist of real number measurements of a particular variable, the best form of graphing is a histogram. This is a bar chart (column really, but "bar" is used for both horizontal and vertical bars now). See Fig. 6. The data within regularly spaced intervals (cells) are counted as a frequency and plotted as a bar. Any given distribution will be spread over a particular range. The range is the difference between the maximum and minimum values, although it is a good idea to treat separately any datum which greatly extends the range and

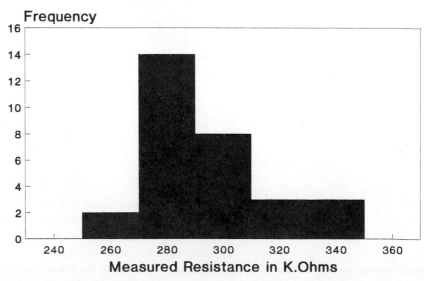

Figure 6
Histogram for sample of carbon composite resistors.

R. Devon, Penn State, 1989

is conspicuously alone. This range will be broken into a number of intervals, all the same size. The larger the number of intervals, the smaller the size of the interval and the fewer data that will fall in that interval. Usually, at least five intervals are used, but the number could be as high as desired. However, the purpose of a histogram is to display the data so that the shape of the distribution is revealed. This means choosing a cell interval large enough to get plenty of data in most of the cells. If the number of data points is very large, it may be possible to use a cell size of 1. In this case, an *XY* line graph of frequency versus value would probably be plotted.

It may be argued that a histogram is always an *XY* graph of frequency versus value and so the data are bivariate. It is true that a histogram is always an *XY* chart, but really only one variable is involved. The *Y* value is simply the frequency of occurrence for the *X* value falling in the various intervals (cells).

c. Bivariate and Multivariate Data

For plotting bivariate (two-variable) and multivariate (multivariable) data, the three main options are bar graphs, scatter plots, and line graphs, although the last includes a wide variety of types.

d. Bar Graphs

A bar graph (Fig. 7) should be chosen when the data occur in aggregates for a somewhat extended period such as a day, month, or year. Data for rainfall or business sales are often presented in this way, for example. However, engineering and scientific data are usually the result of more or less continuous measurements of continuous variations of the phenomena measured. Because of this, scatter plots

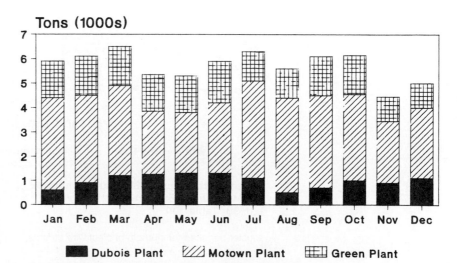

Figure 7
Stacked bar chart for fertilizer production from three chemical plants.

and line graphs are usually more appropriate. Nevertheless, remember the bar graph for data in aggregate form. The histogram, discussed above, is such a case.

Some people prefer to use a bar graph when there are only a few data points to plot. Then a bar graph will make the most of a little. The problem here is that use of this technique may border on deception. A line graph with only three or four points looks exactly like that—a line graph with few data for a very limited data range. The viewer should know instinctively that inferring relationships and trends from it will be very risky. The same graph in bar graph form may be more likely to be taken as a trend-establishing data base. It should not, but it is visually more solid and the void data ranges at either end of all graphs are typically less prominent on bar graphs. This is particularly true when a pseudo 3-D effect is present.

Bar graphs come in three main varieties: simple, clustered, and stacked. The last two are a means of showing more than one set of data on one graph. If you cluster three bars at each data point, you accomplish the equivalent of three line graphs. Whether you stack or cluster depends on whether the sum of all three values is meaningful. If the sum is not meaningful, you should cluster and not stack. If it is meaningful, you may choose to stack, and you should do so if it is a meaning that you wish to convey.

If you cluster three bars at a data point and these three values vary along the same new dimension, you will be creating a graph with a third dimension (Fig. 8). It is often possible in contemporary software to display the 3-D nature in oblique or isometric form with the third dimension shown on a third axis. The equivalent for a line graph would be a 3-D surface. Note that Fig. 8 has a pseudo 3-D effect that should not be confused with a real 3-D graph.

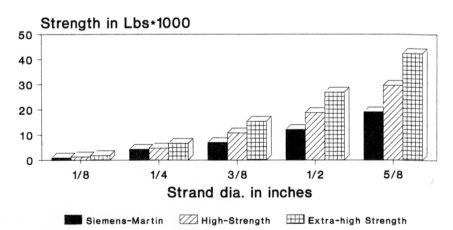

Adapted from Mark's Standard Handbook
for Mechanical Engineers, 8th Ed.,
p.8-90, Table 100.

Figure 8
Cluster bar chart for strength of steel wire strands.

e. Scatter Plots

Scatter plots are like line graphs without the lines. The lines are not drawn because the points are so scattered that there is a real question as to whether a relationship exists between the two variables (or three, if it is a 3-D graph). Scatter may occur because of random measurement errors or because of a weak or non-existent relationship between two variables.

If it appears that the points, although scattered, do indicate a relationship, then a best-fit curve may be drawn. The technique for finding the best fit is statistical and is known as *regression*. Regression may be linear, as in Fig. 9, that is, for finding the straight line which best fits the data. Or regression may be curvilinear, where the best curve is derived using a polynomial series up to a chosen power (for example, a second-order parabola). In both linear and curvilinear regression, the method is often the same. In the common least-squares method, the differences between each data point and an assumed line are squared and then added for the data series. The line chosen is the one for which this sum is minimum. However, regression is only one approach of matching lines to data, and soon we discuss another method, interpolation.

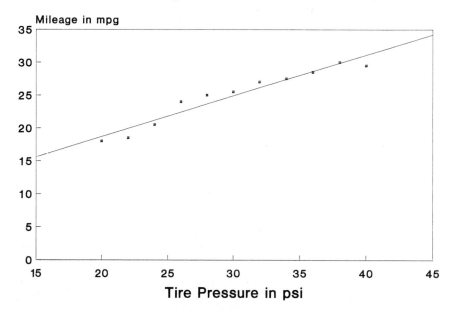

Figure 9
Linear regression on frictional data.

Most good graphing software will produce both linear and curvilinear fits for the scatter plot. Do be careful in using the resulting line. If there is a lot of scatter, the relationship is weak. If there is little scatter, the relationship is strong. So the same regression line could represent a weak or a strong relationship. You can tell approximately how strong the relationship is by looking at the scatter. A more accurate way is to use the correlation coefficient. This is a figure that varies between +1 (no scatter, positive slope) and −1 (no scatter, negative slope). A correlation coefficient of 0 means that there is no relationship between the two variables. The really important value, however, is the square of the correlation coefficient. If the correlation figure is 0.5, say, then variations in the X variable account for 0.5×0.5, or 0.25, of the variance (variation) in the Y value. So whenever you obtain a regression line for a scatter plot, be sure to report the correlation coefficient also. The coefficient should be given with any software package that produces regression lines. Unfortunately, this is not always true, and in general engineers need to use software which provides all the necessary statistical and curve-fitting methods and parametric values (not to mention enough significant figures).

f. Regression: Cause and Effect

If you do establish a regression line or curve, it represents the regression of X on Y. This line shows the relationship between the independent variable X and the dependent variable Y. The line may be used to predict the value of Y for any given value of X, within the range of X values established by the original graph. Predictions that fall outside this range are hypothetical extrapolations which may prove incorrect when tested. Never base your designs on hypothetical extrapolations. The *Challenger* space shuttle was lost because the booster rockets were deployed at a temperature below the tested range and the O-ring seals failed. Engineers who knew this and tried to stop the launch were overruled.

How do you decide which is the dependent variable and which the independent variable? It really is a matter of theory. The dependent variable is your main concern. For example, you may be concerned with the ultimate strength of a long column that fails by buckling. Its ultimate strength is the dependent variable. What might affect this? Two obvious factors are the length of the column and the geometry of the cross section. Either could be the independent variable, which is varied while the other is kept constant. In this example changes in the X variable may be thought of as causing changes in the Y variable. This cause-and-effect relationship often exists between the independent and the dependent variables and is one way to decide which is which.

However, a relationship between two variables that is displayed by a regression line or a line graph does not necessarily imply a cause-and-effect relationship. Quite possibly a totally different variable was responsible for both, or the relationship may be entirely coincidental. Commonly this happens when both variables are a function of time. For example, if you plot the accumulated income of a resident of Pennsylvania versus the accumulated rainfall in Pennsylvania over the course of a year, you will get a very high correlation with very little scatter. Nevertheless, thunderstorms do not lead to bonuses.

g. Interpolation

Where data do not have a lot of scatter and there is some interest in generating a line through the points, the problem becomes one of interpolation rather than regression. The main reason why lines are drawn through data is to generate a line for reading off intermediate values between the measured data points. Reading off these values is known as *interpolation,* because a value is deduced based on measured values on either side of it.

If the points all lie on a straight line, it is easy to draw the line. For any other situation, either you join the points with straight segments between points or you search for a curve that will provide a smooth result. If you choose a curve, you will be faced with a great many different possibilities. The mathematical techniques used for interpolation are not without risk, as discussed elsewhere (for example, Chapra and Canale, 1986). Suffice it to say that there are no guaranteed ways of getting the ''correct'' curve, and it is possible to get some very odd results by using certain methods under the wrong conditions. If you use a curve that fits the points, you can predict from it a variety of in-between values. This is the point of interpolation, of course. If your predictions are repeatedly confirmed by further testing, you may, in fact, come to view the curve as correct—with some justification.

As discussed above for regression lines, to make predictions outside the plotted data range is to engage in extrapolation. This is done only with great caution, that is, for the purposes of making hypotheses only.

h. Line Graphs

A line graph has a great deal in common with a regression line graph developed from a scatter plot. It differs in that the points are joined without an attempt to get a best-fit straight line or curve. The result is often fairly jagged, unless you are plotting a mathematical function or use interpolation, as discussed above. The statistical variation that is quite probably present is, in effect, ignored. This makes sense when the data do not exhibit great random variability and random measurement errors are small as well. In Fig. 10A the data are plotted for a tension test through to the fracture point. A subset of the same data is plotted in Fig. 10B, to show more clearly the data in the working elastic range of the material.

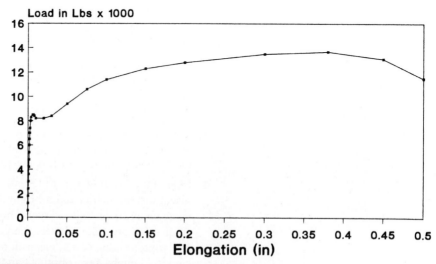

Figure 10A
Line graph for a tension test.

Initial dia. .505 in, L=2.0 in.
J. Conway, Penn State(1989)

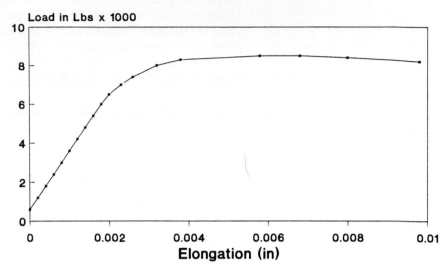

Tension Test for SAE
Annealed Steel

Initial dia. .505 in, L=2.0 in.
J. Conway, Penn State(1989)

Figure 10B
Subset of data of Fig. 10A plotted over a smaller range.

Line graphs are also useful for displaying several dependent variables on the same graph with a common independent variable. This introduces a need to discriminate between different lines on the same graph. There are six techniques for doing this.

1. You may use different symbols for the data points for the different variables. If two or more of the lines are very close to each other anywhere on the graph, this technique may not be adequate to prevent ambiguity. More important, although the points are clearly distinguished, the lines as a whole are not clear, and this inhibits the interpretation of the graphs in their entirety—particularly as they relate to each other.

2. Different line types avoid the pitfalls of the first method, although the first method is quite adequate in many cases and may be readily used in conjunction with the second method. Line types may be varied by using dashes, dots, and other symbols.

3. Line thickness is an effective tool for distinguishing between lines. It has the disadvantage of seeming to make the variable with the heaviest line the most important, which is rarely the case.

4. Lines may be drawn in different colors, too. Color adds very powerful visual discrimination and a bright attractive image to a graph. The disadvantages are that: not everyone has color output facilities (for example, color monitor, color plotter); photocopying color pieces produces black-and-white results, which means a much higher reproduction cost for color copies through, say, printing; and 5 to 10 percent of the population is

color-blind to some degree. Because of the last disadvantage it is good to use some auxiliary techniques as well, if you decide to use color. For example, if you vary the line type or width as well as the line color, it will be possible to distinguish between the lines in black and white. With respect to varying degrees of color blindness, do not use red and green because they are particularly hard to distinguish. Blue and yellow are good choices.

5. Labeling lines by their variables is highly desirable if there are more than two lines on the same graph. In some cases it may be all you need to distinguish between two lines.

6. Use area graphs. These are discussed below. They involve stacking the variables, which is not always appropriate. However, the different shading patterns beneath each line are very effective in differentiating the lines. Of course, in an area graph the lines never cross (although they can touch), and this is helpful for reading a graph.

Usually, multiple lines on the same graph imply that not only is the independent variable common to all, but also the units and scale are the same for the dependent variable. However, it is possible to construct a Y axis on both sides of the graph, as in Fig. 11. This permits two entirely different dependent variables to be used. In such a case proper labeling is particularly important. Most, but not all, software packages do this.

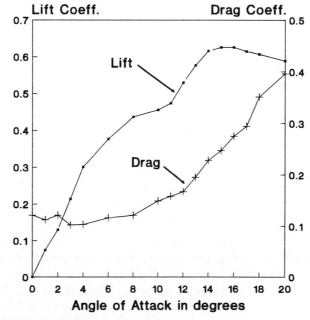

Figure 11
Graph of aerodynamic data using two Y axes.

5. SPECIAL FORMS FOR GRAPHING DATA

a. Area Graphs

An area graph is a particular type of multiple-line graph which is similar to the stacked bar graph. Instead of plotting several lines separately, the values are added cumulatively, as in Fig. 12. So after the first line is plotted, the second line is plotted as a sum of the values at each point for both the first line and the second line. This process is continued until the top, last line is drawn. This line represents the sum of all the values at each point. As in the stacked bar graph, the area graph is used only where the summation of the values has a meaning and that meaning is to be conveyed to the reader. Most software will provide an area graph feature and different shading between the lines to help the reader assess the relative contributions of each. Unfortunately, this shading often involves parallel lines which usually produce a distracting, shimmering, moiré effect. Solid-color shading avoids this problem, although it wears out plotter pens quickly and is not very helpful for the color-blind if more than one area is solid.

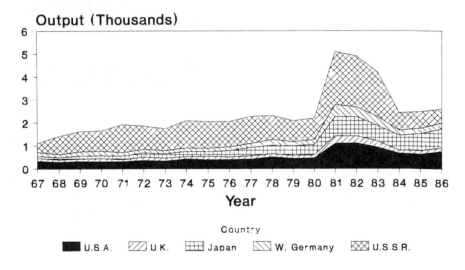

Publishing Frequency for Ceramics R&D

Figure 12
Area graph for selected publication rates.

Period covered 1967-86.
T. Devon, R. Roy (1988)

b. The 100 Percent Graphs

These graphs are a useful variant of the area graph. Instead of plotting several line graphs with the values summed, the percentage contribution of each at each value is plotted. See Fig. 13. The result is like an area graph where the final top line is always a horizontal line representing 100 percent.

The 100 percent graph represents a switch from absolute values to relative values. What is displayed are the relative sizes of the variables. The contribution of each to the whole is very clearly shown. When this is what you wish to communicate, the 100 percent graph is one of the best ways to do it. The 100 percent graph could

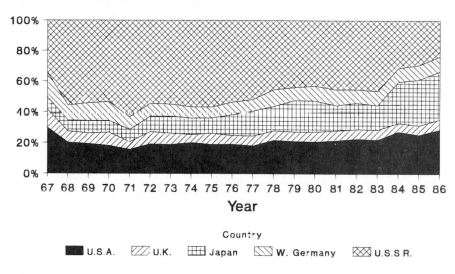

Publishing Frequency for Ceramics R&D

Country

U.S.A.   U.K.   Japan   W. Germany   U.S.S.R.

Figure 13
Data of Fig. 12 shown as a
100 percent graph.

Period covered 1967–86

be used in a stacked bar graph form for aggregate data. Also note that a pie chart is a 100 percent graph for univariate data.

When a 100 percent graph or other relative graphing techniques, such as index and ratio graphs (discussed below), are used, it is important to note on the graph (or in the accompanying text) the absolute values. This reminds the reader of the magnitudes involved.

c. Index Graphs

The index graph seen in Fig. 14 is also based on relative data, but in this case the comparison is internal to each variable and not between variables. This is accomplished by showing the value of a variable relative to a base value (index) for the same independent variable. In this case, all the variables are given a value of 100 at the initial X value. Then as X varies, each variable is plotted as a percentage of its true base value at the point when it was assigned a value of 100. So each line shows the percentage change over time based on the value at the start. For example, if the dependent variable is pressure, the independent variable is time, the initial value at time $= 0$ is 400 lb/in^2, and the pressure at time $= 3$ s is 300 lb/in^2, then at time $= 0$ you will plot 100 and at time $= 3$ s you will plot 75.

In a 100 percent graph, you show the relative contribution of each variable to the sum. In an index graph you show the *change* in each variable relative to its value at a given time. This point is common to all the dependent variables being plotted. Then you use the index graph to compare the changes in a group of variables over a chosen period. Be careful in choosing the index point. By accident or design, there are ample opportunities in an index graph to create very different effects.

Although index graphs usually have the 100 value at the initial X value, this value could, in principle, be placed at any of the X values or even at a value not

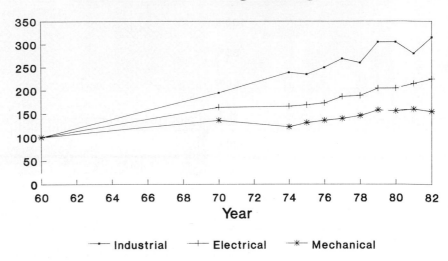

Growth Rates in Engineering, 1960-82

Industrial   Electrical   Mechanical

Figure 14
An index chart showing growth rates
in three fields of engineering.

**Number of practitioners relative to 1960
as a base of 100. Adapted approximately
from Engineering Education & Practice**

shown. Also, unlike in 100 percent and area graphs, the sum of the dependent variables in an index graph does *not* have to be meaningful.

d. Ratio Graphs

This is the last form of relative graph that we discuss. The term *relative graph* refers to graphs which portray the contributions of variables relative to each other, rather than their absolute values. The ratio graph is used when we want to compare the relative strengths of two different dependent variables. Refer to Fig. 15. The value of one variable is divided by the value of the other variable, and the result is plotted. It is very simple to do. Most software will not explicitly provide this option, but it is easy to create the values since most software packages provide the simple spreadsheet function of dividing one column of values by another. As described so far, the ratio graph is very similar to the 100 percent graph for two variables. It produces much the same result, but with a single line, that is, with much less ink. The ratio graph will work only for two variables, but several ratio lines may be produced on the same graph. At times the interest lies in the ratio of one variable to another, not the relative contribution of each to a whole, which may or may not have meaning.

e. Logarithmic and Semilogarithmic Graphs

When the data ranges of values involve powers of 10 above 2 or 3, for example, greater than 3 to 3000, consider using logarithms. With a base-10 logarithm, each power of 10 is 1 unit on the scale. So, for example, 3.6*10**6 will involve plotting the value of log 3.6 between the sixth and seventh divisions on the scale (assuming the first division represented the 10). Note that 10**6 means 10 to the sixth power.

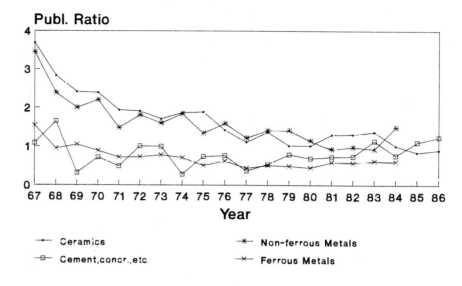

T. Devon, R. Roy (1988)

Figure 15
Ratio graph showing relative publishing rates in selected research topics.

Clearly, then, logarithms provide an incredible means of compressing very large data ranges. In a semilog graph only one data range is very large, so only one axis uses a log scale. See Fig. 16 for an example.

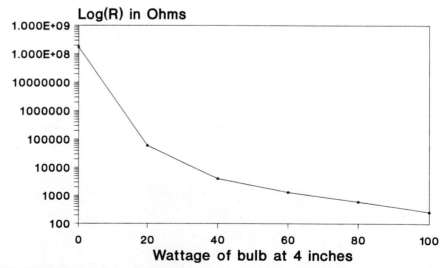

Bulb Wattage measured indirectly
Lab data, R. Devon, Penn State, 1989.

Figure 16
Semilog graph showing the performance of a photoconductive cell.

Most software will provide logarithmic graphing automatically, but there are several features that you should be aware of. If the graph was not plotted automatically, you have two choices. Either you use log graph paper and then just enter the values, using the provided grid, or else you divide the scale into equal divisions for each power of 10 and place the actual log values (for example, log 3.6 = .5563) in the correct power-of-10 division. So, in our example, the value of 3.6 is placed over the halfway mark in the division. On log graph paper, the paper is already ruled with the logarithmic "distortion," so you do not have to look up the logarithm of the number. On the contrary, within the accuracy of your eyesight, you can find the logarithm of a number from log graph paper by superimposing, or juxtaposing, a linear scale onto the log scale.

Another unusual feature of a log scale is the way in which it approaches zero. The logarithm of a value is not defined for negative or zero values. Therefore, log scales cannot be used for data ranges which include zero or negative values. If all the data are negative, they can be treated in terms of their absolute values. If the data contain both positive and negative values, the origin has to be shifted to permit plotting of the data in their entirety.

However, although the logarithms of zero and negative numbers do not exist, there are positive numbers for which the logarithm is negative. Since log 1 is 0, all positive numbers between 0 and 1 produce a negative logarithm. The smaller the number, the larger the negative value of the logarithm. In fact, it goes by powers of -10. For example, the logarithm of $3.6*10**-2$ is $-1 + .5563$, or -1.4437. So the logarithm of positive nonzero numbers passes through zero and may be indefinitely large in either the positive or the negative direction. This is true for the logarithm to any base (for example, 10, e, 2). The value e is the base of natural logarithms, equal to approximately 2.72.

Log graphs greatly improve the spread of the data in the range of the lowest values where a conventional line graph would cause them to bunch. However, log graphs badly bunch the data at the top end of the scale. For example, the values 1 to 1000 may be displayed in the lower three divisions of a log scale while values in the range of 10^7 to 10^8, which number 90,000,000, are all placed in one division only. One result may be a log graph which appears to be a straight line. If an inference is to be made to this effect, then a closer look should be taken at just the log graph of the higher ranges. Figure 17 is an example of data plotted on log-log paper.

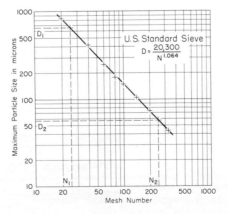

Figure 17
Maximum particle size by mesh number for U.S. standard sieves on log-log graph.

One of the great values of a log graph is that if it is a straight line, then a relationship between the two values may be easily derived. The slope of the log graph is the power to which the independent variable is raised. The method for doing this is covered in Sec. 8.

6. USING PRESENTATION GRAPHICS SOFTWARE

Although all the commercial software packages available are different and it is not possible to provide explicit training for any of them here, a terminology has evolved that is common to many of them, and it is worth introducing some of the terms here.

When you first enter the program, you will be asked what type of graph you wish to draw. The typology of the preceding section should help you make that decision. Some options that you are familiar with may not be offered in the software you are using, but others may be. And certain options may exist but not be explicitly listed in the preliminary menus. Nevertheless, you should have no trouble at this stage.

After you have chosen the graph type, you will be required to enter the data. At this point, a convention that is common to presentation graphics software may confuse you. For most modes of entry (for example, calendar), the X values are assumed to have a regular increment, and you will be required to provide a starting value, an ending value, and an increment value for the X values. If your X values do not increment in a regular fashion, be sure to get into the right data type—it will probably be called *numeric* or *number*. If your X values increment regularly, you simply have to enter a column of figures for your Y data. *Note:* Each set of data is referred to as a *series*. Getting into the right column often is no more complicated than using the arrow keys or the Tab key. Once in the column, you should stay in the column by pressing Enter after typing in each value.

At this point, in many packages you can plot the graph just by pressing a designated function key. Somewhere on your screen you should find a message telling you which function key to press for plotting, for setting drawing details, and for help. When you wish to stop what you are doing or move to a higher-level menu, the Esc (escape) key can be used.

In some software the title, subtitle, and footnote are all entered as you enter the data table the first time, although they may be changed at any time. In other packages you have to look for the features that let you title and label your graph. Some software restricts where you can place text; other software will let you put any text anywhere.

If you change your mind about the way you wish to graph your data, or if you wish to produce different graphs of those data, it is usually easy to change the graph type. Remember to save each version that you want to keep under a different name.

Somewhere in the software there may be options for shading, pseudo 3-D effects, and so on. Try to minimize the chart junk. Remember, you are a professional trying to communicate technical information accurately.

■ 7. DETAILS OF DRAWING

The quality of the final product depends heavily on the way in which the details of the graph are done. Fonts that are too large, lines that are too heavy, labeling that is too crowded, and graphs that list no data source are all examples of details that mark a bad product.

a. Choice of Graph

The first decision is whether to graph. Some very simple data are better summarized statistically or in tabular form. Once the decision has been made to graph, you must choose the graph form which best summarizes the data. If you decide to summarize them in a special way, such as a 100 percent or ratio graph, you should indicate the absolute values involved either in the text or in another graph. Do not select the data and the graph form to present the data with a slant that helps your argument but distorts the data.

b. Choice of Scales

Select scales that spread the data across the graph. Do not create a graph with data bunched in one corner. *Note:* Your scales do *not* have to begin at zero.

c. Title and Source of the Graph

The graph must always have a title, and the title must describe the graph. The source of the data in the graph should be cited in a footnote. Most presentation graphics software have the capacity to enter a title, subtitle, and footnote. The title can be ''Fig. 22,'' say, and the subtitle can be the description. The footnote should be placed discreetly at the bottom.

d. Fonts

There are many choices of font style and size in contemporary software. The temptation is to choose styles that are too ornate or sizes that are too large. Font lines that are too thick attract too much attention and blur when reduced. Also remember that lowercase letters are easier to read than uppercase ones. The labels should be somewhat smaller than the titles, and the footnote should be a little smaller than other labels.

e. Labeling

In addition to the title, subtitle, and footnote, the axes must be labeled and the units given. Some people like to use aligned lettering for the Y axis, but the Y axis label placed horizontally at the top of the axis is easier to read. By now the graph is getting crowded. However, labels for the lines of multiple-line graphs are worth including. The divisions on the axes should be marked, but it is a good idea to only put occasional values, to reduce crowding.

f. Displaying Points and Grids

Many line graphs provide the option of not actually displaying the points. The advantage is that the points tend to detract from the image of the line. On a bar graph the value is clearly the end of the bar, and sometimes the actual numeric value is entered next to this line. On line graphs the exact value of the plotted point is not always clear, particularly if it is at the top of a sharp peak and the line is thick. The goal is to be able to ascertain the plotted values fairly accurately. To this end, keep your lines reasonably thin and/or display the points. A rule of thumb might be to make the axes thin and your graph lines about double the thickness of the axis lines. Unfortunately most software does not include the option of drawing the points as well as the lines. Grid lines can help the viewer to read the graph, but grids introduce a lot of ''nondata'' ink and should be avoided, if possible. If grid lines are plotted, they should be drawn as lightly as possible.

g. Spatial Organization

Do not crowd the material. Keep the lines and labels well spaced. Arrange the total picture so that there is a good balance to the graph. Remember that the purpose of the graph is to display a summary of the data. The graph of the values should be prominent.

h. Legends

A legend is placed at the bottom or side of a graph to identify the lines or area shading used for each independent (X) variable. Legends are supplied automatically in most high-quality software. This is helpful since it is not always possible to label a graph line independently.

8. ANALYTICAL POWER OF GRAPHS

Whether graphs are generated from data or from mathematical functions, they make a number of distinct contributions to our understanding of the relationship(s) represented by the graph.

1. The graph is a visual image which summarizes both the data and the relationship between the variables in a graphic form that is usually far simpler, and thus far easier to understand and to remember, than data in a table or than a function as a formula.

2. Some relationships may be expressed algebraically in a way that is almost impossible to visualize. Other relationships may not be amenable to exact methods such as calculus for finding out characteristics of the curve. With a graph you can see the general trend, you can see where the roots are (where the line crosses the X axis), and you can see maxima, minima, points of inflection, and asymptotes (Fig. 18). A *point of inflection* is where the curvature reverses, such as from convex to concave. An *asymptote* is that straight line which the relationship approaches at infinity. Note, how-

Characteristics of a Curve
$$Y = 2 - 15X + 2X^2$$

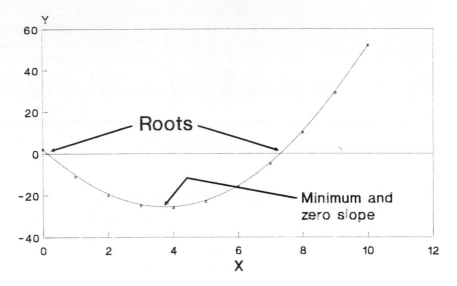

Figure 18
Characteristics of a simple quadratic curve.

ever, that even though it is always possible to graph data or a function, it is sometimes necessary to radically change the scale in order to see the effect of very large values. Similarly, you can zoom in and magnify the relationship over a tiny, but eccentric, range of values. Note that Fig. 19B is an enlarged portion of Fig. 19A. Many distributions are represented by 3-D surfaces (an example is given in Fig. 20).

Graph of $Y = X^{2/3} - 4X$
Range −5 to +5

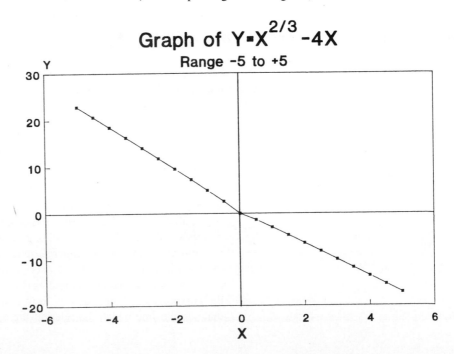

Figure 19A
Graph of a function within broad ranges of X and Y values.

Graph of $Y = X^{2/3} - 4X$
Range −0.015 to +0.05

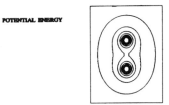

Figure 19B
Data of Fig. 19A zoomed to show data near origin.

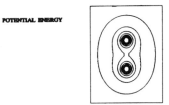

Figure 20
Potential energy depicted with 3-D surface, by Graftool.

3. By obtaining a straight line on a linear or a log graph for a set of data, it is possible to obtain the equation of the line that represents the data. This has already been shown for regression, but it may be obtained directly from the graph if random scatter is not a significant factor. See the sections below on linear, power, and exponential relationships.

4. When we find roots for the relationship between two variables, we find those values of the independent variable for which the dependent variable will be zero. This occurs when the graph crosses the X axis. The X axis is a line which represents $Y = 0$. The roots, then, are those X values which represent the primary relationship *and* the $Y = 0$ line. In general, we can find the values of X which satisfy the primary relationship *and* any other line by finding the intersection of the two lines. This is very easy to do graphically, and it may also be easy to do algebraically. In Fig. 21 the

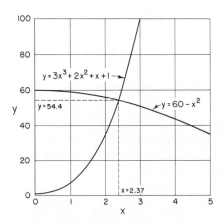

Figure 21
Solution of two simultaneous equations.

graphs of two functions intersect at $X = 2.37$ and $Y = 54.4$. These values of X and Y satisfy both equations. In other words, the intersection represents the solution of the two functions considered as simultaneous equations. While an algebraic solution is easy to obtain and more readily available to many significant figures, the graphical solution also depicts the functions themselves. This is useful if we want to consider changes in one or both of the functions and would like to know what sort of effect it might have on the solution. For example, if $Y = 60 - X^2$ is changed to $Y = 59 - X^2$, then we can easily see from the present graph that the solution decreases slightly in its X value, but the Y value decreases by almost 1.

9. COMMENTS

1. It is often suggested that solutions obtained from graphs are not very accurate. Sometimes you do not need much accuracy, and graphs can give you a visual check on your result that algebra and calculus do not. Also by zooming in on your value, you can get an increasingly accurate result. This is particularly easy to do if you plot your data, or your mathematical function, by writing a computer program. However, it is particularly hard to get accurate results for points of inflection from a graph.

2. Another way to graph data and functions is to write a computer program to do so. A general-purpose program for plotting rectilinear XY data is not too hard to write (Chapra and Canale, 1986, p. 353). However, with so many software packages available which do far more than just plot rectilinear XY data, there is not much point in writing your own (beyond the pleasure of the challenge). Writing programs that plot functions and that let you zoom in on their eccentricities is even easier than writing a data-plotting program, and they are less likely to be found in commercial software (Devon and Feng, 1989, chap. 10).

3. There is a very powerful area of graphical analysis known as *nomography*. This was developed to speed up the solution of mathematical equations with three or more variables that are repeatedly used. It has been rendered largely obsolete by nongraphical techniques used on computers, and so it is not covered in this text. For more information on this method, which rendered excellent service in the past, see French, Vierck, and Foster (1984).

10. LINEAR FIRST-ORDER RELATIONSHIPS

When data are plotted and the result is close to a straight line, the line may be drawn and its equation derived via two methods: the slope-intercept method and the selected-points method. Both methods yield an equation of the form $y = a + bx$, where the values of a and b are determined from the data by analyzing the graph.

a. Slope-Intercept Method

The intercept of a straight line is the value of a, that is, the value of y when $x = 0$. To put it another way, the intercept is the value of y where the line crosses the y axis (the $x = 0$ line), hence its name. In the slope-intercept method, we begin by reading the value of the intercept from the graph. This means that we have already drawn our best straight line by eye. If we do this for the line in Fig. 22, we get $a = 5$. So the equation of the line is

$$y = 5 + 1.1x$$

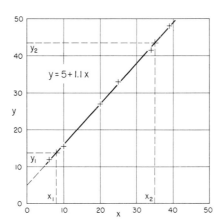

Figure 22
Graphical derivative of equation of a straight line.

We still need to determine the value of b, where b is actually the slope of the line because it specifies exactly how y will react to changes in x. The slope of the line is easily determined by choosing two points on the line and finding the ratio of the change in y divided by the change in x. In the slope-intercept method, we do not look for actual data points, but because we already have the line drawn, we take convenient values from the graph of the line. However, this means that the equation of the line so derived is no more representative of the data than the drawn line is.

So, in Fig. 22, two points, (x_1, y_1) and (x_2, y_2), are chosen, and the slope is

$$b = \frac{y_2 - y_1}{x_2 - x_1} = \frac{43.5 - 13.8}{35.0 - 8.0} = \frac{29.7}{27} = 1.1$$

This gives us the equation of the line:

$$y = 5 + 1.1x$$

b. Selected-Points Method

This method differs from the slope-intercept method because the whole equation is derived from two points, including the intercept. In the slope-intercept method, the intercept was read off the graph. This can be done only where the data range for the x axis includes zero, which is often not the case.

Once again we select points (x_1, y_1) and (x_2, y_2), but this time we also include the general case (x, y), where (x, y) represents any point on the line. The equation may now be found by similar triangles from

$$\frac{y - y_1}{x - x_1} = \frac{y_2 - y_1}{x_2 - x_1}$$

Substituting the values for the two points gives

$$\frac{y - 13.8}{x - 8.0} = \frac{43.5 - 13.8}{35.0 - 8.0}$$
$$y - 13.8 = 1.1\,(x - 8.0)$$

So

$$y = 5.0 + 1.1x$$

This gives us the same result as before. This is to be expected since we used exactly the same line. The only discrepancies would be found from reading values from the graph, which may introduce small variations in the answers.

c. Method of Least Squares

As discussed earlier, this is a regression technique for determining the best straight line through a set of points exhibiting scatter. For more information on this method, see Chapra and Canale (1986, p. 444).

11. NONLINEAR RELATIONSHIPS

a. Power Equations

A *power relationship* refers to the cases where one or more of the variables in the relationship are raised to a power. The simple form of power relationships is expressed by

$$y = ax^b$$

If we plot a family of curves for various values of b (Fig. 23A), we can see that they are all curves. However, if we take the logarithm of both sides of the equation, we get a family of straight lines (Fig. 23B) represented by

$$\log y = \log a + b \log x$$

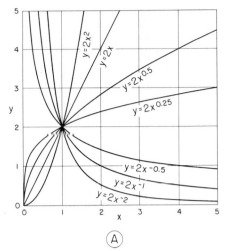 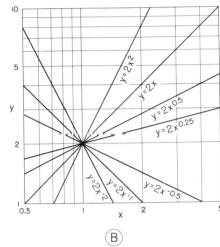

Figure 23
Power equations in linear and log forms.

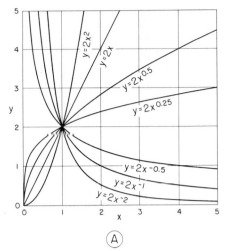

Figure 24
Derivation of a power equation from a log-log graph.

Both log a and b are constants, so this is the equation of a straight line where log x and log y are variables and b is the slope. Log a is the intercept, or value of log y when log x is zero. And log x is zero when $x = 1$. A straight-line graph could also be obtained here with a semilog graph where the logarithm is taken for only the right side of the equation. For some complex relationships, both x and y may be raised to a power, which makes the log-log graph particularly attractive.

Often empirical data appear to be curvilinear. If they are plotted on a log-log or semilog graph, a straight line may result. When it does, the actual power equation relating the variables may be determined. The power b is the slope of the log-log graph. The value of the constant a is the antilogarithm of the value of log y when $x = 1$. Or, more simply, a is equal to y when $x = 1$, that is, when log $x = 0$. Using the method of selected points for the data in Fig. 24, we get

$$
\begin{array}{ll}
x_1 = 2.5 & y_1 = 3.8 \\
x_2 = 55.0 & y_2 = 26.5
\end{array}
$$

So

$$
\frac{\log y - \log 3.8}{\log x - \log 2.5} = \frac{\log 26.5 - \log 3.8}{\log 55.0 - \log 2.5}
$$

In base-10 logarithms, this is

$$
\log y = .330 + .628 \log x
$$

Taking antilogarithms, we get

$$
y = 2.14x^{.628}
$$

b. Exponential Equations

Exponential equations also express nonlinear relationships which form curvilinear graphs. They differ from power relationships because the x variable appears as a power itself. The power, while variable, is made from a constant base, such as 10 or e. The constant e (approximately equal to 2.71) is the base for natural logarithms

$$y = ae^{bx} \qquad y = a(10^{bx})$$

If you examine these equations, you will see that when $x = 0$, the value of y is a. So the equations represent a family of curves through the point $(0, a)$, as shown in Fig. 25A. In Fig. 25B, the same family of curves is reduced to straight lines. This is achieved by taking logarithms of the exponential equations

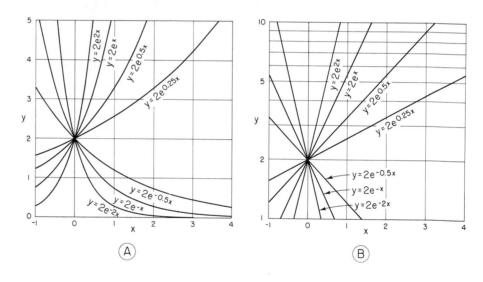

Figure 25
Exponential equations in linear and semilog forms.

$$\ln y = \ln a + bx \ln e$$

which gives

$$\ln y = \ln a + bx \qquad \ln e = 1$$

For the base-10 equation,

$$\log y = \log a + bx \qquad \log 10 = 1$$

The straight-line graphs may be obtained by plotting either $\ln y$ or $\log y$ versus x. Alternatively, the values of y could be placed directly on the log scale of a semilog graph (Fig. 25B).

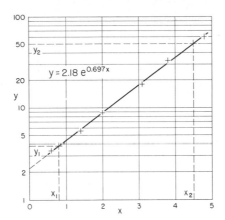

Figure 26
Derivation of the equation of a line
from a semilog graph.

Conversely, where data are plotted on a semilog graph, as in Fig. 26, the equation of the relationship may be determined by deriving the equation of the straight line. Drawing on the method of selected points for the graph in Fig. 26, we use these points:

$$
\begin{aligned}
x_1 &= .8 & y_1 &= 3.8 \\
x_2 &= 4.5 & y_2 &= 50
\end{aligned}
$$

This gives the equation of the line as

$$
\frac{\ln y - \ln 3.8}{x - .8} = \frac{\ln 50 - \ln 3.8}{4.5 - .8}
$$
$$
\ln y = .777 + .697x
$$
$$
y = 2.18e^{.697x}
$$

Using base-10 logarithms, we get

$$
\frac{\log y - \log 3.8}{x - .8} = \frac{\log 50 - \log 3.8}{4.5 - .8}
$$
$$
\log y = .338 + .302x
$$
$$
y = 2.18(10^{.302x})
$$

Note that when the same line is expressed in either base e or base 10, the constant a is the same. (As stated earlier, the value of a is the value of y when $x = 0$.) The different base only produces a different coefficient for the power x.

There are a great many applications for exponential equations. Compound interest on capital is an exponential relationship, for example. So, too, is the decay of radio activity or the response of a temperature transducer, such as a thermometer or a thermocouple, to a change in temperature. If you think about it, the rate at which y changes is a factor of the base. If $b = 1$, for instance, we could write

$$
y = ae^x
$$

Consider the successive values of $x = 2$ and $x = 3$. This produces two y values, the second of which is e times the first. This is equally true for any two successive integer values of x. In other words, as x varies, y varies by a constant factor. If $b = -1$, then for successive integer values of x the value of y is reduced by e or 10, as the case may be.

BIBLIOGRAPHY

■ Chapra, Stephen C., and Raymond P. Canale: *Introduction to Computing for Engineers*, McGraw-Hill, New York, 1986.

■ Devon, Richard F., and Wu-chun Feng: *Fortran at the Keyboard*, Kendall/Hunt, Dubuque, Iowa, 1989.

■ Devon, Tonia K., and Rustum Roy: "Changing National Origins of Materials Research: Implications for Science and Technology Policy," *Materials Research Society Bulletin*, vol. 13, no. 12, December 1988.

■ French, Thomas E., Charles J. Vierck, and Robert J. Foster: *Graphic Science and Design*, McGraw-Hill, New York, 1984.

■ Tufte, Edward: *The Visual Display of Quantitative Information*, Graphics Press, Cheshire, Conn., 1983.

PROBLEMS

Applied Load, lb/in²	Elongation per Inch of Length
0	0
3,000	.00011
5,000	.00018
10,000	.00033
15,000	.00051
20,000	.00067
25,000	.00083
30,000	.00099
35,000	.00115
40,000	.00134
42,000	.00142

Problem 1

1. The data given below were obtained in a tension test of a machine-steel bar. Plot the data on rectangular coordinates, using the elongation as the independent variable and the applied load as the dependent variable.

2. The data given below were obtained from a test of an automobile engine. Plot curves on rectangular coordinate paper, showing the relation between fuel used per brake horsepower-hour and brake horsepower developed. Show also the relation between thermal efficiency and brake horsepower developed, assuming the heat value of the gasoline to be 19,000 Btu/lb.

r/min	Length of Run, min	Fuel per Run, lb	bhp
1006	11.08	1.0	5.5
1001	4.25	.5	8.5
997	7.53	1.0	13.0
1000	5.77	1.0	16.3
1002	2.38	.5	21.1

Problem 2

3. From the data below, plot curves showing the "thinking distance" and "braking distance." From these curves, plot the sum curve "total distance." Call it "Automobile Minimum Travel Distances When Stopping—Average Driver."

mi/h	ft/s	Thinking Distance, ft	Braking Distance, ft
20	29	22	18
30	44	33	40
40	59	44	71
50	74	55	111
60	88	66	160
70	103	77	218

Problem 3

Temperature T, °C	Resistance R, $\mu\Omega$
14.0	96.00
19.2	97.76
25.0	100.50
30.0	102.14
36.5	105.00
40.1	105.75
45.0	108.20
52.0	110.60

Problem 4

4. Measurement of the electric resistance of a 1-ft length of no. 0 AWG standard annealed copper wire at various temperatures resulted in the data shown in the accompanying table.

After plotting the data on uniform rectangular coordinates with resistance as the ordinate and temperature as the abscissa, evaluate constants a and b in the linear equation $R = a + bT$ relating the variables.

5. Creep-strength tests of a high-chromium (23 to 27 percent) ferritic steel used in high-temperature service resulted in the stress values to produce a 1 percent deformation in 10,000 h at various temperatures, tabulated as shown.

After plotting the data on semilogarithmic coordinates with stress as the ordinate on a logarithmic scale and temperature as the abscissa on a uniform scale, evaluate constants a and b in the exponential equation $S = a10^{bT}$ relating the variables.

Temperature T, °C	Stress S, kPa
540	35,500
590	14,400
650	8,600
700	3,900
760	2,200

Problem 5

Preliminary plots should be made on rectilinear coordinates for data in the following problems so that the equation form may be determined. Further preliminary plots of the data should be made on the correct coordinate system required for rectification. Constants of the equations may be obtained graphically from an accurate rectified plot of the data or numerically. The completed plot of the data should include scales with proper graduations, calibrations, legends, and the equation with constants evaluated for the data as part of a descriptive title.

6. Spark-gap breakdown voltages for smooth spherical electrodes 25 cm in diameter and in clean dry air at 25°C and 760 mm are tabulated as shown for various gap lengths:

Gap Length L, cm	Peak Voltage V, kV
5	.16
10	.32
15	.48
20	.64
25	.81
30	.98
35	1.15
40	1.32
45	1.49
50	1.66
60	2.01
70	2.37
80	2.74
90	3.11
100	3.49

Problem 6

7. Heat losses from horizontal bare-iron hot-water pipes at 180°F to still ambient air at 75°F are tabulated as shown.

Pipe Size D, in	Heat Loss H, Btu/(ft·day)
1	1,896
1¼	2,398
1½	2,746
2	3,430
2½	4,140
3	5,054
3½	5,771
4	6,493
4½	7,211
5	8,020
6	9,530
8	12,442
10	15,528
12	18,418
14	20,140
16	23,088
18	25,998

Problem 7

APPENDIXES

APPENDIX 1 **TRIGONOMETRIC FUNCTIONS**

Angle	Sine		Cosine		Tangent		Cotangent		Angle
	Nat.	Log.	Nat.	Log.	Nat.	Log.	Nat.	Log.	
0° 00′	.0000	∞	1.0000	0.0000	.0000	∞	∞	∞	90° 00′
10	.0029	7.4637	1.0000	0000	.0029	7.4637	343.77	2.5363	50
20	.0058	7648	1.0000	0000	.0058	7648	171.89	2352	40
30	.0087	9408	1.0000	0000	.0087	9409	114.59	0591	30
40	.0116	8.0658	.9999	0000	.0116	8.0658	85.940	1.9342	20
50	.0145	1627	.9999	0000	.0145	1627	68.750	8373	10
1° 00′	.0175	8.2419	.9998	9.9999	.0175	8.2419	57.290	1.7581	89° 00′
10	.0204	3088	.9998	9999	.0204	3089	49.104	6911	50
20	.0233	3668	.9997	9999	.0233	3669	42.964	6331	40
30	.0262	4179	.9997	9999	.0262	4181	38.188	5819	30
40	.0291	4637	.9996	9998	.0291	4638	34.368	5362	20
50	.0320	5050	.9995	9998	.0320	5053	31.242	4947	10
2° 00′	.0349	8.5428	.9994	9.9997	.0349	8.5431	28.636	1.4569	88° 00′
10	.0378	5776	.9993	9997	.0378	5779	26.432	4221	50
20	.0407	6097	.9992	9996	.0407	6101	24.542	3899	40
30	.0436	6397	.9990	9996	.0437	6401	22.904	3599	30
40	.0465	6677	.9989	9995	.0466	6682	21.470	3318	20
50	.0494	6940	.9988	9995	.0495	6945	20.206	3055	10
3° 00′	.0523	8.7188	.9986	9.9994	.0524	8.7194	19.081	1.2806	87° 00′
10	.0552	7423	.9985	9993	.0553	7429	18.075	2571	50
20	.0581	7645	.9983	9993	.0582	7652	17.169	2348	40
30	.0610	7857	.9981	9992	.0612	7865	16.350	2135	30
40	.0640	8059	.9980	9991	.0641	8067	15.605	1933	20
50	.0669	8251	.9978	9990	.0670	8261	14.924	1739	10
4° 00′	.0698	8.8436	.9976	9.9989	.0699	8.8446	14.301	1.1554	86° 00′
10	.0727	8613	.9974	9989	.0729	8624	13.727	1376	50
20	.0756	8783	.9971	9988	.0758	8795	13.197	1205	40
30	.0785	8946	.9969	9987	.0787	8960	12.706	1040	30
40	.0814	9104	.9967	9986	.0816	9118	12.251	0882	20
50	.0843	9256	.9964	9985	.0846	9272	11.826	0728	10
5° 00′	.0872	8.9403	.9962	9.9983	.0875	8.9420	11.430	1.0580	85° 00′
10	.0901	9545	.9959	9982	.0904	9563	11.059	0437	50
20	.0929	9682	.9957	9981	.0934	9701	10.712	0299	40
30	.0958	9816	.9954	9980	.0963	9836	10.385	0164	30
40	.0987	9945	.9951	9979	.0992	9966	10.078	0034	20
50	.1016	9.0070	.9948	9977	.1022	9.0093	9.7882	0.9907	10
6° 00′	.1045	9.0192	.9945	9.9976	.1051	9.0216	9.5144	0.9784	84° 00′
10	.1074	0311	.9942	9975	.1080	0336	9.2553	9664	50
20	.1103	0426	.9939	9973	.1110	0453	9.0098	9547	40
30	.1132	0539	.9936	9972	.1139	0567	8.7769	9433	30
40	.1161	0648	.9932	9971	.1169	0678	8.5555	9322	20
50	.1190	0755	.9929	9969	.1198	0786	8.3450	9214	10
7° 00′	.1219	9.0859	.9925	9.9968	.1228	9.0891	8.1443	0.9109	83° 00′
10	.1248	0961	.9922	9966	.1257	0995	7.9530	9005	50
20	.1276	1060	.9918	9964	.1287	1096	7.7704	8904	40
	Nat.	Log.	Nat.	Log.	Nat.	Log.	Nat.	Log.	
Angle	Cosine		Sine		Cotangent		Tangent		Angle

Angle	Sine		Cosine		Tangent		Cotangent		Angle
	Nat.	Log.	Nat.	Log.	Nat.	Log.	Nat.	Log.	
30	.1305	1157	.9914	9963	.1317	1194	7.5958	8806	30
40	.1334	1252	.9911	9961	.1346	1291	7.4287	8709	20
50	.1363	1345	.9907	9959	.1376	1385	7.2687	8615	10
8° 00′	.1392	9.1436	.9903	9.9958	.1405	9.1478	7.1154	0.8522	82° 00′
10	.1421	1525	.9899	9956	.1435	1569	6.9682	8431	50
20	.1449	1612	.9894	9954	.1465	1658	6.8269	8342	40
30	.1478	1697	.9890	9952	.1495	1745	6.6912	8255	30
40	.1507	1781	.9886	9950	.1524	1831	6.5606	8169	20
50	.1536	1863	.9881	9948	.1554	1915	6.4348	8085	10
9° 00′	.1564	9.1943	.9877	9.9946	.1584	9.1997	6.3138	0.8003	81° 00′
10	.1593	2022	.9872	9944	.1614	2078	6.1970	7922	50
20	.1622	2100	.9868	9942	.1644	2158	6.0844	7842	40
30	.1650	2176	.9863	9940	.1673	2236	5.9758	7764	30
40	.1679	2251	.9858	9938	.1703	2313	5.8708	7687	20
50	.1708	2324	.9853	9936	.1733	2389	5.7694	7611	10
10° 00′	.1736	9.2397	.9848	9.9934	.1763	9.2463	5.6713	0.7537	80° 00′
10	.1765	2468	.9843	9931	.1793	2536	5.5764	7464	50
20	.1794	2538	.9838	9929	.1823	2609	5.4845	7391	40
30	.1822	2606	.9833	9927	.1853	2680	5.3955	7320	30
40	.1851	2674	.9827	9924	.1883	2750	5.3093	7250	20
50	.1880	2740	.9822	9922	.1914	2819	5.2257	7181	10
11° 00′	.1908	9.2806	.9816	9.9919	.1944	9.2887	5.1446	0.7113	79° 00′
10	.1937	2870	.9811	9917	.1974	2953	5.0658	7047	50
20	.1965	2934	.9805	9914	.2004	3020	4.9894	6980	40
30	.1994	2997	.9799	9912	.2035	3085	4.9152	6915	30
40	.2022	3058	.9793	9909	.2065	3149	4.8430	6851	20
50	.2051	3119	.9787	9907	.2095	3212	4.7729	6788	10
12° 00′	.2079	9.3179	.9781	9.9904	.2126	9.3275	4.7046	0.6725	78° 00′
10	.2108	3238	.9775	9901	.2156	3336	4.6382	6664	50
20	.2136	3296	.9769	9899	.2186	3397	4.5736	6603	40
30	.2164	3353	.9763	9896	.2217	3458	4.5107	6542	30
40	.2193	3410	.9757	9893	.2247	3517	4.4494	6483	20
50	.2221	3466	.9750	9890	.2278	3576	4.3897	6424	10
13° 00′	.2250	9.3521	.9744	9.9887	.2309	9.3634	4.3315	0.6366	77° 00′
10	.2278	3575	.9737	9884	.2339	3691	4.2747	6309	50
20	.2306	3629	.9730	9881	.2370	3748	4.2193	6252	40
30	.2334	3682	.9724	9878	.2401	3804	4.1653	6196	30
40	.2363	3734	.9717	9875	.2432	3859	4.1126	6141	20
50	.2391	3786	.9710	9872	.2462	3914	4.0611	6086	10
14° 00′	.2419	9.3837	.9703	9.9869	.2493	9.3968	4.0108	0.6032	76° 00′
10	.2447	3887	.9696	9866	.2524	4021	3.9617	5979	50
20	.2476	3937	.9689	9863	.2555	4074	3.9136	5926	40
30	.2504	3986	.9681	9859	.2586	4127	3.8667	5873	30
40	.2532	4035	.9674	9856	.2617	4178	3.8208	5822	20
50	.2560	4083	.9667	9853	.2648	4230	3.7760	5770	10
	Nat.	Log.	Nat.	Log.	Nat.	Log.	Nat.	Log.	
Angle	Cosine		Sine		Cotangent		Tangent		Angle

Angle	Sine		Cosine		Tangent		Cotangent		Angle
	Nat.	Log.	Nat.	Log.	Nat.	Log.	Nat.	Log.	
15° 00′	.2588	9.4130	.9659	9.9849	.2679	9.4281	3.7321	0.5719	75° 00′
10	.2616	4177	.9652	9846	.2711	4331	3.6891	5669	50
20	.2644	4223	.9644	9843	.2742	4381	3.6470	5619	40
30	.2672	4269	.9636	9839	.2773	4430	3.6059	5570	30
40	.2700	4314	.9628	9836	.2805	4479	3.5656	5521	20
50	.2728	4359	.9621	9832	.2836	4527	3.5261	5473	10
16° 00′	.2756	9.4403	.9613	9.9828	.2867	9.4575	3.4874	0.5425	74° 00′
10	.2784	4447	.9605	9825	.2899	4622	3.4495	5378	50
20	.2812	4491	.9596	9821	.2931	4669	3.4124	5331	40
30	.2840	4533	.9588	9817	.2962	4716	3.3759	5284	30
40	.2868	4576	.9580	9814	.2994	4762	3.3402	5238	20
50	.2896	4618	.9572	9810	.3026	4808	3.3052	5192	10
17° 00′	.2924	9.4659	.9563	9.9806	.3057	9.4853	3.2709	0.5147	73° 00′
10	.2952	4700	.9555	9802	.3089	4898	3.2371	5102	50
20	.2979	4741	.9546	9798	.3121	4943	3.2041	5057	40
30	.3007	4781	.9537	9794	.3153	4987	3.1716	5013	30
40	.3035	4821	.9528	9790	.3185	5031	3.1397	4969	20
50	.3062	4861	.9520	9786	.3217	5075	3.1084	4925	10
18° 00′	.3090	9.4900	.9511	9.9782	.3249	9.5118	3.0777	0.4882	72° 00′
10	.3118	4939	.9502	9778	.3281	5161	3.0475	4839	50
20	.3145	4977	.9492	9774	.3314	5203	3.0178	4797	40
30	.3173	5015	.9483	9770	.3346	5245	2.9887	4755	30
40	.3201	5052	.9474	9765	.3378	5287	2.9600	4713	20
50	.3228	5090	.9465	9761	.3411	5329	2.9319	4671	10
19° 00′	.3256	9.5126	.9455	9.9757	.3443	9.5370	2.9042	0.4630	71° 00′
10	.3283	5163	.9446	9752	.3476	5411	2.8770	4589	50
20	.3311	5199	.9436	9748	.3508	5451	2.8502	4549	40
30	.3338	5235	.9426	9743	.3541	5491	2.8239	4509	30
40	.3365	5270	.9417	9739	.3574	5531	2.7980	4469	20
50	.3393	5306	.9407	9734	.3607	5571	2.7725	4429	10
20° 00′	.3420	9.5341	.9397	9.9730	.3640	9.5611	2.7475	0.4389	70° 00′
10	.3448	5375	.9387	9725	.3673	5650	2.7228	4350	50
20	.3475	5409	.9377	9721	.3706	5689	2.6985	4311	40
30	.3502	5443	.9367	9716	.3739	5727	2.6746	4273	30
40	.3529	5477	.9356	9711	.3772	5766	2.6511	4234	20
50	.3557	5510	.9346	9706	.3805	5804	2.6279	4196	10
21° 00′	.3584	9.5543	.9336	9.9702	.3839	9.5842	2.6051	0.4158	69° 00′
10	.3611	5576	.9325	9697	.3872	5879	2.5826	4121	50
20	.3638	5609	.9315	9692	.3906	5917	2.5605	4083	40
30	.3665	5641	.9304	9687	.3939	5954	2.5386	4046	30
40	.3692	5673	.9293	9682	.3973	5991	2.5172	4009	20
50	.3719	5704	.9283	9677	.4006	6028	2.4960	3972	10
22° 00′	.3746	9.5736	.9272	9.9672	.4040	9.6064	2.4751	0.3936	68° 00′
10	.3773	5767	.9261	9667	.4074	6100	2.4545	3900	50
20	.3800	5798	.9250	9661	.4108	6136	2.4342	3864	40
	Nat.	Log.	Nat.	Log.	Nat.	Log.	Nat.	Log.	
Angle	Cosine		Sine		Cotangent		Tangent		Angle

Angle	Sine		Cosine		Tangent		Cotangent		Angle
	Nat.	Log.	Nat.	Log.	Nat.	Log.	Nat.	Log.	
30	.3827	5828	.9239	9656	.4142	6172	2.4142	3828	30
40	.3854	5859	.9228	9651	.4176	6208	2.3945	3792	20
50	.3881	5889	.9216	9646	.4210	6243	2.3750	3757	10
23° 00′	.3907	9.5919	.9205	9.9640	4245	9.6279	2.3559	0.3721	67° 00′
10	.3934	5948	.9194	9635	.4279	6314	2.3369	3686	50
20	.3961	5978	.9182	9629	.4314	6348	2.3183	3652	40
30	.3987	6007	.9171	9624	.4348	6383	2.2998	3617	30
40	.4014	6036	.9159	9618	.4383	6417	2.2817	3583	20
50	.4041	6065	.9147	9613	.4417	6452	2.2637	3548	10
24° 00′	.4067	9.6093	.9135	9.9607	.4452	9.6486	2.2460	0.3514	66° 00′
10	.4094	6121	.9124	9602	.4487	6520	2.2286	3480	50
20	.4120	6149	.9112	9596	.4522	6553	2.2113	3447	40
30	.4147	6177	.9100	9590	.4557	6587	2.1943	3413	30
40	.4173	6205	.9088	9584	.4592	6620	2.1775	3380	20
50	.4200	6232	.9075	9579	.4628	6654	2.1609	3346	10
25° 00′	.4226	9.6259	.9063	9.9573	.4663	9.6687	2.1445	0.3313	65° 00′
10	.4253	6286	.9051	9567	.4699	6720	2.1283	3280	50
20	.4279	6313	.9038	9561	.4734	6752	2.1123	3248	40
30	.4305	6340	.9026	9555	.4770	6785	2.0965	3215	30
40	.4331	6366	.9013	9549	.4806	6817	2.0809	3183	20
50	.4358	6392	.9001	9543	.4841	6850	2.0655	3150	10
26° 00′	.4384	9.6418	.8988	9.9537	.4877	9.6882	2.0503	0.3118	64° 00′
10	.4410	6444	.8975	9530	.4913	6914	2.0353	3086	50
20	.4436	6470	.8962	9524	.4950	6946	2.0204	3054	40
30	.4462	6495	.8949	9518	.4986	6977	2.0057	3023	30
40	.4488	6521	.8936	9512	.5022	7009	1.9912	2991	20
50	.4514	6546	.8923	9505	.5059	7040	1.9768	2960	10
27° 00′	.4540	9.6570	.8910	9.9499	.5095	9.7072	1.9626	0.2928	63° 00′
10	.4566	6595	.8897	9492	.5132	7103	1.9486	2897	50
20	.4592	6620	.8884	9486	.5169	7134	1.9347	2866	40
30	.4617	6644	.8870	9479	.5206	7165	1.9210	2835	30
40	.4643	6668	.8857	9473	.5243	7196	1.9074	2804	20
50	.4669	6692	.8843	9466	.5280	7226	1.8940	2774	10
28° 00′	.4695	9.6716	.8829	9.9459	.5317	9.7257	1.8807	0.2743	62° 00′
10	.4720	6740	.8816	9453	.5354	7287	1.8676	2713	50
20	.4746	6763	.8802	9446	.5392	7317	1.8546	2683	40
30	.4772	6787	.8788	9439	.5430	7348	1.8418	2652	30
40	.4797	6810	.8774	9432	.5467	7378	1.8291	2622	20
50	.4823	6833	.8760	9425	.5505	7408	1.8165	2592	10
29° 00′	.4848	9.6856	.8746	9.9418	.5543	9.7438	1.8040	0.2562	61° 00′
10	.4874	6878	.8732	9411	.5581	7467	1.7917	2533	50
20	.4899	6901	.8718	9404	.5619	7497	1.7796	2503	40
30	.4924	6923	.8704	9397	.5658	7526	1.7675	2474	30
40	.4950	6946	.8689	9390	.5696	7556	1.7556	2444	20
50	.4975	6968	.8675	9383	.5735	7585	1.7437	2415	10
	Nat.	Log.	Nat.	Log.	Nat.	Log.	Nat.	Log.	
Angle	Cosine		Sine		Cotangent		Tangent		Angle

Angle	Sine		Cosine		Tangent		Cotangent		Angle
	Nat.	Log.	Nat.	Log.	Nat.	Log.	Nat.	Log.	
30° 00′	.5000	9.6990	.8660	9.9375	.5774	9.7614	1.7321	0.2386	60° 00′
10	.5025	7012	.8646	9368	.5812	7644	1.7205	2356	50
20	.5050	7033	.8631	9361	.5851	7673	1.7090	2327	40
30	.5075	7055	.8616	9353	.5890	7701	1.6977	2299	30
40	.5100	7076	.8601	9346	.5930	7730	1.6864	2270	20
50	.5125	7097	.8587	9338	.5969	7759	1.6753	2241	10
31° 00′	.5150	9.7118	.8572	9.9331	.6009	9.7788	1.6643	0.2212	59° 00′
10	.5175	7139	.8557	9323	.6048	7816	1.6534	2184	50
20	.5200	7160	.8542	9315	.6088	7845	1.6426	2155	40
30	.5225	7181	.8526	9308	.6128	7873	1.6319	2127	30
40	.5250	7201	.8511	9300	.6168	7902	1.6212	2098	20
50	.5275	7222	.8496	9292	.6208	7930	1.6107	2070	10
32° 00′	.5299	9.7242	.8480	9.9284	.6249	9.7958	1.6003	0.2042	58° 00′
10	.5324	7262	.8465	9276	.6289	7986	1.5900	2014	50
20	.5348	7282	.8450	9268	.6330	8014	1.5798	1986	40
30	.5373	7302	.8434	9260	.6371	8042	1.5697	1958	30
40	.5398	7322	.8418	9252	.6412	8070	1.5597	1930	20
50	.5422	7342	.8403	9244	.6453	8097	1.5497	1903	10
33° 00′	.5446	9.7361	.8387	9.9236	.6494	9.8125	1.5399	0.1875	57° 00′
10	.5471	7380	.8371	9228	.6536	8153	1.5301	1847	50
20	.5495	7400	.8355	9219	.6577	8180	1.5204	1820	40
30	.5519	7419	.8339	9211	.6619	8208	1.5108	1792	30
40	.5544	7438	.8323	9203	.6661	8235	1.5013	1765	20
50	.5568	7457	.8307	9194	.6703	8263	1.4919	1737	10
34° 00′	.5592	9.7476	.8290	9.9186	.6745	9.8290	1.4826	0.1710	56° 00′
10	.5616	7494	.8274	9177	.6787	8317	1.4733	1683	50
20	.5640	7513	.8258	9169	.6830	8344	1.4641	1656	40
30	.5664	7531	.8241	9160	.6873	8371	1.4550	1629	30
40	.5688	7550	.8225	9151	.6916	8398	1.4460	1602	20
50	.5712	7568	.8208	9142	.6959	8425	1.4370	1575	10
35° 00′	.5736	9.7586	.8192	9.9134	.7002	9.8452	1.4281	0.1548	55° 00′
10	.5760	7604	.8175	9125	.7046	8479	1.4193	1521	50
20	.5783	7622	.8158	9116	.7089	8506	1.4106	1494	40
30	.5807	7640	.8141	9107	.7133	8533	1.4019	1467	30
40	.5831	7657	.8124	9098	.7177	8559	1.3934	1441	20
50	.5854	7675	.8107	9089	.7221	8586	1.3848	1414	10
36° 00′	.5878	9.7692	.8090	9.9080	.7265	9.8613	1.3764	0.1387	54° 00′
10	.5901	7710	.8073	9070	.7310	8639	1.3680	1361	50
20	.5925	7727	.8056	9061	.7355	8666	1.3597	1334	40
30	.5948	7744	.8039	9052	.7400	8692	1.3514	1308	30
40	.5972	7761	.8021	9042	.7445	8718	1.3432	1282	20
50	.5995	7778	.8004	9033	.7490	8745	1.3351	1255	10
37° 00′	.6018	9.7795	.7986	9.9023	.7536	9.8771	1.3270	0.1229	53° 00′
10	.6041	7811	.7969	9014	.7581	8797	1.3190	1203	50
20	.6065	7828	.7951	9004	.7627	8824	1.3111	1176	40
	Nat.	Log.	Nat.	Log.	Nat.	Log.	Nat.	Log.	
Angle	Cosine		Sine		Cotangent		Tangent		Angle

Angle	Sine		Cosine		Tangent		Cotangent		Angle
	Nat.	Log.	Nat.	Log.	Nat.	Log.	Nat.	Log.	
30	.6088	7844	.7934	8995	.7673	8850	1.3032	1150	30
40	.6111	7861	.7916	8985	.7720	8876	1.2954	1124	20
50	.6134	7877	.7898	8975	.7766	8902	1.2876	1098	10
38° 00′	.6157	9.7893	.7880	9.8965	.7813	9.8928	1.2799	0.1072	52° 00′
10	.6180	7910	.7862	8955	.7860	8954	1.2723	1046	50
20	.6202	7926	.7844	8945	.7907	8980	1.2647	1020	40
30	.6225	7941	.7826	8935	.7954	9006	1.2572	0994	30
40	.6248	7957	.7808	8925	.8002	9032	1.2497	0968	20
50	.6271	7973	.7790	8915	.8050	9058	1.2423	0942	10
39° 00′	.6293	9.7989	.7771	9.8905	.8098	9.9084	1.2349	0.0916	51° 00′
10	.6316	8004	.7753	8895	.8146	9110	1.2276	0890	50
20	.6338	8020	.7735	8884	.8195	9135	1.2203	0865	40
30	.6361	8035	.7716	8874	.8243	9161	1.2131	0839	30
40	.6383	8050	.7698	8864	.8292	9187	1.2059	0813	20
50	.6406	8066	.7679	8853	.8342	9212	1.1988	0788	10
40° 00′	.6428	9.8081	.7660	9.8843	.8391	9.9238	1.1918	0.0762	50° 00′
10	.6450	8096	.7642	8832	.8441	9264	1.1847	0736	50
20	.6472	8111	.7623	8821	.8491	9289	1.1778	0711	40
30	.6494	8125	.7604	8810	.8541	9315	1.1708	0685	30
40	.6517	8140	.7585	8800	.8591	9341	1.1640	0659	20
50	.6539	8155	.7566	8789	.8642	9366	1.1571	0634	10
41° 00′	.6561	9.8169	.7547	9.8778	.8693	9.9392	1.1504	0.0608	49° 00′
10	.6583	8184	.7528	8767	.8744	9417	1.1436	0583	50
20	.6604	8198	.7509	8756	.8796	9443	1.1369	0557	40
30	.6626	8213	.7490	8745	.8847	9468	1.1303	0532	30
40	.6648	8227	.7470	8733	.8899	9494	1.1237	0506	20
50	.6670	8241	.7451	8722	.8952	9519	1.1171	0481	10
42° 00′	.6691	9.8255	.7431	9.8711	.9004	9.9544	1.1106	0.0456	48° 00′
10	.6713	8269	.7412	8699	.9057	9570	1.1041	0430	50
20	.6734	8283	.7392	8688	.9110	9595	1.0977	0405	40
30	.6756	8297	.7373	8676	.9163	9621	1.0913	0379	30
40	.6777	8311	.7353	8665	.9217	9646	1.0850	0354	20
50	.6799	8324	.7333	8653	.9271	9671	1.0786	0329	10
43° 00′	.6820	9.8338	.7314	9.8641	.9325	9.9697	1.0724	0.0303	47° 00′
10	.6841	8351	.7294	8629	.9380	9722	1.0661	0278	50
20	.6862	8365	.7274	8618	.9435	9747	1.0599	0253	40
30	.6884	8378	.7254	8606	.9490	9772	1.0538	0228	30
40	.6905	8391	.7234	8594	.9545	9798	1.0477	0202	20
50	.6926	8405	.7214	8582	.9601	9823	1.0416	0177	10
44° 00′	.6947	9.8418	.7193	9.8569	.9657	9.9848	1.0355	0.0152	46° 00′
10	.6967	8431	.7173	8557	.9713	9874	1.0295	0126	50
20	.6988	8444	.7153	8545	.9770	9899	1.0235	0101	40
30	.7009	8457	.7133	8532	.9827	9924	1.0176	0076	30
40	.7030	8469	.7112	8520	.9884	9949	1.0117	0051	20
50	.7050	8482	.7092	8507	.9942	9975	1.0058	0025	10
45° 00′	.7071	9.8495	.7071	9.8495	1.0000	0.0000	1.0000	0.0000	45° 00′
	Nat.	Log.	Nat.	Log.	Nat.	Log.	Nat.	Log	
Angle	Cosine		Sine		Cotangent		Tangent		Angle

APPENDIX 2 DECIMAL INCH-MILLIMETER CONVERSIONS

Decimal Equivalents of Inch Fractions

Fraction	Equiv.	Fraction	Equiv.	Fraction	Equiv.	Fraction	Equiv.
1/64	0.015625	17/64	0.265625	33/64	0.515625	49/64	0.765625
1/32	0.03125	9/32	0.28125	17/32	0.53125	25/32	0.78125
3/64	0.046875	19/64	0.296875	35/64	0.546875	51/64	0.796875
1/16	0.0625	5/16	0.3125	9/16	0.5625	13/16	0.8125
5/64	0.078125	21/64	0.328125	37/64	0.578125	53/64	0.828125
3/32	0.09375	11/32	0.34375	19/32	0.59375	27/32	0.84375
7/64	0.109375	23/64	0.359375	39/64	0.609375	55/64	0.859375
1/8	0.1250	3/8	0.3750	5/8	0.6250	7/8	0.8750
9/64	0.140625	25/64	0.390625	41/64	0.640625	57/64	0.890625
5/32	0.15625	13/32	0.40625	21/32	0.65625	29/32	0.90625
11/64	0.171875	27/64	0.421875	43/64	0.671875	59/64	0.921875
3/16	0.1875	7/16	0.4375	11/16	0.6875	15/16	0.9375
13/64	0.203125	29/64	0.453125	45/64	0.703125	61/64	0.953125
7/32	0.21875	15/32	0.46875	23/32	0.71875	31/32	0.96875
15/64	0.234375	31/64	0.484375	47/64	0.734375	63/64	0.984375
1/4	0.2500	1/2	0.5000	3/4	0.7500	1	1.0000

Metric Equivalents

Mm	In.*	Mm	In.	In.	Mm †	In.	Mm
1 = 0.0394		17 = 0.6693		1/32 = 0.794		17/32 = 13.494	
2 = 0.0787		18 = 0.7087		1/16 = 1.588		9/16 = 14.288	
3 = 0.1181		19 = 0.7480		3/32 = 2.381		19/32 = 15.081	
4 = 0.1575		20 = 0.7874		1/8 = 3.175		5/8 = 15.875	
5 = 0.1969		21 = 0.8268		5/32 = 3.969		21/32 = 16.669	
6 = 0.2362		22 = 0.8662		3/16 = 4.762		11/16 = 17.462	
7 = 0.2756		23 = 0.9055		7/32 = 5.556		23/32 = 18.256	
8 = 0.3150		24 = 0.9449		1/4 = 6.350		3/4 = 19.050	
9 = 0.3543		25 = 0.9843		9/32 = 7.144		25/32 = 19.844	
10 = 0.3937		26 = 1.0236		5/16 = 7.938		13/16 = 20.638	
11 = 0.4331		27 = 1.0630		11/32 = 8.731		27/32 = 21.431	
12 = 0.4724		28 = 1.1024		3/8 = 9.525		7/8 = 22.225	
13 = 0.5118		29 = 1.1418		13/32 = 10.319		29/32 = 23.019	
14 = 0.5512		30 = 1.1811		7/16 = 11.112		15/16 = 23.812	
15 = 0.5906		31 = 1.2205		15/32 = 11.906		31/32 = 24.606	
16 = 0.6299		32 = 1.2599		1/2 = 12.700		1 = 25.400	

*Rounded to fourth decimal place.
†Rounded to third decimal place.

APPENDIX 3 SI UNIT PREFIXES

Multiplication factor	Prefix	Symbol	Pronunciation (USA)*	Term (USA)	Term (other countries)
$1\ 000\ 000\ 000\ 000\ 000\ 000 = 10^{18}$	exa	E	as in Texas	one quintillion†	one trillion
$1\ 000\ 000\ 000\ 000\ 000 = 10^{15}$	peta	P	as in petal	one quadrillion†	one thousand billion
$1\ 000\ 000\ 000\ 000 = 10^{12}$	tera	T	as in terrace	one trillion†	one billion
$1\ 000\ 000\ 000 = 10^{9}$	giga	G	jig' a (a as in about)	one billion†	one millard
$1\ 000\ 000 = 10^{6}$	mega	M	as in megaphone	one million	
$1\ 000 = 10^{3}$	kilo	k	as in kilowatt	one thousand	
$100 = 10^{2}$	hecto	h	heck′toe	one hundred	
$10 = 10$	deka	da	deck′ a (a as in about)	ten	
$0.1 = 10^{-1}$	deci	d	as in decimal	one tenth	
$0.01 = 10^{-2}$	centi	c	as in sentiment	one hundredth	
$0.001 = 10^{-3}$	milli	m	as in military	one thousandth	
$0.000\ 001 = 10^{-6}$	micro	μ	as in microphone	one millionth	one milliardth
$0.000\ 000\ 001 = 10^{-9}$	nano	n	nan' oh (nan as in Nancy)	one billionth†	one billionth
$0.000\ 000\ 000\ 001 = 10^{-12}$	pico	p	peek′ oh	one trillionth†	one thousand billionth
$0.000\ 000\ 000\ 000\ 001 = 10^{-15}$	femto	f	fem′ toe (fem as in feminine)	one quadrillionth†	one trillionth
$0.000\ 000\ 000\ 000\ 000\ 001 = 10^{-18}$	atto	a	as in anatomy	one quintillionth†	

Abstracted from material by American National Metric Council, 1977.

*The first syllable of every prefix is accented to ensure that the prefix will retain its identity.

†These terms should be avoided in technical writing because the denominations above one million and below one millionth are different in most countries, as indicated in the last column. Instead, use the prefixes or 10 raised to an integral power.

APPENDIX 4   COMMON SI UNITS

Quantity	Some common units	Symbol	Equivalent	Symbol
Length	kilometer	km		
	meter	m		
	centimeter	cm		
	millimeter	mm		
	micrometer	μm		
Area	square kilometer	km^2		
	square hectometer	hm^2	hectare	ha
	square meter	m^2		
	square centimeter	cm^2		
	square millimeter	mm^2		
Volume	cubic meter	m^3		
	cubic decimeter	dm^3	liter	L
	cubic centimeter	cm^3	milliliter	mL
Plane angle	degree	°		
Speed or velocity	meter per second	m/s		
	kilometer per hour	km/h		
Acceleration	meter per second squared	m/s^2		
Frequency	megahertz	MHz		
	kilohertz	kHz		
	hertz	Hz		
Rotational frequency	revolution per second	r/s		
	revolution per minute	r/min		
Mass	megagram	Mg	metric ton	t
	kilogram	kg		
	gram	g		
	milligram	mg		
Density	kilogram per cubic meter	kg/m^3	gram per liter	g/L
Force	kilonewton	kN		
	newton	N		
Moment of force	newton-meter	N·m		
Pressure (or vacuum)	kilopascal	kPa		
Stress	megapascal	MPa		
Viscosity (dynamic)	millipascal second	mPa·s		
Viscosity (kinematic)	square millimeter per second	mm^2/s		
Energy, work, or quantity of heat	joule	J		
	kilowatthour	kW·h	kilowatthour	kWh
Power, or heat flow rate	kilowatt	kW		
	watt	W		
Temperature, or temperature interval	kelvin	K		
	degree Celsius	°C		
Electric current	ampere	A		

APPENDIX 4 COMMON SI UNITS (CONT.)

Quantity	Some common units	Symbol	Equivalent	Symbol
Quantity of electricity	coulomb	C		
	ampere-hour	A·h		Ah
Electromotive force	volt	V		
Electric resistance	ohm	Ω		
Luminous intensity	candela	cd		
Luminous flux	lumen	lm		
Illuminance	lux	lx		
Sound level	decibel	dB		

Abstracted from material by American National Metric Council, 1977.

APPENDIX 5   **LENGTH OF CHORD FOR CIRCLE ARCS OF 1-IN. RADIUS**

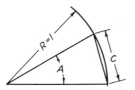

°	0′	10′	20′	30′	40′	50′
0	0.0000	0.0029	0.0058	0.0087	0.0116	0.0145
1	0.0175	0.0204	0.0233	0.0262	0.0291	0.0320
2	0.0349	0.0378	0.0407	0.0436	0.0465	0.0494
3	0.0524	0.0553	0.0582	0.0611	0.0640	0.0669
4	0.0698	0.0727	0.0756	0.0785	0.0814	0.0843
5	0.0872	0.0901	0.0931	0.0960	0.0989	0.1018
6	0.1047	0.1076	0.1105	0.1134	0.1163	0.1192
7	0.1221	0.1250	0.1279	0.1308	0.1337	0.1366
8	0.1395	0.1424	0.1453	0.1482	0.1511	0.1540
9	0.1569	0.1598	0.1627	0.1656	0.1685	0.1714
10	0.1743	0.1772	0.1801	0.1830	0.1859	0.1888
11	0.1917	0.1946	0.1975	0.2004	0.2033	0.2062
12	0.2091	0.2119	0.2148	0.2177	0.2206	0.2235
13	0.2264	0.2293	0.2322	0.2351	0.2380	0.2409
14	0.2437	0.2466	0.2495	0.2524	0.2553	0.2582
15	0.2611	0.2639	0.2668	0.2697	0.2726	0.2755
16	0.2783	0.2812	0.2841	0.2870	0.2899	0.2927
17	0.2956	0.2985	0.3014	0.3042	0.3071	0.3100
18	0.3129	0.3157	0.3186	0.3215	0.3244	0.3272
19	0.3301	0.3330	0.3358	0.3387	0.3416	0.3444
20	0.3473	0.3502	0.3530	0.3559	0.3587	0.3616
21	0.3645	0.3673	0.3702	0.3730	0.3759	0.3788
22	0.3816	0.3845	0.3873	0.3902	0.3930	0.3959
23	0.3987	0.4016	0.4044	0.4073	0.4101	0.4130
24	0.4158	0.4187	0.4215	0.4244	0.4272	0.4300
25	0.4329	0.4357	0.4386	0.4414	0.4442	0.4471
26	0.4499	0.4527	0.4556	0.4584	0.4612	0.4641
27	0.4669	0.4697	0.4725	0.4754	0.4782	0.4810
28	0.4838	0.4867	0.4895	0.4923	0.4951	0.4979
29	0.5008	0.5036	0.5064	0.5092	0.5120	0.5148
30	0.5176	0.5204	0.5233	0.5251	0.5289	0.5317
31	0.5345	0.5373	0.5401	0.5429	0.5457	0.5485
32	0.5513	0.5541	0.5569	0.5597	0.5625	0.5652
33	0.5680	0.5708	0.5736	0.5764	0.5792	0.5820
34	0.5847	0.5875	0.5903	0.5931	0.5959	0.5986
35	0.6014	0.6042	0.6070	0.6097	0.6125	0.6153
36	0.6180	0.6208	0.6236	0.6263	0.6291	0.6319
37	0.6346	0.6374	0.6401	0.6429	0.6456	0.6484
38	0.6511	0.6539	0.6566	0.6594	0.6621	0.6649
39	0.6676	0.6704	0.6731	0.6758	0.6786	0.6813
40	0.6840	0.6868	0.6895	0.6922	0.6950	0.6977
41	0.7004	0.7031	0.7059	0.7086	0.7113	0.7140
42	0.7167	0.7195	0.7222	0.7249	0.7276	0.7303
43	0.7330	0.7357	0.7384	0.7411	0.7438	0.7465
44	0.7492	0.7519	0.7546	0.7573	0.7600	0.7627
45 *	0.7654	0.7681	0.7707	0.7734	0.7761	0.7788

* For angles between 45° and 90°, draw 90° angle and lay off complement from 90° line.

APPENDIX 6 USA STANDARD PREFERRED LIMITS AND FITS FOR
CYLINDRICAL PARTS [ANSI B4.1—1967 (1974)]

APPENDIX 6A RUNNING AND SLIDING FITS

Limits are in thousandths of an inch.

Limits for hole and shaft are applied algebraically to the basic size to obtain the limits of size for the parts.

Data in bold face are in accordance with ABC agreements.

Symbols H5, g5, etc., are Hole and Shaft designations used in ABC System

Nominal Size Range Inches		Class RC 1			Class RC 2			Class RC 3			Class RC 4		
		Limits of Clearance	Standard Limits		Limits of Clearance	Standard Limits		Limits of Clearance	Standard Limits		Limits of Clearance	Standard Limits	
Over	To		Hole H5	Shaft g4		Hole H6	Shaft g5		Hole H7	Shaft f6		Hole H8	Shaft f7
0	− 0.12	0.1 0.45	+ 0.2 0	− 0.1 − 0.25	0.1 0.55	+ 0.25 0	− 0.1 − 0.3	0.3 0.95	+ 0.4 0	− 0.3 − 0.55	0.3 1.3	+ 0.6 0	− 0.3 − 0.7
0.12	− 0.24	0.15 0.5	+ 0.2 0	− 0.15 − 0.3	0.15 0.65	+ 0.3 0	− 0.15 − 0.35	0.4 1.2	+ 0.5 0	− 0.4 − 0.7	0.4 1.6	+ 0.7 0	− 0.4 − 0.9
0.24	− 0.40	0.2 0.6	+ 0.25 0	− 0.2 − 0.35	0.2 0.85	+ 0.4 0	− 0.2 − 0.45	0.5 1.5	+ 0.6 0	− 0.5 − 0.9	0.5 2.0	+ 0.9 0	− 0.5 − 1.1
0.40	− 0.71	0.25 0.75	+ 0.3 0	− 0.25 − 0.45	0.25 0.95	+ 0.4 0	− 0.25 − 0.55	0.6 1.7	+ 0.7 0	− 0.6 − 1.0	0.6 2.3	+ 1.0 0	− 0.6 − 1.3
0.71	− 1.19	0.3 0.95	+ 0.4 0	− 0.3 − 0.55	0.3 1.2	+ 0.5 0	− 0.3 − 0.7	0.8 2.1	+ 0.8 0	− 0.8 − 1.3	0.8 2.8	+ 1.2 0	− 0.8 − 1.6
1.19	− 1.97	0.4 1.1	+ 0.4 0	− 0.4 − 0.7	0.4 1.4	+ 0.6 0	− 0.4 − 0.8	1.0 2.6	+ 1.0 0	− 1.0 − 1.6	1.0 3.6	+ 1.6 0	− 1.0 − 2.0
1.97	− 3.15	0.4 1.2	+ 0.5 0	− 0.4 − 0.7	0.4 1.6	+ 0.7 0	− 0.4 − 0.9	1.2 3.1	+ 1.2 0	− 1.2 − 1.9	1.2 4.2	+ 1.8 0	− 1.2 − 2.4
3.15	− 4.73	0.5 1.5	+ 0.6 0	− 0.5 − 0.9	0.5 2.0	+ 0.9 0	− 0.5 − 1.1	1.4 3.7	+ 1.4 0	− 1.4 − 2.3	1.4 5.0	+ 2.2 0	− 1.4 − 2.8
4.73	− 7.09	0.6 1.8	+ 0.7 0	− 0.6 − 1.1	0.6 2.3	+ 1.0 0	− 0.6 − 1.3	1.6 4.2	+ 1.6 0	− 1.6 − 2.6	1.6 5.7	+ 2.5 0	− 1.6 − 3.2
7.09	− 9.85	0.6 2.0	+ 0.8 0	− 0.6 − 1.2	0.6 2.6	+ 1.2 0	− 0.6 − 1.4	2.0 5.0	+ 1.8 0	− 2.0 − 3.2	2.0 6.6	+ 2.8 0	− 2.0 − 3.8
9.85	−12.41	0.8 2.3	+ 0.9 0	− 0.8 − 1.4	0.7 2.8	+ 1.2 0	− 0.7 − 1.6	2.5 5.7	+ 2.0 0	− 2.5 − 3.7	2.2 7.2	+ 3.0 0	− 2.2 − 4.2
12.41	−15.75	1.0 2.7	+ 1.0 0	− 1.0 − 1.7	0.7 3.1	+ 1.4 0	− 0.7 − 1.7	3.0 6.6	+ 2.2 0	− 3.0 − 4.4	2.5 8.2	+ 3.5 0	− 2.5 − 4.7
15.75	−19.69	1.2 3.0	+ 1.0 0	− 1.2 − 2.0	0.8 3.4	+ 1.6 0	− 0.8 − 1.8	4.0 8.1	+ 2.5 0	− 4.0 − 5.6	2.8 9.3	+ 4.0 0	− 2.8 − 5.3
19.69	−30.09	1.6 3.7	+ 1.2 0	− 1.6 − 2.5	1.6 4.8	+ 2.0 0	− 1.6 − 2.8	5.0 10.0	+ 3.0 0	− 5.0 − 7.0	5.0 13.0	+ 5.0 0	− 5.0 − 8.0
30.09	−41.49	2.0 4.6	+ 1.6 0	− 2.0 − 3.0	2.0 6.1	+ 2.5 0	− 2.0 − 3.6	6.0 12.5	+ 4.0 0	− 6.0 − 8.5	6.0 16.0	+ 6.0 0	− 6.0 −10.0
41.49	−56.19	2.5 5.7	+ 2.0 0	− 2.5 − 3.7	2.5 7.5	+ 3.0 0	− 2.5 − 4.5	8.0 16.0	+ 5.0 0	− 8.0 −11.0	8.0 21.0	+ 8.0 0	− 8.0 −13.0
56.19	−76.39	3.0 7.1	+ 2.5 0	− 3.0 − 4.6	3.0 9.5	+ 4.0 0	− 3.0 − 5.5	10.0 20.0	+ 6.0 0	−10.0 −14.0	10.0 26.0	+10.0 0	−10.0 −16.0
76.39	−100.9	4.0 9.0	+ 3.0 0	− 4.0 − 6.0	4.0 12.0	+ 5.0 0	− 4.0 − 7.0	12.0 25.0	+ 8.0 0	−12.0 −17.0	12.0 32.0	+12.0 0	−12.0 −20.0
100.9	−131.9	5.0 11.5	+ 4.0 0	− 5.0 − 7.5	5.0 15.0	+ 6.0 0	− 5.0 − 9.0	16.0 32.0	+10.0 0	−16.0 −22.0	16.0 42.0	+16.0 0	−16.0 −26.0
131.9	−171.9	6.0 14.0	+ 5.0 0	− 6.0 − 9.0	6.0 19.0	+ 8.0 0	− 6.0 −11.0	18.0 38.0	+12.0 0	−18.0 −26.0	18.0 50.0	+20.0 0	−18.0 −30.0
171.9	−200	8.0 18.0	+ 6.0 0	− 8.0 −12.0	8.0 22.0	+10.0 0	− 8.0 −12.0	22.0 48.0	+16.0 0	−22.0 −32.0	22.0 63.0	+25.0 0	−22.0 −38.0

APPENDIX 6A   (CONT.)

RUNNING AND SLIDING FITS

Limits are in thousandths of an inch.

Limits for hole and shaft are applied algebraically to the basic size to obtain the limits of size for the parts

Data in bold face are in accordance with ABC agreements

Symbols H8, e7, etc., are Hole and Shaft designations used in ABC System

Class RC 5			Class RC 6			Class RC 7			Class RC 8			Class RC 9			Nominal Size Range Inches	
Limits of Clearance	Hole H8	Shaft e7	Limits of Clearance	Hole H9	Shaft e8	Limits of Clearance	Hole H9	Shaft d8	Limits of Clearance	Hole H10	Shaft c9	Limits of Clearance	Hole H11	Shaft	Over	To
0.6	+ 0.6	− 0.6	0.6	+ 1.0	− 0.6	1.0	+ 1.0	− 1.0	2.5	+ 1.6	− 2.5	4.0	+ 2.5	− 4.0	0	0.12
1.6	− 0	− 1.0	2.2	− 0	− 1.2	2.6	0	− 1.6	5.1	0	− 3.5	8.1	0	− 5.6		
0.8	+ 0.7	− 0.8	0.8	+ 1.2	− 0.8	1.2	+ 1.2	− 1.2	2.8	+ 1.8	− 2.8	4.5	+ 3.0	− 4.5	0.12	0.24
2.0	− 0	− 1.3	2.7	− 0	− 1.5	3.1	0	− 1.9	5.8	0	− 4.0	9.0	0	− 6.0		
1.0	+ 0.9	− 1.0	1.0	+ 1.4	− 1.0	1.6	+ 1.4	− 1.6	3.0	+ 2.2	− 3.0	5.0	+ 3.5	− 5.0	0.24	0.40
2.5	− 0	− 1.6	3.3	− 0	− 1.9	3.9	0	− 2.5	6.6	0	− 4.4	10.7	0	− 7.2		
1.2	+ 1.0	− 1.2	1.2	+ 1.6	− 1.2	2.0	+ 1.6	− 2.0	3.5	+ 2.8	− 3.5	6.0	+ 4.0	− 6.0	0.40	0.71
2.9	− 0	− 1.9	3.8	− 0	− 2.2	4.6	0	− 3.0	7.9	0	− 5.1	12.8	− 0	− 8.8		
1.6	+ 1.2	− 1.6	1.6	+ 2.0	− 1.6	2.5	+ 2.0	− 2.5	4.5	+ 3.5	− 4.5	7.0	+ 5.0	− 7.0	0.71	1.19
3.6	− 0	− 2.4	4.8	− 0	− 2.8	5.7	0	− 3.7	10.0	0	− 6.5	15.5	0	− 10.5		
2.0	+ 1.6	− 2.0	2.0	+ 2.5	− 2.0	3.0	+ 2.5	− 3.0	5.0	+ 4.0	− 5.0	8.0	+ 6.0	− 8.0	1.19	1.97
4.6	− 0	− 3.0	6.1	− 0	− 3.6	7.1	0	− 4.6	11.5	0	− 7.5	18.0	0	− 12.0		
2.5	+ 1.8	− 2.5	2.5	+ 3.0	− 2.5	4.0	+ 3.0	− 4.0	6.0	+ 4.5	− 6.0	9.0	+ 7.0	− 9.0	1.97	3.15
5.5	− 0	− 3.7	7.3	− 0	− 4.3	8.8	0	− 5.8	13.5	0	− 9.0	20.5	0	− 13.5		
3.0	+ 2.2	− 3.0	3.0	+ 3.5	− 3.0	5.0	+ 3.5	− 5.0	7.0	+ 5.0	− 7.0	10.0	+ 9.0	− 10.0	3.15	4.73
6.6	− 0	− 4.4	8.7	− 0	− 5.2	10.7	0	− 7.2	15.5	0	− 10.5	24.0	0	− 15.0		
3.5	+ 2.5	− 3.5	3.5	+ 4.0	− 3.5	6.0	+ 4.0	− 6.0	8.0	+ 6.0	− 8.0	12.0	+ 10.0	− 12.0	4.73	7.09
7.6	− 0	− 5.1	10.0	− 0	− 6.0	12.5	0	− 8.5	18.0	0	− 12.0	28.0	0	− 18.0		
4.0	+ 2.8	− 4.0	4.0	+ 4.5	− 4.0	7.0	+ 4.5	− 7.0	10.0	+ 7.0	− 10.0	15.0	+ 12.0	− 15.0	7.09	9.85
8.6	− 0	− 5.8	11.3	0	− 6.8	14.3	0	− 9.8	21.5	0	− 14.5	34.0	0	− 22.0		
5.0	+ 3.0	− 5.0	5.0	+ 5.0	− 5.0	8.0	+ 5.0	− 8.0	12.0	+ 8.0	− 12.0	18.0	+ 12.0	− 18.0	9.85	12.41
10.0	0	− 7.0	13.0	0	− 8.0	16.0	0	− 11.0	25.0	0	− 17.0	38.0	0	− 26.0		
6.0	+ 3.5	− 6.0	6.0	+ 6.0	− 6.0	10.0	+ 6.0	− 10.0	14.0	+ 9.0	− 14.0	22.0	+ 14.0	− 22.0	12.41	15.75
11.7	0	− 8.2	15.5	0	− 9.5	19.5	0	13.5	29.0	0	− 20.0	45.0	0	− 31.0		
8.0	+ 4.0	− 8.0	8.0	+ 6.0	− 8.0	12.0	+ 6.0	− 12.0	16.0	+10.0	− 16.0	25.0	+ 16.0	− 25.0	15.75	19.69
14.5	0	−10.5	18.0	0	−12.0	22.0	0	− 16.0	32.0	0	− 22.0	51.0	0	− 35.0		
10.0	+ 5.0	−10.0	10.0	+ 8.0	−10.0	16.0	+ 8.0	− 16.0	20.0	+12.0	− 20.0	30.0	+ 20.0	− 30.0	19.69	30.09
18.0	0	−13.0	23.0	0	−15.0	29.0	0	− 21.0	40.0	0	− 28.0	62.0	0	− 42.0		
12.0	+ 6.0	−12.0	12.0	+10.0	−12.0	20.0	+10.0	− 20.0	25.0	+16.0	− 25.0	40.0	+ 25.0	− 40.0	30.09	41.49
22.0	0	−16.0	28.0	0	−18.0	36.0	0	− 26.0	51.0	0	− 35.0	81.0	0	− 56.0		
16.0	+ 8.0	−16.0	16.0	+12.0	−16.0	25.0	+12.0	− 25.0	30.0	+20.0	− 30.0	50.0	+ 30.0	− 50.0	41.49	56.19
29.0	0	−21.0	36.0	0	−24.0	45.0	0	− 33.0	62.0	0	− 42.0	100	0	− 70.0		
20.0	+10.0	−20.0	20.0	+16.0	−20.0	30.0	+16.0	− 30.0	40.0	+25.0	− 40.0	60.0	+ 40.0	− 60.0	56.19	76.39
36.0	0	−26.0	46.0	0	−30.0	56.0	0	− 40.0	81.0	0	− 56.0	125	0	− 85.0		
25.0	+12.0	−25.0	25.0	+20.0	−25.0	40.0	+20.0	− 40.0	50.0	+30.0	− 50.0	80.0	+ 50.0	− 80.0	76.39	100.9
45.0	0	−33.0	57.0	0	−37.0	72.0	0	− 52.0	100	0	− 70.0	160	0	−110		
30.0	+16.0	−30.0	30.0	+25.0	−30.0	50.0	+25.0	− 50.0	60.0	+40.0	− 60.0	100	+ 60.0	−100	100.9	131.9
56.0	0	−40.0	71.0	0	−46.0	91.0	0	− 66.0	125	0	− 85.0	200	0	−140		
35.0	+20.0	−35.0	35.0	+30.0	−35.0	60.0	+30.0	− 60.0	80.0	+50.0	− 80.0	130	+ 80.0	−130	131.9	171.9
67.0	0	−47.0	85.0	0	−55.0	110.0	0	− 80.0	160	0	−110	260	0	−180		
45.0	+25.0	−45.0	45.0	+40.0	−45.0	80.0	+40.0	− 80.0	100	+60.0	−100	150	+100	−150	171.9	200
86.0	0	−61.0	110.0	0	−70.0	145.0	0	−105.0	200	0	−140	310	0	−210		

APPENDIX 6B   LOCATIONAL CLEARANCE FITS

Limits are in thousandths of an inch.

Limits for hole and shaft are applied algebraically to the basic size to obtain the limits of size for the parts.

Data in bold face are in accordance with ABC agreements.

Symbols H6, h5, etc., are Hole and Shaft designations used in ABC System

Nominal Size Range Inches Over — To	LC 1 Limits of Clearance	LC 1 Hole H6	LC 1 Shaft h5	LC 2 Limits of Clearance	LC 2 Hole H7	LC 2 Shaft h6	LC 3 Limits of Clearance	LC 3 Hole H8	LC 3 Shaft h7	LC 4 Limits of Clearance	LC 4 Hole H10	LC 4 Shaft h9	LC 5 Limits of Clearance	LC 5 Hole H7	LC 5 Shaft g6
0 — 0.12	0 / 0.45	+0.25 / −0	+0 / −0.2	0 / 0.65	+0.4 / −0	+0 / −0.25	0 / 1	+0.6 / −0	+0 / −0.4	0 / 2.6	+1.6 / −0	+0 / −1.0	0.1 / 0.75	+0.4 / −0	−0.1 / −0.35
0.12 — 0.24	0 / 0.5	+0.3 / −0	+0 / −0.2	0 / 0.8	+0.5 / −0	+0 / −0.3	0 / 1.2	+0.7 / −0	+0 / −0.5	0 / 3.0	+1.8 / −0	+0 / −1.2	0.15 / 0.95	+0.5 / −0	−0.15 / −0.45
0.24 — 0.40	0 / 0.65	+0.4 / −0	+0 / −0.25	0 / 1.0	+0.6 / −0	+0 / −0.4	0 / 1.5	+0.9 / −0	+0 / −0.6	0 / 3.6	+2.2 / −0	+0 / −1.4	0.2 / 1.2	+0.6 / −0	−0.2 / −0.6
0.40 — 0.71	0 / 0.7	+0.4 / −0	+0 / −0.3	0 / 1.1	+0.7 / −0	+0 / −0.4	0 / 1.7	+1.0 / −0	+0 / −0.7	0 / 4.4	+2.8 / −0	+0 / −1.6	0.25 / 1.35	+0.7 / −0	−0.25 / −0.65
0.71 — 1.19	0 / 0.9	+0.5 / −0	+0 / −0.4	0 / 1.3	+0.8 / −0	+0 / −0.5	0 / 2	+1.2 / −0	+0 / −0.8	0 / 5.5	+3.5 / −0	+0 / −2.0	0.3 / 1.6	+0.8 / −0	−0.3 / −0.8
1.19 — 1.97	0 / 1.0	+0.6 / −0	+0 / −0.4	0 / 1.6	+1.0 / −0	+0 / −0.6	0 / 2.6	+1.6 / −0	+0 / −1	0 / 6.5	+4.0 / −0	+0 / −2.5	0.4 / 2.0	+1.0 / −0	−0.4 / −1.0
1.97 — 3.15	0 / 1.2	+0.7 / −0	+0 / −0.5	0 / 1.9	+1.2 / −0	+0 / −0.7	0 / 3	+1.8 / −0	+0 / −1.2	0 / 7.5	+4.5 / −0	+0 / −3	0.4 / 2.3	+1.2 / −0	−0.4 / −1.1
3.15 — 4.73	0 / 1.5	+0.9 / −0	+0 / −0.6	0 / 2.3	+1.4 / −0	+0 / −0.9	0 / 3.6	+2.2 / −0	+0 / −1.4	0 / 8.5	+5.0 / −0	+0 / −3.5	0.5 / 2.8	+1.4 / −0	−0.5 / −1.4
4.73 — 7.09	0 / 1.7	+1.0 / −0	+0 / −0.7	0 / 2.6	+1.6 / −0	+0 / −1.0	0 / 4.1	+2.5 / −0	+0 / −1.6	0 / 10	+6.0 / −0	+0 / −4	0.6 / 3.2	+1.6 / −0	−0.6 / −1.6
7.09 — 9.85	0 / 2.0	+1.2 / −0	+0 / −0.8	0 / 3.0	+1.8 / −0	+0 / −1.2	0 / 4.6	+2.8 / −0	+0 / −1.8	0 / 11.5	+7.0 / −0	+0 / −4.5	0.6 / 3.6	+1.8 / −0	−0.6 / −1.8
9.85 — 12.41	0 / 2.1	+1.2 / −0	+0 / −0.9	0 / 3.2	+2.0 / −0	+0 / −1.2	0 / 5	+3.0 / −0	+0 / −2.0	0 / 13	+8.0 / −0	+0 / −5	0.7 / 3.9	+2.0 / −0	−0.7 / −1.9
12.41 — 15.75	0 / 2.4	+1.4 / −0	+0 / −1.0	0 / 3.6	+2.2 / −0	+0 / −1.4	0 / 5.7	+3.5 / −0	+0 / −2.2	0 / 15	+9.0 / −0	+0 / −6	0.7 / 4.3	+2.2 / −0	−0.7 / −2.1
15.75 — 19.69	0 / 2.6	+1.6 / −0	+0 / −1.0	0 / 4.1	+2.5 / −0	+0 / −1.6	0 / 6.5	+4 / −0	+0 / −2.5	0 / 16	+10.0 / −0	+0 / −6	0.8 / 4.9	+2.5 / −0	−0.8 / −2.4
19.69 — 30.09	0 / 3.2	+2.0 / −0	+0 / −1.2	0 / 5.0	+3 / −0	+0 / −2	0 / 8	+5 / −0	+0 / −3	0 / 20	+12.0 / −0	+0 / −8	0.9 / 5.9	+3.0 / −0	−0.9 / −2.9
30.09 — 41.49	0 / 4.1	+2.5 / −0	+0 / −1.6	0 / 6.5	+4 / −0	+0 / −2.5	0 / 10	+6 / −0	+0 / −4	0 / 26	+16.0 / −0	+0 / −10	1.0 / 7.5	+4.0 / −0	−1.0 / −3.5
41.49 — 56.19	0 / 5.0	+3.0 / −0	+0 / −2.0	0 / 8.0	+5 / −0	+0 / −3	0 / 13	+8 / −0	+0 / −5	0 / 32	+20.0 / −0	+0 / −12	1.2 / 9.2	+5.0 / −0	−1.2 / −4.2
56.19 — 76.39	0 / 6.5	+4.0 / −0	+0 / −2.5	0 / 10	+6 / −0	+0 / −4	0 / 16	+10 / −0	+0 / −6	0 / 41	+25.0 / −0	+0 / −16	1.2 / 11.2	+6.0 / −0	−1.2 / −5.2
76.39 — 100.9	0 / 8.0	+5.0 / −0	+0 / −3.0	0 / 13	+8 / −0	+0 / −5	0 / 20	+12 / −0	+0 / −8	0 / 50	+30.0 / −0	+0 / −20	1.4 / 14.4	+8.0 / −0	−1.4 / −6.4
100.9 — 131.9	0 / 10.0	+6.0 / −0	+0 / −4.0	0 / 16	+10 / −0	+0 / −6	0 / 26	+16 / −0	+0 / −10	0 / 65	+40.0 / −0	+0 / −25	1.6 / 17.6	+10.0 / −0	−1.6 / −7.6
131.9 — 171.9	0 / 13.0	+8.0 / −0	+0 / −5.0	0 / 20	+12 / −0	+0 / −8	0 / 32	+20 / −0	+0 / −12	0 / 80	+50.0 / −0	+0 / −30	1.8 / 21.8	+12.0 / −0	−1.8 / −9.8
171.9 — 200	0 / 16.0	+10.0 / −0	+0 / −6.0	0 / 26	+16 / −0	+0 / −10	0 / 41	+25 / −0	+0 / −16	0 / 100	+60.0 / −0	+0 / −40	1.8 / 27.8	+16.0 / −0	−1.8 / −11.8

APPENDIX 6B   (CONT.)

LOCATIONAL CLEARANCE FITS

Limits are in thousandths of an inch.

Limits for hole and shaft are applied algebraically to the basic size to obtain the limits of size for the parts.

Data in bold face are in accordance with ABC agreements.

Symbols H9, f8, etc., are Hole and Shaft designations used in ABC System

Class LC 6			Class LC 7			Class LC 8			Class LC 9			Class LC 10			Class LC 11			Nominal Size Range Inches	
Limits of Clearance	Standard Limits		Limits of Clearance	Standard Limits		Limits of Clearance	Standard Limits		Limits of Clearance	Standard Limits		Limits of Clearance	Standard Limits		Limits of Clearance	Standard Limits			
	Hole H9	Shaft f8		Hole H10	Shaft e9		Hole H10	Shaft d9		Hole H11	Shaft c10		Hole H12	Shaft		Hole H13	Shaft	Over	To
0.3 1.9	+ 1.0 0	− 0.3 − 0.9	0.6 3.2	+ 1.6 0	− 0.6 − 1.6	1.0 3.6	+ 1.6 − 0	− 1.0 − 2.0	2.5 6.6	+ 2.5 − 0	− 2.5 − 4.1	4 12	+ 4 − 0	− 4 − 8	5 17	+ 6 − 0	− 5 − 11	0 −	0.12
0.4 2.3	+ 1.2 0	− 0.4 − 1.1	0.8 3.8	+ 1.8 0	− 0.8 − 2.0	1.2 4.2	+ 1.8 − 0	− 1.2 − 2.4	2.8 7.6	+ 3.0 − 0	− 2.8 − 4.6	4.5 14.5	+ 5 − 0	− 4.5 − 9.5	6 20	+ 7 − 0	− 6 − 13	0.12 −	0.24
0.5 2.8	+ 1.4 0	− 0.5 − 1.4	1.0 4.6	+ 2.2 0	− 1.0 − 2.4	1.6 5.2	+ 2.2 − 0	− 1.6 − 3.0	3.0 8.7	+ 3.5 − 0	− 3.0 − 5.2	5 17	+ 6 − 0	− 5 − 11	7 25	+ 9 − 0	− 7 − 16	0.24 −	0.40
0.6 3.2	+ 1.6 0	− 0.6 − 1.6	1.2 5.6	+ 2.8 0	− 1.2 − 2.8	2.0 6.4	+ 2.8 − 0	− 2.0 − 3.6	3.5 10.3	+ 4.0 − 0	− 3.5 − 6.3	6 20	+ 7 − 0	− 6 − 13	8 28	+ 10 − 0	− 8 − 18	0.40 −	0.71
0.8 4.0	+ 2.0 0	− 0.8 − 2.0	1.6 7.1	+ 3.5 0	− 1.6 − 3.6	2.5 8.0	+ 3.5 − 0	− 2.5 − 4.5	4.5 13.0	+ 5.0 − 0	− 4.5 − 8.0	7 23	+ 8 − 0	− 7 − 15	10 34	+ 12 − 0	− 10 − 22	0.71 −	1.19
1.0 5.1	+ 2.5 0	− 1.0 − 2.6	2.0 8.5	+ 4.0 0	− 2.0 − 4.5	3.0 9.5	+ 4.0 − 0	− 3.0 − 5.5	5 15	+ 6 − 0	− 5 − 9	8 28	+ 10 − 0	− 8 − 18	12 44	+ 16 − 0	− 12 − 28	1.19 −	1.97
1.2 6.0	+ 3.0 0	− 1.2 − 3.0	2.5 10.0	+ 4.5 0	− 2.5 − 5.5	4.0 11.5	+ 4.5 − 0	− 4.0 − 7.0	6 17.5	+ 7 − 0	− 6 − 10.5	10 34	+ 12 − 0	− 10 − 22	14 50	+ 18 − 0	− 14 − 32	1.97 −	3.15
1.4 7.1	+ 3.5 0	− 1.4 − 3.6	3.0 11.5	+ 5.0 0	− 3.0 − 6.5	5.0 13.5	+ 5.0 − 0	− 5.0 − 8.5	7 21	+ 9 − 0	− 7 − 12	11 39	+ 14 − 0	− 11 − 25	16 60	+ 22 − 0	− 16 − 38	3.15 −	4.73
1.6 8.1	+ 4.0 0	− 1.6 − 4.1	3.5 13.5	+ 6.0 0	− 3.5 − 7.5	6 16	+ 6 − 0	− 6 −10	8 24	+ 10 − 0	− 8 − 14	12 44	+ 16 − 0	− 12 − 28	18 68	+ 25 − 0	− 18 − 43	4.73 −	7.09
2.0 9.3	+ 4.5 0	− 2.0 − 4.8	4.0 15.5	+ 7.0 0	− 4.0 − 8.5	7 18.5	+ 7 − 0	− 7 −11.5	10 29	+ 12 − 0	− 10 − 17	16 52	+ 18 − 0	− 16 − 34	22 78	+ 28 − 0	− 22 − 50	7.09 −	9.85
2.2 10.2	+ 5.0 0	− 2.2 − 5.2	4.5 17.5	+ 8.0 0	− 4.5 − 9.5	7 20	+ 8 − 0	− 7 −12	12 32	+ 12 − 0	− 12 − 20	20 60	+ 20 − 0	− 20 − 40	28 88	+ 30 − 0	− 28 − 58	9.85 −	12.41
2.5 12.0	+ 6.0 0	− 2.5 − 6.0	5.0 20.0	+ 9.0 0	− 5 −11	8 23	+ 9 − 0	− 8 −14	14 37	+ 14 − 0	− 14 − 23	22 66	+ 22 − 0	− 22 − 44	30 100	+ 35 − 0	− 30 − 65	12.41 −	15.75
2.8 12.8	+ 6.0 0	− 2.8 − 6.8	5.0 21.0	+ 10.0 0	− 5 −11	9 25	+10 − 0	− 9 −15	16 42	+ 16 − 0	− 16 − 26	25 75	+ 25 − 0	− 25 − 50	35 115	+ 40 − 0	− 35 − 75	15.75 −	19.69
3.0 16.0	+ 8.0 0	− 3.0 − 8.0	6.0 26.0	+12.0 − 0	− 6 −14	10 30	+12 −0	−10 −18	18 50	+ 20 − 0	− 18 − 30	28 88	+ 30 − 0	− 28 − 58	40 140	+ 50 − 0	− 40 − 90	19.69 −	30.09
3.5 19.5	+10.0 0	− 3.5 − 9.5	7.0 33.0	+16.0 − 0	− 7 −17	12 38	+16 − 0	−12 −22	20 61	+ 25 − 0	− 20 − 36	30 110	+ 40 − 0	− 30 − 70	45 165	+ 60 − 0	− 45 −105	30.09 −	41.49
4.0 24.0	+12.0 0	− 4.0 −12.0	8.0 40.0	+20.0 − 0	− 8 −20	14 46	+20 − 0	−14 −26	25 75	+ 30 − 0	− 25 − 45	40 140	+ 50 − 0	− 40 − 90	60 220	+ 80 − 0	− 60 −140	41.49 −	56.19
4.5 30.5	+16.0 0	− 4.5 −14.5	9.0 50.0	+25.0 − 0	− 9 −25	16 57	+25 − 0	−16 −32	30 95	+ 40 − 0	− 30 − 55	50 170	+ 60 − 0	− 50 110	70 270	+100 − 0	− 70 −170	56.19 −	76.39
5.0 37.0	+20.0 0	− 5 −17	10.0 60.0	+30.0 − 0	−10 −30	18 68	+30 − 0	−18 −38	35 115	+ 50 − 0	− 35 − 65	50 210	+ 80 − 0	− 50 −130	80 330	+125 − 0	− 80 −205	76.39 −	100.9
6.0 47.0	+25.0 0	− 6 −22	12.0 67.0	+40.0 − 0	−12 −27	20 85	+40 − 0	−20 −45	40 140	+ 60 − 0	− 40 − 80	60 260	+100 − 0	− 60 −160	90 410	+160 − 0	− 90 −250	100.9 −	131.9
7.0 57.0	+30.0 0	− 7 −27	14.0 94.0	+50.0 − 0	−14 −44	25 105	+50 − 0	−25 −55	50 180	+ 80 − 0	− 50 −100	80 330	+125 − 0	− 80 −205	100 500	+200 − 0	−100 −300	131.9 −	171.9
7.0 72.0	+40.0 0	− 7 −32	14.0 114.0	+60.0 − 0	−14 −54	25 125	+60 − 0	−25 −65	50 210	+100 − 0	− 50 −110	90 410	+160 − 0	− 90 −250	125 625	+250 − 0	−125 −375	171.9 −	200

APPENDIX 6C LOCATIONAL TRANSITIONAL FITS

Limits are in thousandths of an inch.

Limits for hole and shaft are applied algebraically to the basic size to obtain the limits of size for the mating parts.

Data in bold face are in accordance with ABC agreements.

"Fit" represents the maximum interference (minus values) and the maximum clearance (plus values).

Symbols H7, js6, etc., are Hole and Shaft designations used in ABC System

Nominal Size Range Inches Over – To	Class LT 1 Fit	Class LT 1 Hole H7	Class LT 1 Shaft js6	Class LT 2 Fit	Class LT 2 Hole H8	Class LT 2 Shaft js7	Class LT 3 Fit	Class LT 3 Hole H7	Class LT 3 Shaft k6	Class LT 4 Fit	Class LT 4 Hole H8	Class LT 4 Shaft k7	Class LT 5 Fit	Class LT 5 Hole H7	Class LT 5 Shaft n6	Class LT 6 Fit	Class LT 6 Hole H7	Class LT 6 Shaft n7
0 – 0.12	−0.10 / +0.50	+0.4 / −0	+0.10 / −0.10	−0.2 / +0.8	+0.6 / −0	+0.2 / −0.2							−0.5 / +0.15	+0.4 / −0	+0.5 / +0.25	−0.65 / +0.15	+0.4 / −0	+0.65 / +0.25
0.12 – 0.24	−0.15 / +0.65	+0.5 / −0	+0.15 / −0.15	−0.25 / +0.95	+0.7 / −0	+0.25 / −0.25							−0.6 / +0.2	+0.5 / −0	+0.6 / +0.3	−0.8 / +0.2	+0.5 / −0	+0.8 / +0.3
0.24 – 0.40	−0.2 / +0.8	+0.6 / −0	+0.2 / −0.2	−0.3 / +1.2	+0.9 / −0	+0.3 / −0.3	−0.5 / +0.5	+0.6 / −0	+0.5 / +0.1	−0.7 / +0.8	+0.9 / −0	+0.7 / +0.1	−0.8 / +0.2	+0.6 / −0	+0.8 / +0.4	−1.0 / +0.2	+0.6 / −0	+1.0 / +0.4
0.40 – 0.71	−0.2 / +0.9	+0.7 / −0	+0.2 / −0.2	−0.35 / +1.35	+1.0 / −0	+0.35 / −0.35	−0.5 / +0.6	+0.7 / −0	+0.5 / +0.1	−0.8 / +0.9	+1.0 / −0	+0.8 / +0.1	−0.9 / +0.2	+0.7 / −0	+0.9 / +0.5	−1.2 / +0.2	+0.7 / −0	+1.2 / +0.5
0.71 – 1.19	−0.25 / +1.05	+0.8 / −0	+0.25 / −0.25	−0.4 / +1.6	+1.2 / −0	+0.4 / −0.4	−0.6 / +0.7	+0.8 / −0	+0.6 / +0.1	−0.9 / +1.1	+1.2 / −0	+0.9 / +0.1	−1.1 / +0.2	+0.8 / −0	+1.1 / +0.6	−1.4 / +0.2	+0.8 / −0	+1.4 / +0.6
1.19 – 1.97	−0.3 / +1.3	+1.0 / −0	+0.3 / −0.3	−0.5 / +2.1	+1.6 / −0	+0.5 / −0.5	−0.7 / +0.9	+1.0 / −0	+0.7 / +0.1	−1.1 / +1.5	+1.6 / −0	+1.1 / +0.1	−1.3 / +0.3	+1.0 / −0	+1.3 / +0.7	−1.7 / +0.3	+1.0 / −0	+1.7 / +0.7
1.97 – 3.15	−0.3 / +1.5	+1.2 / −0	+0.3 / −0.3	−0.6 / +2.4	+1.8 / −0	+0.6 / −0.6	−0.8 / +1.1	+1.2 / −0	+0.8 / +0.1	−1.3 / +1.7	+1.8 / −0	+1.3 / +0.1	−1.5 / +0.4	+1.2 / −0	+1.5 / +0.8	−2.0 / +0.4	+1.2 / −0	+2.0 / +0.8
3.15 – 4.73	−0.4 / +1.8	+1.4 / −0	+0.4 / −0.4	−0.7 / +2.9	+2.2 / −0	+0.7 / −0.7	−1.0 / +1.3	+1.4 / −0	+1.0 / +0.1	−1.5 / +2.1	+2.2 / −0	+1.5 / +0.1	−1.9 / +0.4	+1.4 / −0	+1.9 / +1.0	−2.4 / +0.4	+1.4 / −0	+2.4 / +1.0
4.73 – 7.09	−0.5 / +2.1	+1.6 / −0	+0.5 / −0.5	−0.8 / +3.3	+2.5 / −0	+0.8 / −0.8	−1.1 / +1.5	+1.6 / −0	+1.1 / +0.1	−1.7 / +2.4	+2.5 / −0	+1.7 / +0.1	−2.2 / +0.4	+1.6 / −0	+2.2 / +1.2	−2.8 / +0.4	+1.6 / −0	+2.8 / +1.2
7.09 – 9.85	−0.6 / +2.4	+1.8 / −0	+0.6 / −0.6	−0.9 / +3.7	+2.8 / −0	+0.9 / −0.9	−1.4 / +1.6	+1.8 / −0	+1.4 / +0.2	−2.0 / +2.6	+2.8 / −0	+2.0 / +0.2	−2.6 / +0.4	+1.8 / −0	+2.6 / +1.4	−3.2 / +0.4	+1.8 / −0	+3.2 / +1.4
9.85 – 12.41	−0.6 / +2.6	+2.0 / −0	+0.6 / −0.6	−1.0 / +4.0	+3.0 / −0	+1.0 / −1.0	−1.4 / +1.8	+2.0 / −0	+1.4 / +0.2	−2.2 / +2.8	+3.0 / −0	+2.2 / +0.2	−2.6 / +0.6	+2.0 / −0	+2.6 / +1.4	−3.4 / +0.6	+2.0 / −0	+3.4 / +1.4
12.41 – 15.75	−0.7 / +2.9	+2.2 / −0	+0.7 / −0.7	−1.0 / +4.5	+3.5 / −0	+1.0 / −1.0	−1.6 / +2.0	+2.2 / −0	+1.6 / +0.2	−2.4 / +3.3	+3.5 / −0	+2.4 / +0.2	−3.0 / +0.6	+2.2 / −0	+3.0 / +1.6	−3.8 / +0.6	+2.2 / −0	+3.8 / +1.6
15.75 – 19.69	−0.8 / +3.3	+2.5 / −0	+0.8 / −0.8	−1.2 / +5.2	+4.0 / −0	+1.2 / −1.2	−1.8 / +2.3	+2.5 / −0	+1.8 / +0.2	−2.7 / +3.8	+4.0 / −0	+2.7 / +0.2	−3.4 / +0.7	+2.5 / −0	+3.4 / +1.8	−4.3 / +0.7	+2.5 / −0	+4.3 / +1.8

APPENDIX 6D   LOCATIONAL INTERFERENCE FITS

Limits are in thousandths of an inch.
Limits for hole and shaft are applied algebraically to the
basic size to obtain the limits of size for the parts.

Data in bold face are in accordance with ABC agreements,
Symbols H7, p6, etc., are Hole and Shaft designations
used in ABC System

Nominal Size Range Inches (Over — To)	Class LN 1 Limits of Interference	Class LN 1 Standard Limits Hole H6	Class LN 1 Standard Limits Shaft n5	Class LN 2 Limits of Interference	Class LN 2 Standard Limits Hole H7	Class LN 2 Standard Limits Shaft p6	Class LN 3 Limits of Interference	Class LN 3 Standard Limits Hole H7	Class LN 3 Standard Limits Shaft r6
0 — 0.12	0 / 0.45	+ 0.25 / − 0	+0.45 / +0.25	0 / 0.65	+ 0.4 / − 0	+ 0.65 / + 0.4	0.1 / 0.75	+ 0.4 / − 0	+ 0.75 / + 0.5
0.12 — 0.24	0 / 0.5	+ 0.3 / − 0	+0.5 / +0.3	0 / 0.8	+ 0.5 / − 0	+ 0.8 / + 0.5	0.1 / 0.9	+ 0.5 / 0	+ 0.9 / + 0.6
0.24 — 0.40	0 / 0.65	+ 0.4 / − 0	+0.65 / +0.4	0 / 1.0	+ 0.6 / − 0	+ 1.0 / + 0.6	0.2 / 1.2	+ 0.6 / − 0	+ 1.2 / + 0.8
0.40 — 0.71	0 / 0.8	+ 0.4 / − 0	+0.8 / +0.4	0 / 1.1	+ 0.7 / − 0	+ 1.1 / + 0.7	0.3 / 1.4	+ 0.7 / − 0	+ 1.4 / + 1.0
0.71 — 1.19	0 / 1.0	+ 0.5 / − 0	+1.0 / +0.5	0 / 1.3	+ 0.8 / − 0	+ 1.3 / + 0.8	0.4 / 1.7	+ 0.8 / − 0	+ 1.7 / + 1.2
1.19 — 1.97	0 / 1.1	+ 0.6 / − 0	+1.1 / +0.6	0 / 1.6	+ 1.0 / − 0	+ 1.6 / + 1.0	0.4 / 2.0	+ 1.0 / − 0	+ 2.0 / + 1.4
1.97 — 3.15	0.1 / 1.3	+ 0.7 / − 0	+1.3 / +0.8	0.2 / 2.1	+ 1.2 / − 0	+ 2.1 / + 1.4	0.4 / 2.3	+ 1.2 / − 0	+ 2.3 / + 1.6
3.15 — 4.73	0.1 / 1.6	+ 0.9 / − 0	+1.6 / +1.0	0.2 / 2.5	+ 1.4 / − 0	+ 2.5 / + 1.6	0.6 / 2.9	+ 1.4 / − 0	+ 2.9 / + 2.0
4.73 — 7.09	0.2 / 1.9	+ 1.0 / − 0	+1.9 / +1.2	0.2 / 2.8	+ 1.6 / − 0	+ 2.8 / + 1.8	0.9 / 3.5	+ 1.6 / − 0	+ 3.5 / + 2.5
7.09 — 9.85	0.2 / 2.2	+ 1.2 / − 0	+2.2 / +1.4	0.2 / 3.2	+ 1.8 / − 0	+ 3.2 / + 2.0	1.2 / 4.2	+ 1.8 / − 0	+ 4.2 / + 3.0
9.85 — 12.41	0.2 / 2.3	+ 1.2 / − 0	+2.3 / +1.4	0.2 / 3.4	+ 2.0 / − 0	+ 3.4 / + 2.2	1.5 / 4.7	+ 2.0 / − 0	+ 4.7 / + 3.5
12.41 — 15.75	0.2 / 2.6	+ 1.4 / − 0	+2.6 / +1.6	0.3 / 3.9	+ 2.2 / − 0	+ 3.9 / + 2.5	2.3 / 5.9	+ 2.2 / − 0	+ 5.9 / + 4.5
15.75 — 19.69	0.2 / 2.8	+ 1.6 / − 0	+2.8 / +1.8	0.3 / 4.4	+ 2.5 / − 0	+ 4.4 / + 2.8	2.5 / 6.6	+ 2.5 / − 0	+ 6.6 / + 5.0
19.69 — 30.09		+ 2.0 / − 0		0.5 / 5.5	+ 3 / − 0	+ 5.5 / + 3.5	4 / 9	+ 3 / − 0	+ 9 / + 7
30.09 — 41.49		+ 2.5 / − 0		0.5 / 7.0	+ 4 / − 0	+ 7.0 / + 4.5	5 / 11.5	+ 4 / − 0	+11.5 / + 9
41.49 — 56.19		+ 3.0 / − 0		1 / 9	+ 5 / − 0	+ 9 / + 6	7 / 15	+ 5 / − 0	+15 / +12
56.19 — 76.39		+ 4.0 / − 0		1 / 11	+ 6 / − 0	+11 / + 7	10 / 20	+ 6 / − 0	+20 / +16
76.39 — 100.9		+ 5.0 / − 0		1 / 14	+ 8 / − 0	+14 / + 9	12 / 25	+ 8 / − 0	+25 / +20
100.9 — 131.9		+ 6.0 / − 0		2 / 18	+10 / − 0	+18 / +12	15 / 31	+10 / − 0	+31 / +25
131.9 — 171.9		+ 8.0 / − 0		4 / 24	+12 / − 0	+24 / +16	18 / 38	+12 / − 0	+38 / +30
171.9 — 200		+10.0 / − 0		4 / 30	+16 / − 0	+30 / +20	24 / 50	+16 / − 0	+50 / +40

APPENDIX 6E FORCE AND SHRINK FITS

Limits are in thousandths of an inch.

Limits for hole and shaft are applied algebraically to the basic size to obtain the limits of size for the parts.

Data in bold face are in accordance with ABC agreements.

Symbols H7, s6, etc., are Hole and Shaft designations used in ABC System

Nominal Size Range Inches Over — To	Class FN 1 Limits of Interference	Class FN 1 Standard Limits Hole H6	Class FN 1 Standard Limits Shaft	Class FN 2 Limits of Interference	Class FN 2 Standard Limits Hole H7	Class FN 2 Standard Limits Shaft s6	Class FN 3 Limits of Interference	Class FN 3 Standard Limits Hole H7	Class FN 3 Standard Limits Shaft t6	Class FN 4 Limits of Interference	Class FN 4 Standard Limits Hole H7	Class FN 4 Standard Limits Shaft u6	Class FN 5 Limits of Interference	Class FN 5 Standard Limits Hole H8	Class FN 5 Standard Limits Shaft x7
0 — 0.12	0.05 0.5	+0.25 − 0	+ 0.5 + 0.3	0.2 0.85	+0.4 − 0	+ 0.85 + 0.6				0.3 0.95	+0.4 − 0	+ 0.95 + 0.7	0.3 1.3	+0.6 − 0	+ 1.3 + 0.9
0.12 — 0.24	0.1 0.6	+0.3 − 0	+ 0.6 + 0.4	0.2 1.0	+0.5 − 0	+ 1.0 + 0.7				0.4 1.2	+0.5 − 0	+ 1.2 + 0.9	0.5 1.7	+ 0.7 − 0	+ 1.7 + 1.2
0.24 — 0.40	0.1 0.75	+0.4 − 0	+ 0.75 + 0.5	0.4 1.4	+0.6 − 0	+ 1.4 + 1.0				0.6 1.6	+0.6 − 0	+ 1.6 + 1.2	0.5 2.0	+ 0.9 − 0	+ 2.0 + 1.4
0.40 — 0.56	0.1 0.8	+0.4 − 0	+ 0.8 + 0.5	0.5 1.6	+0.7 − 0	+ 1.6 + 1.2				0.7 1.8	+ 0.7 − 0	+ 1.8 + 1.4	0.6 2.3	+ 1.0 − 0	+ 2.3 + 1.6
0.56 — 0.71	0.2 0.9	+0.4 − 0	+ 0.9 + 0.6	0.5 1.6	+0.7 − 0	+ 1.6 + 1.2				0.7 1.8	+0.7 − 0	+ 1.8 + 1.4	0.8 2.5	+ 1.0 − 0	+ 2.5 + 1.8
0.71 — 0.95	0.2 1.1	+0.5 − 0	+ 1.1 + 0.7	0.6 1.9	+0.8 − 0	+ 1.9 + 1.4				0.8 2.1	+0.8 − 0	+ 2.1 + 1.6	1.0 3.0	+ 1.2 − 0	+ 3.0 + 2.2
0.95 — 1.19	0.3 1.2	+0.5 − 0	+ 1.2 + 0.8	0.6 1.9	+0.8 − 0	+ 1.9 + 1.4	0.8 2.1	+0.8 − 0	+ 2.1 + 1.6	1.0 2.3	+0·8 − 0	+ 2.3 + 1.8	1.3 3.3	+ 1.2 − 0	+ 3.3 + 2.5
1.19 — 1.58	0.3 1.3	+0.6 − 0	+ 1.3 + 0.9	0.8 2.4	+1.0 − 0	+ 2.4 + 1.8	1.0 2.6	+1.0 − 0	+ 2.6 + 2.0	1.5 3.1	+1.0 − 0	+ 3.1 + 2.5	1.4 4.0	+ 1.6 − 0	+ 4.0 + 3.0
1.58 — 1.97	0.4 1.4	+0.6 − 0	+ 1.4 + 1.0	0.8 2.4	+1.0 − 0	+ 2.4 + 1.8	1.2 2.8	+1.0 − 0	+ 2.8 + 2.2	1.8 3.4	+1.0 − 0	+ 3.4 + 2.8	2.4 5.0	+ 1.6 − 0	+ 5.0 + 4.0
1.97 — 2.56	0.6 1.8	+0.7 − 0	+ 1.8 + 1.3	0.8 2.7	+1.2 − 0	+ 2.7 + 2.0	1.3 3.2	+1.2 − 0	+ 3.2 + 2.5	2.3 4.2	+1.2 − 0	+ 4.2 + 3.5	3.2 6.2	+ 1.8 − 0	+ 6.2 + 5.0
2.56 — 3.15	0.7 1.9	+0.7 − 0	+ 1.9 + 1.4	1.0 2.9	+1.2 − 0	+ 2.9 + 2.2	1.8 3.7	+1.2 − 0	+ 3.7 + 3.0	2.8 4.7	+1.2 − 0	+ 4.7 + 4.0	4.2 7.2	+ 1.8 − 0	+ 7.2 + 6.0
3.15 — 3.94	0.9 2.4	+0.9 − 0	+ 2.4 + 1.8	1.4 3.7	+1.4 − 0	+ 3.7 + 2.8	2.1 4.4	+1.4 − 0	+ 4.4 + 3.5	3.6 5.9	+1.4 − 0	+ 5.9 + 5.0	4.8 8.4	+ 2.2 − 0	+ 8.4 + 7.0
3.94 — 4.73	1.1 2.6	+0.9 − 0	+ 2.6 + 2.0	1.6 3.9	+1.4 − 0	+ 3.9 + 3.0	2.6 4.9	+1.4 − 0	+ 4.9 + 4.0	4.6 6.9	+1.4 − 0	+ 6.9 + 6.0	5.8 9.4	+ 2.2 − 0	+ 9.4 + 8.0
4.73 — 5.52	1.2 2.9	+1.0 − 0	+ 2.9 + 2.2	1.9 4.5	+1.6 − 0	+ 4.5 + 3.5	3.4 6.0	+1.6 − 0	+ 6.0 + 5.0	5.4 8.0	+1.6 − 0	+ 8.0 + 7.0	7.5 11.6	+ 2.5 − 0	+11.6 +10.0
5.52 — 6.30	1.5 3.2	+1.0 − 0	+ 3.2 + 2.5	2.4 5.0	+1.6 − 0	+ 5.0 + 4.0	3.4 6.0	+1.6 − 0	+ 6.0 + 5.0	5.4 8.0	+1.6 − 0	+ 8.0 + 7.0	9.5 13.6	+ 2.5 − 0	+13.6 +12.0
6.30 — 7.09	1.8 3.5	+1.0 − 0	+ 3.5 + 2.8	2.9 5.5	+1.6 − 0	+ 5.5 + 4.5	4.4 7.0	+1.6 − 0	+ 7.0 + 6.0	6.4 9.0	+1.6 − 0	+ 9.0 + 8.0	9.5 13.6	+ 2.5 − 0	+13.6 +12.0
7.09 — 7.88	1.8 3.8	+1.2 − 0	+ 3.8 + 3.0	3.2 6.2	+1.8 − 0	+ 6.2 + 5.0	5.2 8.2	+1.8 − 0	+ 8.2 + 7.0	7.2 10.2	+1.8 − 0	+10.2 + 9.0	11.2 15.8	+ 2.8 − 0	+15.8 +14.0
7.88 — 8.86	2.3 4.3	+1.2 − 0	+ 4.3 + 3.5	3.2 6.2	+1.8 − 0	+ 6.2 + 5.0	5.2 8.2	+1.8 − 0	+ 8.2 + 7.0	8.2 11.2	+1.8 − 0	+11.2 +10.0	13.2 17.8	+ 2.8 − 0	+17.8 +16.0
8.86 — 9.85	2.3 4.3	+1.2 − 0	+ 4.3 + 3.5	4.2 7.2	+1.8 − 0	+ 7.2 + 6.0	6.2 9.2	+1.8 − 0	+ 9.2 + 8.0	10.2 13.2	+1.8 − 0	+13.2 +12.0	13.2 17.8	+ 2.8 − 0	+17.8 +16.0
9.85 — 11.03	2.8 4.9	+1.2 − 0	+ 4.9 + 4.0	4.0 7.2	+2.0 − 0	+ 7.2 + 6.0	7.0 10.2	+2.0 − 0	+10.2 + 9.0	10.0 13.2	+2.0 − 0	+13.2 +12.0	15.0 20.0	+ 3.0 − 0	+20.0 +18.0
11.03 — 12.41	2.8 4.9	+1.2 − 0	+ 4.9 + 4.0	5.0 8.2	+2.0 − 0	+ 8.2 + 7.0	7.0 10.2	+2.0 − 0	+10.2 + 9.0	12.0 15.2	+2.0 − 0	+15.2 +14.0	17.0 22.0	+ 3.0 − 0	+22.0 +20.0
12.41 — 13.98	3.1 5.5	+1.4 − 0	+ 5.5 + 4.5	5.8 9.4	+2.2 − 0	+ 9.4 + 8.0	7.8 11.4	+2.2 − 0	+11.4 +10.0	13.8 17.4	+2.2 − 0	+17.4 +16.0	18.5 24.2	+ 3.5 + 0	+24.2 +22.0
13.98 — 15.75	3.6 6.1	+1.4 − 0	+ 6.1 + 5.0	5.8 9.4	+2.2 − 0	+ 9.4 + 8.0	9.8 13.4	+2.2 − 0	+13.4 +12.0	15.8 19.4	+2.2 − 0	+19.4 +18.0	21.5 27.2	+ 3.5 − 0	+27.2 +25.0
15.75 — 17.72	4.4 7.0	+1.6 − 0	+ 7.0 + 6.0	6.5 10.6	+2.5 − 0	+10.6 + 9.0	9.5 13.6	+2.5 − 0	+13.6 +12.0	17.5 21.6	+2.5 − 0	+21.6 +20.0	24.0 30.5	+ 4.0 − 0	+30.5 +28.0
17.72 — 19.69	4.4 7.0	+1.6 − 0	+ 7.0 + 6.0	7.5 11.6	+2.5 − 0	+11.6 +10.0	11.5 15.6	+2.5 − 0	+15.6 +14.0	19.5 23.6	+2.5 − 0	+23.6 +22.0	26.0 32.5	+ 4.0 − 0	+32.5 +30.0

APPENDIX 6E   (CONT.)

FORCE AND SHRINK FITS

Limits are in thousandths of an inch.

Limits for hole and shaft are applied algebraically to the basic size to obtain the limits of size for the parts.

Data in bold face are in accordance with ABC agreements.

Symbols H7, s6, etc., are Hole and Shaft designations used in ABC System

Nominal Size Range Inches Over — To	Class FN 1 Limits of Interference	Standard Limits Hole H6	Shaft	Class FN 2 Limits of Interference	Standard Limits Hole H7	Shaft s6	Class FN 3 Limits of Interference	Standard Limits Hole H7	Shaft t6	Class FN 4 Limits of Interference	Standard Limits Hole H7	Shaft u6	Class FN 5 Limits of Interference	Standard Limits Hole H8	Shaft x7
19.69 — 24.34	6.0 9.2	+ 2.0 − 0	+ 9.2 + 8.0	9.0 14.0	+ 3.0 − 0	+ 14.0 + 12.0	15.0 20.0	+ 3.0 − 0	+ 20.0 + 18.0	22.0 27.0	+ 3.0 − 0	+ 27.0 + 25.0	30.0 38.0	+ 5.0 − 0	+ 38.0 + 35.0
24.34 — 30.09	7.0 10.2	+ 2.0 − 0	+10.2 + 9.0	11.0 16.0	+ 3.0 − 0	+ 16.0 + 14.0	17.0 22.0	+ 3.0 − 0	+ 22.0 + 20.0	27.0 32.0	+ 3.0 − 0	+ 32.0 + 30.0	35.0 43.0	+ 5.0 − 0	+ 43.0 + 40.0
30.09 — 35.47	7.5 11.6	+ 2.5 − 0	+11.6 +10.0	14.0 20.5	+ 4.0 − 0	+ 20.5 + 18.0	21.0 27.5	+ 4.0 − 0	+ 27.5 + 25.0	31.0 37.5	+ 4.0 − 0	+ 37.5 + 35.0	44.0 54.0	+ 6.0 − 0	+ 54.0 + 50.0
35.47 — 41.49	9.5 13.6	+ 2.5 − 0	+13.6 +12.0	16.0 22.5	+ 4.0 − 0	+ 22.5 + 20.0	24.0 30.5	+ 4.0 − 0	+ 30.5 + 28.0	36.0 43.5	+ 4.0 − 0	+ 43.5 + 40.0	54.0 64.0	+ 6.0 − 0	+ 64.0 + 60.0
41.49 — 48.28	11.0 16.0	+ 3.0 − 0	+16.0 +14.0	17.0 25.0	+ 5.0 − 0	+ 25.0 + 22.0	30.0 38.0	+ 5.0 − 0	+ 38.0 + 35.0	45.0 53.0	+ 5.0 − 0	+ 53.0 + 50.0	62.0 75.0	+ 8.0 − 0	+ 75.0 + 70.0
48.28 — 56.19	13.0 18.0	+ 3.0 − 0	+18.0 +16.0	20.0 28.0	+ 5.0 − 0	+ 28.0 + 25.0	35.0 43.0	+ 5.0 − 0	+ 43.0 + 40.0	55.0 63.0	+ 5.0 − 0	+ 63.0 + 60.0	72.0 85.0	+ 8.0 − 0	+ 85.0 + 80.0
56.19 — 65.54	14.0 20.5	+ 4.0 − 0	+20.5 +18.0	24.0 34.0	+ 6.0 − 0	+ 34.0 + 30.0	39.0 49.0	+ 6.0 − 0	+ 49.0 + 45.0	64.0 74.0	+ 6.0 − 0	+ 74.0 + 70.0	90.0 106	+10.0 − 0	+106 +100
65.54 — 76.39	18.0 24.5	+ 4.0 − 0	+24.5 +22.0	29.0 39.0	+ 6.0 − 0	+ 39.0 + 35.0	44.0 54.0	+ 6.0 − 0	+ 54.0 + 50.0	74.0 84.0	+ 6.0 − 0	+ 84.0 + 80.0	110 126	+10.0 − 0	+126 +120
76.39 — 87.79	20.0 28.0	+ 5.0 − 0	+28.0 +25.0	32.0 45.0	+ 8.0 − 0	+ 45.0 + 40.0	52.0 65.0	+ 8.0 − 0	+ 65.0 + 60.0	82.0 95.0	+ 8.0 − 0	+ 95.0 + 90.0	128 148	+12.0 − 0	+148 +140
87.79 — 100.9	23.0 31.0	+ 5.0 − 0	+31.0 +28.0	37.0 50.0	+ 8.0 − 0	+ 50.0 + 45.0	62.0 75.0	+ 8.0 − 0	+ 75.0 + 70.0	92.0 105	+ 8.0 − 0	+105 +100	148 168	+12.0 − 0	+168 +160
100.9 — 115.3	24.0 34.0	+ 6.0 − 0	+34.0 +30.0	40.0 56.0	+10.0 − 0	+ 56.0 + 50.0	70.0 86.0	+10.0 − 0	+ 86.0 + 80.0	110 126	+10.0 − 0	+126 +120	164 190	+16.0 − 0	+190 +180
115.3 — 131.9	29.0 39.0	+ 6.0 − 0	+39.0 +35.0	50.0 66.0	+10.0 − 0	+ 66.0 + 60.0	80.0 96.0	+10.0 − 0	+ 96.0 + 90.0	130 146	+10.0 − 0	+146 +140	184 210	+16.0 − 0	+210 +200
131.9 — 152.2	37.0 50.0	+ 8.0 − 0	+50.0 +45.0	58.0 78.0	+12.0 − 0	+ 78.0 + 70.0	88.0 108	+12.0 − 0	+108 +100	148 168	+12.0 − 0	+168 +160	200 232	+20.0 − 0	+232 +220
152.2 — 171.9	42.0 55.0	+ 8.0 − 0	+55.0 +50.0	68.0 88.0	+12.0 − 0	+ 88.0 + 80.0	108 128	+12.0 − 0	+128 +120	168 188	+12.0 − 0	+188 +180	230 262	+20.0 − 0	+262 +250
171.9 — 200	50.0 66.0	+10.0 − 0	+66.0 +60.0	74.0 100	+16.0 − 0	+100 + 90	124 150	+16.0 − 0	+150 +140	184 210	+16.0 − 0	+210 +200	275 316	+ 2.5 − 0	+316 +300

APPENDIX 7 ANSI PREFERRED METRIC LIMITS AND FITS (ANSI B4.2—1978)

PREFERRED HOLE BASIS CLEARANCE FITS

Dimensions in mm.

BASIC SIZE		LOOSE RUNNING			FREE RUNNING			CLOSE RUNNING			SLIDING			LOCATIONAL CLEARANCE		
		Hole H11	Shaft c11	Fit	Hole H9	Shaft d9	Fit	Hole H8	Shaft f7	Fit	Hole H7	Shaft g6	Fit	Hole H7	Shaft h6	Fit
1	MAX	1.060	0.940	0.180	1.025	0.980	0.070	1.014	0.994	0.030	1.010	0.998	0.018	1.010	1.000	0.016
	MIN	1.000	0.880	0.060	1.000	0.955	0.020	1.000	0.984	0.006	1.000	0.992	0.002	1.000	0.994	0.000
1.2	MAX	1.260	1.140	0.180	1.225	1.180	0.070	1.214	1.194	0.030	1.210	1.198	0.018	1.210	1.200	0.016
	MIN	1.200	1.080	0.060	1.200	1.155	0.020	1.200	1.184	0.006	1.200	1.192	0.002	1.200	1.194	0.000
1.6	MAX	1.660	1.540	0.180	1.625	1.580	0.070	1.614	1.594	0.030	1.610	1.598	0.018	1.610	1.600	0.016
	MIN	1.600	1.480	0.060	1.600	1.555	0.020	1.600	1.584	0.006	1.600	1.592	0.002	1.600	1.594	0.000
2	MAX	2.060	1.940	0.180	2.025	1.980	0.070	2.014	1.994	0.030	2.010	1.998	0.018	2.010	2.000	0.016
	MIN	2.000	1.880	0.060	2.000	1.955	0.020	2.000	1.984	0.006	2.000	1.992	0.002	2.000	1.994	0.000
2.5	MAX	2.560	2.440	0.180	2.525	2.480	0.070	2.514	2.494	0.030	2.510	2.498	0.018	2.510	2.500	0.016
	MIN	2.500	2.380	0.060	2.500	2.455	0.020	2.500	2.484	0.006	2.500	2.492	0.002	2.500	2.494	0.000
3	MAX	3.060	2.940	0.180	3.025	2.980	0.070	3.014	2.994	0.030	3.010	2.998	0.018	3.010	3.000	0.016
	MIN	3.000	2.880	0.060	3.000	2.955	0.020	3.000	2.984	0.006	3.000	2.992	0.002	3.000	2.994	0.000
4	MAX	4.075	3.930	0.220	4.030	3.970	0.090	4.018	3.990	0.040	4.012	3.996	0.024	4.012	4.000	0.020
	MIN	4.000	3.855	0.070	4.000	3.940	0.030	4.000	3.978	0.010	4.000	3.988	0.004	4.000	3.992	0.000
5	MAX	5.075	4.930	0.220	5.030	4.970	0.090	5.018	4.990	0.040	5.012	4.996	0.024	5.012	5.000	0.020
	MIN	5.000	4.855	0.070	5.000	4.940	0.030	5.000	4.978	0.010	5.000	4.988	0.004	5.000	4.992	0.000
6	MAX	6.075	5.930	0.220	6.030	5.970	0.090	6.018	5.990	0.040	6.012	5.996	0.024	6.012	6.000	0.020
	MIN	6.000	5.855	0.070	6.000	5.940	0.030	6.000	5.978	0.010	6.000	5.988	0.004	6.000	5.992	0.000
8	MAX	8.090	7.920	0.260	8.036	7.960	0.112	8.022	7.987	0.050	8.015	7.995	0.029	8.015	8.000	0.024
	MIN	8.000	7.830	0.080	8.000	7.924	0.040	8.000	7.972	0.013	8.000	7.986	0.005	8.000	7.991	0.000
10	MAX	10.090	9.920	0.260	10.036	9.960	0.112	10.022	9.987	0.050	10.015	9.995	0.029	10.015	10.000	0.024
	MIN	10.000	9.830	0.080	10.000	9.924	0.040	10.000	9.972	0.013	10.000	9.986	0.005	10.000	9.991	0.000
12	MAX	12.110	11.905	0.315	12.043	11.950	0.136	12.027	11.984	0.061	12.018	11.994	0.035	12.018	12.000	0.029
	MIN	12.000	11.795	0.095	12.000	11.907	0.050	12.000	11.966	0.016	12.000	11.983	0.006	12.000	11.989	0.000
16	MAX	16.110	15.905	0.315	16.043	15.950	0.136	16.027	15.984	0.061	16.018	15.994	0.035	16.018	16.000	0.029
	MIN	16.000	15.795	0.095	16.000	15.907	0.050	16.000	15.966	0.016	16.000	15.983	0.006	16.000	15.989	0.000
20	MAX	20.130	19.890	0.370	20.052	19.935	0.169	20.033	19.980	0.074	20.021	19.993	0.041	20.021	20.000	0.034
	MIN	20.000	19.760	0.110	20.000	19.883	0.065	20.000	19.959	0.020	20.000	19.980	0.007	20.000	19.987	0.000
25	MAX	25.130	24.890	0.370	25.052	24.935	0.169	25.033	24.980	0.074	25.021	24.993	0.041	25.021	25.000	0.034
	MIN	25.000	24.760	0.110	25.000	24.883	0.065	25.000	24.959	0.020	25.000	24.980	0.007	25.000	24.987	0.000
30	MAX	30.130	29.890	0.370	30.052	29.935	0.169	30.033	29.980	0.074	30.021	29.993	0.041	30.021	30.000	0.034
	MIN	30.000	29.760	0.110	30.000	29.883	0.065	30.000	29.959	0.020	30.000	29.980	0.007	30.000	29.987	0.000

APPENDIX 7A PREFERRED HOLE BASIS CLEARANCE FITS (CONT.)

Dimensions in mm.

BASIC SIZE		LOOSE RUNNING Hole H11	Shaft c11	Fit	FREE RUNNING Hole H9	Shaft d9	Fit	CLOSE RUNNING Hole H8	Shaft f7	Fit	SLIDING Hole H7	Shaft g6	Fit	LOCATIONAL CLEARANCE Hole H7	Shaft h6	Fit
40	MAX	40.160	39.880	0.440	40.062	39.920	0.204	40.039	39.975	0.089	40.025	39.991	0.050	40.025	40.000	0.041
	MIN	40.000	39.720	0.120	40.000	39.858	0.080	40.000	39.950	0.025	40.000	39.975	0.009	40.000	39.984	0.000
50	MAX	50.160	49.870	0.450	50.062	49.920	0.204	50.039	49.975	0.089	50.025	49.991	0.050	50.025	50.000	0.041
	MIN	50.000	49.710	0.130	50.000	49.858	0.080	50.000	49.950	0.025	50.000	49.975	0.009	50.000	49.984	0.000
60	MAX	60.190	59.860	0.520	60.074	59.900	0.248	60.046	59.970	0.106	60.030	59.990	0.059	60.030	60.000	0.049
	MIN	60.000	59.670	0.140	60.000	59.826	0.100	60.000	59.940	0.030	60.000	59.971	0.010	60.000	59.981	0.000
80	MAX	80.190	79.850	0.530	80.074	79.900	0.248	80.046	79.970	0.106	80.030	79.990	0.059	80.030	80.000	0.049
	MIN	80.000	79.660	0.150	80.000	79.826	0.100	80.000	79.940	0.030	80.000	79.971	0.010	80.000	79.981	0.000
100	MAX	100.220	99.830	0.610	100.087	99.880	0.294	100.054	99.964	0.125	100.035	99.988	0.069	100.035	100.000	0.057
	MIN	100.000	99.610	0.170	100.000	99.793	0.120	100.000	99.929	0.036	100.000	99.966	0.012	100.000	99.978	0.000
120	MAX	120.220	119.820	0.620	120.087	119.880	0.294	120.054	119.964	0.125	120.035	119.988	0.069	120.035	120.000	0.057
	MIN	120.000	119.600	0.180	120.000	119.793	0.120	120.000	119.929	0.036	120.000	119.966	0.012	120.000	119.978	0.000
160	MAX	160.250	159.790	0.710	160.100	159.855	0.345	160.063	159.957	0.146	160.040	159.986	0.079	160.040	160.000	0.065
	MIN	160.000	159.540	0.210	160.000	159.755	0.145	160.000	159.917	0.043	160.000	159.961	0.014	160.000	159.975	0.000
200	MAX	200.290	199.760	0.820	200.115	199.830	0.400	200.072	199.950	0.168	200.046	199.985	0.090	200.046	200.000	0.075
	MIN	200.000	199.470	0.240	200.000	199.715	0.170	200.000	199.904	0.050	200.000	199.956	0.015	200.000	199.971	0.000
250	MAX	250.290	249.720	0.860	250.115	249.830	0.400	250.072	249.950	0.168	250.046	249.985	0.090	250.046	250.000	0.075
	MIN	250.000	249.430	0.280	250.000	249.715	0.170	250.000	249.904	0.050	250.000	249.956	0.015	250.000	249.971	0.000
300	MAX	300.320	299.670	0.970	300.130	299.810	0.450	300.081	299.944	0.189	300.052	299.983	0.101	300.052	300.000	0.084
	MIN	300.000	299.350	0.330	300.000	299.680	0.190	300.000	299.892	0.056	300.000	299.951	0.017	300.000	299.968	0.000
400	MAX	400.360	399.600	1.120	400.140	399.790	0.490	400.089	399.938	0.208	400.057	399.982	0.111	400.057	400.000	0.093
	MIN	400.000	399.240	0.400	400.000	399.650	0.210	400.000	399.881	0.062	400.000	399.946	0.018	400.000	399.964	0.000
500	MAX	500.400	499.520	1.280	500.155	499.770	0.540	500.097	499.932	0.228	500.063	499.980	0.123	500.063	500.000	0.103
	MIN	500.000	499.120	0.480	500.000	499.615	0.230	500.000	499.869	0.068	500.000	499.940	0.020	500.000	499.960	0.000

APPENDIX 7B   PREFERRED HOLE BASIS TRANSITION AND INTERFERENCE FITS

Dimensions in mm.

BASIC SIZE		LOCATIONAL TRANSN. Hole H7	Shaft k6	Fit	LOCATIONAL TRANSN. Hole H7	Shaft n6	Fit	LOCATIONAL INTERF. Hole H7	Shaft p6	Fit	MEDIUM DRIVE Hole H7	Shaft s6	Fit	FORCE Hole H7	Shaft u6	Fit
1	MAX	1.010	1.006	0.010	1.010	1.010	0.006	1.010	1.012	0.004	1.010	1.020	-0.004	1.010	1.024	-0.008
	MIN	1.000	1.000	-0.006	1.000	1.004	-0.010	1.000	1.006	-0.012	1.000	1.014	-0.020	1.000	1.018	-0.024
1.2	MAX	1.210	1.206	0.010	1.210	1.210	0.006	1.210	1.212	0.004	1.210	1.220	-0.004	1.210	1.224	-0.008
	MIN	1.200	1.200	-0.006	1.200	1.204	-0.010	1.200	1.206	-0.012	1.200	1.214	-0.020	1.200	1.218	-0.024
1.6	MAX	1.610	1.606	0.010	1.610	1.610	0.006	1.610	1.612	0.004	1.610	1.620	-0.004	1.610	1.624	-0.008
	MIN	1.600	1.600	-0.006	1.600	1.604	-0.010	1.600	1.606	-0.012	1.600	1.614	-0.020	1.600	1.618	-0.024
2	MAX	2.010	2.006	0.010	2.010	2.010	0.006	2.010	2.012	0.004	2.010	2.020	-0.004	2.010	2.024	-0.008
	MIN	2.000	2.000	-0.006	2.000	2.004	-0.010	2.000	2.006	-0.012	2.000	2.014	-0.020	2.000	2.018	-0.024
2.5	MAX	2.510	2.506	0.010	2.510	2.510	0.006	2.510	2.512	0.004	2.510	2.520	-0.004	2.510	2.524	-0.008
	MIN	2.500	2.500	-0.006	2.500	2.504	-0.010	2.500	2.506	-0.012	2.500	2.514	-0.020	2.500	2.518	-0.024
3	MAX	3.010	3.006	0.010	3.010	3.010	0.006	3.010	3.012	0.004	3.010	3.020	-0.004	3.010	3.024	-0.008
	MIN	3.000	3.000	-0.006	3.000	3.004	-0.010	3.000	3.006	-0.012	3.000	3.014	-0.020	3.000	3.018	-0.024
4	MAX	4.012	4.009	0.011	4.012	4.016	0.004	4.012	4.020	0.000	4.012	4.027	-0.007	4.012	4.031	-0.011
	MIN	4.000	4.001	-0.009	4.000	4.008	-0.016	4.000	4.012	-0.020	4.000	4.019	-0.027	4.000	4.023	-0.031
5	MAX	5.012	5.009	0.011	5.012	5.016	0.004	5.012	5.020	0.000	5.012	5.027	-0.007	5.012	5.031	-0.011
	MIN	5.000	5.001	-0.009	5.000	5.008	-0.016	5.000	5.012	-0.020	5.000	5.019	-0.027	5.000	5.023	-0.031
6	MAX	6.012	6.009	0.011	6.012	6.016	0.004	6.012	6.020	0.000	6.012	6.027	-0.007	6.012	6.031	-0.011
	MIN	6.000	6.001	-0.009	6.000	6.008	-0.016	6.000	6.012	-0.020	6.000	6.019	-0.027	6.000	6.023	-0.031
8	MAX	8.015	8.010	0.014	8.015	8.019	0.005	8.015	8.024	0.000	8.015	8.032	-0.008	8.015	8.037	-0.013
	MIN	8.000	8.001	-0.010	8.000	8.010	-0.019	8.000	8.015	-0.024	8.000	8.023	-0.032	8.000	8.028	-0.037
10	MAX	10.015	10.010	0.014	10.015	10.019	0.005	10.015	10.024	0.000	10.015	10.032	-0.008	10.015	10.037	-0.013
	MIN	10.000	10.001	-0.010	10.000	10.010	-0.019	10.000	10.015	-0.024	10.000	10.023	-0.032	10.000	10.028	-0.037
12	MAX	12.018	12.012	0.017	12.018	12.023	0.006	12.018	12.029	0.000	12.018	12.039	-0.010	12.018	12.044	-0.015
	MIN	12.000	12.001	-0.012	12.000	12.012	-0.023	12.000	12.018	-0.029	12.000	12.028	-0.039	12.000	12.033	-0.044
16	MAX	16.018	16.012	0.017	16.018	16.023	0.006	16.018	16.029	0.000	16.018	16.039	-0.010	16.018	16.044	-0.015
	MIN	16.000	16.001	-0.012	16.000	16.012	-0.023	16.000	16.018	-0.029	16.000	16.028	-0.039	16.000	16.033	-0.044
20	MAX	20.021	20.015	0.019	20.021	20.028	0.006	20.021	20.035	-0.001	20.021	20.048	-0.014	20.021	20.054	-0.020
	MIN	20.000	20.002	-0.015	20.000	20.015	-0.028	20.000	20.022	-0.035	20.000	20.035	-0.048	20.000	20.041	-0.054
25	MAX	25.021	25.015	0.019	25.021	25.028	0.006	25.021	25.035	-0.001	25.021	25.048	-0.014	25.021	25.061	-0.027
	MIN	25.000	25.002	-0.015	25.000	25.015	-0.028	25.000	25.022	-0.035	25.000	25.035	-0.048	25.000	25.048	-0.061
30	MAX	30.021	30.015	0.019	30.021	30.028	0.006	30.021	30.035	-0.001	30.021	30.048	-0.014	30.021	30.061	-0.027
	MIN	30.000	30.002	-0.015	30.000	30.015	-0.028	30.000	30.022	-0.035	30.000	30.035	-0.048	30.000	30.048	-0.061

APPENDIX 7B (CONT.)

PREFERRED HOLE BASIS TRANSITION AND INTERFERENCE FITS

Dimensions in mm.

BASIC SIZE		LOCATIONAL TRANSN. Hole H7	Shaft k6	Fit	LOCATIONAL TRANSN. Hole H7	Shaft n6	Fit	LOCATIONAL INTERF. Hole H7	Shaft p6	Fit	MEDIUM DRIVE Hole H7	Shaft s6	Fit	FORCE Hole H7	Shaft u6	Fit
40	MAX	40.025	40.018	0.023	40.025	40.033	0.008	40.025	40.042	-0.001	40.025	40.059	-0.018	40.025	40.076	-0.035
	MIN	40.000	40.002	-0.018	40.000	40.017	-0.033	40.000	40.026	-0.042	40.000	40.043	-0.059	40.000	40.060	-0.076
50	MAX	50.025	50.018	0.023	50.000	50.033	0.008	50.025	50.042	-0.001	50.025	50.059	-0.018	50.025	50.086	-0.045
	MIN	50.000	50.002	-0.018	50.000	50.017	-0.033	50.000	50.026	-0.042	50.000	50.043	-0.059	50.000	50.070	-0.086
60	MAX	60.030	60.021	0.028	60.030	60.039	0.010	60.030	60.051	-0.002	60.030	60.072	-0.023	60.030	60.106	-0.057
	MIN	60.000	60.002	-0.021	60.000	60.020	-0.039	60.000	60.032	-0.051	60.000	60.053	-0.072	60.000	60.087	-0.106
80	MAX	80.030	80.021	0.028	80.030	80.039	0.010	80.030	80.051	-0.002	80.030	80.078	-0.029	80.030	80.121	-0.072
	MIN	80.000	80.002	-0.021	80.000	80.020	-0.039	80.000	80.032	-0.051	80.000	80.059	-0.078	80.000	80.102	-0.121
100	MAX	100.035	100.025	0.032	100.035	100.045	0.012	100.035	100.059	-0.002	100.035	100.093	-0.036	100.035	100.146	-0.089
	MIN	100.000	100.003	-0.025	100.000	100.023	-0.045	100.000	100.037	-0.059	100.000	100.071	-0.093	100.000	100.124	-0.146
120	MAX	120.035	120.025	0.032	120.035	120.045	0.012	120.035	120.059	-0.002	120.035	120.101	-0.044	120.035	120.166	-0.109
	MIN	120.000	120.003	-0.025	120.000	120.023	-0.045	120.000	120.037	-0.059	120.000	120.079	-0.101	120.000	120.144	-0.166
160	MAX	160.040	160.028	0.037	160.040	160.052	0.013	160.040	160.068	-0.003	160.040	160.125	-0.060	160.040	160.215	-0.150
	MIN	160.000	160.003	-0.028	160.000	160.027	-0.052	160.000	160.043	-0.068	160.000	160.100	-0.125	160.000	160.190	-0.215
200	MAX	200.046	200.033	0.042	200.046	200.060	0.015	200.046	200.079	-0.004	200.046	200.151	-0.076	200.046	200.265	-0.190
	MIN	200.000	200.004	-0.033	200.000	200.031	-0.060	200.000	200.050	-0.079	200.000	200.122	-0.151	200.000	200.236	-0.265
250	MAX	250.046	250.033	0.042	250.046	250.060	0.015	250.046	250.079	-0.004	250.046	250.169	-0.094	250.046	250.313	-0.238
	MIN	250.000	250.004	-0.033	250.000	250.031	-0.060	250.000	250.050	-0.079	250.000	250.140	-0.169	250.000	250.284	-0.313
300	MAX	300.052	300.036	0.048	300.052	300.066	0.018	300.052	300.088	-0.004	300.052	300.202	-0.118	300.052	300.382	-0.298
	MIN	300.000	300.004	-0.036	300.000	300.034	-0.066	300.000	300.056	-0.088	300.000	300.170	-0.202	300.000	300.350	-0.382
400	MAX	400.057	400.040	0.053	400.057	400.073	0.020	400.057	400.098	-0.005	400.057	400.244	-0.151	400.057	400.471	-0.378
	MIN	400.000	400.004	-0.040	400.000	400.037	-0.073	400.000	400.062	-0.098	400.000	400.208	-0.244	400.000	400.435	-0.471
500	MAX	500.063	500.045	0.058	500.063	500.080	0.023	500.063	500.108	-0.005	500.063	500.292	-0.189	500.063	500.580	-0.477
	MIN	500.000	500.005	-0.045	500.000	500.040	-0.080	500.000	500.068	-0.108	500.000	500.252	-0.292	500.000	500.540	-0.580

APPENDIX 7C PREFERRED SHAFT BASIS CLEARANCE FITS

Dimensions in mm.

BASIC SIZE		LOOSE RUNNING Hole C11	Shaft h11	Fit	FREE RUNNING Hole D9	Shaft h9	Fit	CLOSE RUNNING Hole F8	Shaft h7	Fit	SLIDING Hole G7	Shaft h6	Fit	LOCATIONAL CLEARANCE Hole H7	Shaft h6	Fit
1	MAX	1.120	1.000	0.180	1.045	1.000	0.070	1.020	1.000	0.030	1.012	1.000	0.018	1.010	1.000	0.016
	MIN	1.060	0.940	0.060	1.020	0.975	0.020	1.006	0.990	0.006	1.002	0.994	0.002	1.000	0.994	0.000
1.2	MAX	1.320	1.200	0.180	1.245	1.200	0.070	1.220	1.200	0.030	1.212	1.200	0.018	1.210	1.200	0.016
	MIN	1.260	1.140	0.060	1.220	1.175	0.020	1.206	1.190	0.006	1.202	1.194	0.002	1.200	1.194	0.000
1.6	MAX	1.720	1.600	0.180	1.645	1.600	0.070	1.620	1.600	0.030	1.612	1.600	0.018	1.610	1.600	0.016
	MIN	1.660	1.540	0.060	1.620	1.575	0.020	1.606	1.590	0.006	1.602	1.594	0.002	1.600	1.594	0.000
2	MAX	2.120	2.000	0.180	2.045	2.000	0.070	2.020	2.000	0.030	2.012	2.000	0.018	2.010	2.000	0.016
	MIN	2.060	1.940	0.060	2.020	1.975	0.020	2.006	1.990	0.006	2.002	1.994	0.002	2.000	1.994	0.000
2.5	MAX	2.620	2.500	0.180	2.545	2.500	0.070	2.520	2.500	0.030	2.512	2.500	0.018	2.510	2.500	0.016
	MIN	2.560	2.440	0.060	2.520	2.475	0.020	2.506	2.490	0.006	2.502	2.494	0.002	2.500	2.494	0.000
3	MAX	3.120	3.000	0.180	3.045	3.000	0.070	3.020	3.000	0.030	3.012	3.000	0.018	3.010	3.000	0.016
	MIN	3.060	2.940	0.060	3.020	2.975	0.020	3.006	2.990	0.006	3.002	2.994	0.002	3.000	2.994	0.000
4	MAX	4.145	4.000	0.220	4.060	4.000	0.090	4.028	4.000	0.040	4.016	4.000	0.024	4.012	4.000	0.020
	MIN	4.070	3.925	0.070	4.030	3.970	0.030	4.010	3.988	0.010	4.004	3.992	0.004	4.000	3.992	0.000
5	MAX	5.145	5.000	0.220	5.060	5.000	0.090	5.028	5.000	0.040	5.016	5.000	0.024	5.012	5.000	0.020
	MIN	5.070	4.925	0.070	5.030	4.970	0.030	5.010	4.988	0.010	5.004	4.992	0.004	5.000	4.992	0.000
6	MAX	6.145	6.000	0.220	6.060	6.000	0.090	6.028	6.000	0.040	6.016	6.000	0.024	6.012	6.000	0.020
	MIN	6.070	5.925	0.070	6.030	5.970	0.030	6.010	5.988	0.010	6.004	5.992	0.004	6.000	5.992	0.000
8	MAX	8.170	8.000	0.260	8.076	8.000	0.112	8.035	8.000	0.050	8.020	8.000	0.029	8.015	8.000	0.024
	MIN	8.080	7.910	0.080	8.040	7.964	0.040	8.013	7.985	0.013	8.005	7.991	0.005	8.000	7.991	0.000
10	MAX	10.170	10.000	0.260	10.076	10.000	0.112	10.035	10.000	0.050	10.020	10.000	0.029	10.015	10.000	0.024
	MIN	10.080	9.910	0.080	10.040	9.964	0.040	10.013	9.985	0.013	10.005	9.991	0.005	10.000	9.991	0.000
12	MAX	12.205	12.000	0.315	12.093	12.000	0.136	12.043	12.000	0.061	12.024	12.000	0.035	12.018	12.000	0.029
	MIN	12.095	11.890	0.095	12.050	11.957	0.050	12.016	11.982	0.016	12.006	11.989	0.006	12.000	11.989	0.000
16	MAX	16.205	16.000	0.315	16.093	16.000	0.136	16.043	16.000	0.061	16.024	16.000	0.035	16.018	16.000	0.029
	MIN	16.095	15.890	0.095	16.050	15.957	0.050	16.016	15.982	0.016	16.006	15.989	0.006	16.000	15.989	0.000
20	MAX	20.240	20.000	0.370	20.117	20.000	0.169	20.053	20.000	0.074	20.028	20.000	0.041	20.021	20.000	0.034
	MIN	20.110	19.870	0.110	20.065	19.948	0.065	20.020	19.979	0.020	20.007	19.987	0.007	20.000	19.987	0.000
25	MAX	25.240	25.000	0.370	25.117	25.000	0.169	25.053	25.000	0.074	25.028	25.000	0.041	25.021	25.000	0.034
	MIN	25.110	24.870	0.110	25.065	24.948	0.065	25.020	24.979	0.020	25.007	24.987	0.007	25.000	24.987	0.000
30	MAX	30.240	30.000	0.370	30.117	30.000	0.169	30.053	30.000	0.074	30.028	30.000	0.041	30.021	30.000	0.034
	MIN	30.110	29.870	0.110	30.065	29.948	0.065	30.020	29.979	0.020	30.007	29.987	0.007	30.000	29.987	0.000

APPENDIX 7C   (CONT.)

PREFERRED SHAFT BASIS CLEARANCE FITS

Dimensions in mm.

BASIC SIZE		LOOSE RUNNING Hole C11	Shaft h11	Fit	FREE RUNNING Hole D9	Shaft h9	Fit	CLOSE RUNNING Hole F8	Shaft h7	Fit	SLIDING Hole G7	Shaft h6	Fit	LOCATIONAL CLEARANCE Hole H7	Shaft h6	Fit
40	MAX	40.280	40.000	0.440	40.142	40.000	0.204	40.064	40.000	0.089	40.034	40.000	0.050	40.025	40.000	0.041
	MIN	40.120	39.840	0.120	40.080	39.938	0.080	40.025	39.975	0.025	40.009	39.984	0.009	40.000	39.984	0.000
50	MAX	50.290	50.000	0.450	50.142	50.000	0.204	50.064	50.000	0.089	50.034	50.000	0.050	50.025	50.000	0.041
	MIN	50.130	49.840	0.130	50.080	49.938	0.080	50.025	49.975	0.025	50.009	49.984	0.009	50.000	49.984	0.000
60	MAX	60.330	60.000	0.520	60.174	60.000	0.248	60.076	60.000	0.106	60.040	60.000	0.059	60.030	60.000	0.049
	MIN	60.140	59.810	0.140	60.100	59.926	0.100	60.030	59.970	0.030	60.010	59.981	0.010	60.000	59.981	0.000
80	MAX	80.340	80.000	0.530	80.174	80.000	0.248	80.076	80.000	0.106	80.040	80.000	0.059	80.030	80.000	0.049
	MIN	80.150	79.810	0.150	80.100	79.926	0.100	80.030	79.970	0.030	80.010	79.981	0.010	80.000	79.981	0.000
100	MAX	100.390	100.000	0.610	100.207	100.000	0.294	100.090	100.000	0.125	100.047	100.000	0.069	100.035	100.000	0.057
	MIN	100.170	99.780	0.170	100.120	99.913	0.120	100.036	99.965	0.036	100.012	99.978	0.012	100.000	99.978	0.000
120	MAX	120.400	120.000	0.620	120.207	120.000	0.294	120.090	120.000	0.125	120.047	120.000	0.069	120.035	120.000	0.057
	MIN	120.180	119.780	0.180	120.120	119.913	0.120	120.036	119.965	0.036	120.012	119.978	0.012	120.000	119.978	0.000
160	MAX	160.460	160.000	0.710	160.245	160.000	0.345	160.106	160.000	0.146	160.054	160.000	0.079	160.040	160.000	0.065
	MIN	160.210	159.750	0.210	160.145	159.900	0.145	160.043	159.960	0.043	160.014	159.975	0.014	160.000	159.975	0.000
200	MAX	200.530	200.000	0.820	200.285	200.000	0.400	200.122	200.000	0.168	200.061	200.000	0.090	200.046	200.000	0.075
	MIN	200.240	199.710	0.240	200.170	199.885	0.170	200.050	199.954	0.050	200.015	199.971	0.015	200.000	199.971	0.000
250	MAX	250.570	250.000	0.860	250.285	250.000	0.400	250.122	250.000	0.168	250.061	250.000	0.090	250.046	250.000	0.075
	MIN	250.280	249.710	0.280	250.170	249.885	0.170	250.050	249.954	0.050	250.015	249.971	0.015	250.000	249.971	0.000
300	MAX	300.650	300.000	0.970	300.320	300.000	0.450	300.137	300.000	0.189	300.069	300.000	0.101	300.052	300.000	0.084
	MIN	300.330	299.680	0.330	300.190	299.870	0.190	300.056	299.948	0.056	300.017	299.968	0.017	300.000	299.968	0.000
400	MAX	400.760	400.000	1.120	400.350	400.000	0.490	400.151	400.000	0.208	400.075	400.000	0.111	400.057	400.000	0.093
	MIN	400.400	399.640	0.400	400.210	399.860	0.210	400.062	399.943	0.062	400.018	399.964	0.018	400.000	399.964	0.000
500	MAX	500.880	500.000	1.280	500.385	500.000	0.540	500.165	500.000	0.228	500.083	500.000	0.123	500.063	500.000	0.103
	MIN	500.480	499.600	0.480	500.230	499.845	0.230	500.068	499.937	0.068	500.020	499.960	0.020	500.000	499.960	0.000

APPENDIX 7D   PREFERRED SHAFT BASIS TRANSITION AND INTERFERENCE FITS

Dimensions in mm.

BASIC SIZE		LOCATIONAL TRANSN. Hole K7	Shaft h6	Fit	LOCATIONAL TRANSN. Hole N7	Shaft h6	Fit	LOCATIONAL INTERF. Hole P7	Shaft h6	Fit	MEDIUM DRIVE Hole S7	Shaft h6	Fit	FORCE Hole U7	Shaft h6	Fit
1	MAX	1.000	1.000	0.006	0.996	1.000	0.002	0.994	1.000	0.000	0.986	1.000	-0.008	0.982	1.000	-0.012
	MIN	0.990	0.994	-0.010	0.986	0.994	-0.014	0.984	0.994	-0.016	0.976	0.994	-0.024	0.972	0.994	-0.028
1.2	MAX	1.200	1.200	0.006	1.196	1.200	0.002	1.194	1.200	0.000	1.186	1.200	-0.008	1.182	1.200	-0.012
	MIN	1.190	1.194	-0.010	1.186	1.194	-0.014	1.184	1.194	-0.016	1.176	1.194	-0.024	1.172	1.194	-0.028
1.6	MAX	1.600	1.600	0.006	1.596	1.600	0.002	1.594	1.600	0.000	1.586	1.600	-0.008	1.582	1.600	-0.012
	MIN	1.590	1.594	-0.010	1.586	1.594	-0.014	1.584	1.594	-0.016	1.576	1.594	-0.024	1.572	1.594	-0.028
2	MAX	2.000	2.000	0.006	1.996	2.000	0.002	1.994	2.000	0.000	1.986	2.000	-0.008	1.982	2.000	-0.012
	MIN	1.990	1.994	-0.010	1.986	1.994	-0.014	1.984	1.994	-0.016	1.976	1.994	-0.024	1.972	1.994	-0.028
2.5	MAX	2.500	2.500	0.006	2.496	2.500	0.002	2.494	2.500	0.000	2.486	2.500	-0.008	2.482	2.500	-0.012
	MIN	2.490	2.494	-0.010	2.486	2.494	-0.014	2.484	2.494	-0.016	2.476	2.494	-0.024	2.472	2.494	-0.028
3	MAX	3.000	3.000	0.006	2.996	3.000	0.002	2.994	3.000	0.000	2.986	3.000	-0.008	2.982	3.000	-0.012
	MIN	2.990	2.994	-0.010	2.986	2.994	-0.014	2.984	2.994	-0.016	2.976	2.994	-0.024	2.972	2.994	-0.028
4	MAX	4.003	4.000	0.011	3.996	4.000	0.004	3.992	4.000	0.000	3.985	4.000	-0.007	3.981	4.000	-0.011
	MIN	3.991	3.992	-0.009	3.984	3.992	-0.016	3.980	3.992	-0.020	3.973	3.992	-0.027	3.969	3.992	-0.031
5	MAX	5.003	5.000	0.011	4.996	5.000	0.004	4.992	5.000	0.000	4.985	5.000	-0.007	4.981	5.000	-0.011
	MIN	4.991	4.992	-0.009	4.984	4.992	-0.016	4.980	4.992	-0.020	4.973	4.992	-0.027	4.969	4.992	-0.031
6	MAX	6.003	6.000	0.011	5.996	6.000	0.004	5.992	6.000	0.000	5.985	6.000	-0.007	5.981	6.000	-0.011
	MIN	5.991	5.992	-0.009	5.984	5.992	-0.016	5.980	5.992	-0.020	5.973	5.992	-0.027	5.969	5.992	-0.031
8	MAX	8.005	8.000	0.014	7.996	8.000	0.005	7.991	8.000	0.000	7.983	8.000	-0.008	7.978	8.000	-0.013
	MIN	7.990	7.991	-0.010	7.981	7.991	-0.019	7.976	7.991	-0.024	7.968	7.991	-0.032	7.963	7.991	-0.037
10	MAX	10.005	10.000	0.014	9.996	10.000	0.005	9.991	10.000	0.000	9.983	10.000	-0.008	9.978	10.000	-0.013
	MIN	9.990	9.991	-0.010	9.981	9.991	-0.019	9.976	9.991	-0.024	9.968	9.991	-0.032	9.963	9.991	-0.037
12	MAX	12.006	12.000	0.017	11.995	12.000	0.006	11.989	12.000	0.000	11.979	12.000	-0.010	11.974	12.000	-0.015
	MIN	11.988	11.989	-0.012	11.977	11.989	-0.023	11.971	11.989	-0.029	11.961	11.989	-0.039	11.956	11.989	-0.044
16	MAX	16.006	16.000	0.017	15.995	16.000	0.006	15.989	16.000	0.000	15.979	16.000	-0.010	15.974	16.000	-0.015
	MIN	15.988	15.989	-0.012	15.977	15.989	-0.023	15.971	15.989	-0.029	15.961	15.989	-0.039	15.956	15.989	-0.044
20	MAX	20.006	20.000	0.019	19.993	20.000	0.006	19.986	20.000	-0.001	19.973	20.000	-0.014	19.967	20.000	-0.020
	MIN	19.985	19.987	-0.015	19.972	19.987	-0.028	19.965	19.987	-0.035	19.952	19.987	-0.048	19.946	19.987	-0.054
25	MAX	25.006	25.000	0.019	24.993	25.000	0.006	24.986	25.000	-0.001	24.973	25.000	-0.014	24.960	25.000	-0.027
	MIN	24.985	24.987	-0.015	24.972	24.987	-0.028	24.965	24.987	-0.035	24.952	24.987	-0.048	24.939	24.987	-0.061
30	MAX	30.006	30.000	0.019	29.993	30.000	0.006	29.986	30.000	-0.001	29.973	30.000	-0.014	29.960	30.000	-0.027
	MIN	29.985	29.987	-0.015	29.972	29.987	-0.028	29.965	29.987	-0.035	29.952	29.987	-0.048	29.939	29.987	-0.061

APPENDIX 7D   (CONT.)

PREFERRED SHAFT BASIS TRANSITION AND INTERFERENCE FITS

Dimensions in mm.

BASIC SIZE		LOCATIONAL TRANSN. Hole K7	Shaft h6	Fit	LOCATIONAL TRANSN. Hole N7	Shaft h6	Fit	LOCATIONAL INTERF. Hole P7	Shaft h6	Fit	MEDIUM DRIVE Hole S7	Shaft h6	Fit	FORCE Hole U7	Shaft h6	Fit
40	MAX	40.007	40.000	0.023	39.992	40.000	0.008	39.983	40.000	-0.001	39.966	40.000	-0.018	39.949	40.000	-0.035
	MIN	39.982	39.984	-0.018	39.967	39.984	-0.033	39.958	39.984	-0.042	39.941	39.984	-0.059	39.924	39.984	-0.076
50	MAX	50.007	50.000	0.023	49.992	50.000	0.008	49.983	50.000	-0.001	49.966	50.000	-0.018	49.939	50.000	-0.045
	MIN	49.982	49.984	-0.018	49.967	49.984	-0.033	49.958	49.984	-0.042	49.941	49.984	-0.059	49.914	49.984	-0.086
60	MAX	60.009	60.000	0.028	59.991	60.000	0.010	59.979	60.000	-0.002	59.958	60.000	-0.023	59.924	60.000	-0.057
	MIN	59.979	59.981	-0.021	59.961	59.981	-0.039	59.949	59.981	-0.051	59.928	59.981	-0.072	59.894	59.981	-0.106
80	MAX	80.009	80.000	0.028	79.991	80.000	0.010	79.979	80.000	-0.002	79.952	80.000	-0.029	79.909	80.000	-0.072
	MIN	79.979	79.981	-0.021	79.961	79.981	-0.039	79.949	79.981	-0.051	79.922	79.981	-0.078	73.879	79.981	-0.121
100	MAX	100.010	100.000	0.032	99.990	100.000	0.012	99.976	100.000	-0.002	99.942	100.000	-0.036	93.889	100.000	-0.089
	MIN	99.975	99.978	-0.025	99.955	99.978	-0.045	99.941	99.978	-0.059	99.907	99.978	-0.093	93.854	99.978	-0.146
120	MAX	120.010	120.000	0.032	119.990	120.000	0.012	119.976	120.000	-0.002	119.934	120.000	-0.044	119.869	120.000	-0.109
	MIN	119.975	119.978	-0.025	119.955	119.978	-0.045	119.941	119.978	-0.059	119.899	119.978	-0.101	119.834	119.978	-0.166
160	MAX	160.012	160.000	0.037	159.988	160.000	0.013	159.972	160.000	-0.003	159.915	160.000	-0.060	159.825	160.000	-0.150
	MIN	159.972	159.975	-0.028	159.948	159.975	-0.052	159.932	159.975	-0.068	159.875	159.975	-0.125	159.785	159.975	-0.215
200	MAX	200.013	200.000	0.042	199.986	200.000	0.015	199.967	200.000	-0.004	199.895	200.000	-0.076	199.781	200.000	-0.190
	MIN	199.967	199.971	-0.033	199.940	199.971	-0.060	199.921	199.971	-0.079	199.849	199.971	-0.151	199.735	199.971	-0.265
250	MAX	250.013	250.000	0.042	249.986	250.000	0.015	249.967	250.000	-0.004	249.877	250.000	-0.094	249.733	250.000	-0.238
	MIN	249.967	249.971	-0.033	249.940	249.971	-0.060	249.921	249.971	-0.079	249.831	249.971	-0.169	249.687	249.971	-0.313
300	MAX	300.016	300.000	0.048	299.986	300.000	0.018	299.964	300.000	-0.004	299.850	300.000	-0.118	259.670	300.000	-0.298
	MIN	299.964	299.968	-0.036	299.934	299.968	-0.066	299.912	299.968	-0.088	299.798	299.968	-0.202	299.618	299.968	-0.382
400	MAX	400.017	400.000	0.053	399.984	400.000	0.020	399.959	400.000	-0.005	399.813	400.000	-0.151	399.586	400.000	-0.378
	MIN	399.960	399.964	-0.040	399.927	399.964	-0.073	399.902	399.964	-0.098	399.756	399.964	-0.244	399.529	399.964	-0.471
500	MAX	500.018	500.000	0.058	499.983	500.000	0.023	499.955	500.003	-0.005	499.771	500.000	-0.189	499.483	500.000	-0.477
	MIN	499.955	499.960	-0.045	499.920	499.960	-0.080	499.892	499.960	-0.108	499.708	499.960	-0.292	499.420	499.960	-0.580

I N D E X